This hymnal is presented for the glory of God
and in loving memory of

Dorothy Lee Brian

Dec. 22, 1919 – May 24, 1984

HYMNBOOK FOR

Christian Worship

HYMNBOOK FOR

Christian Worship

THE BETHANY PRESS · ST. LOUIS
THE JUDSON PRESS · VALLEY FORGE

Preface

CHRISTIANITY has been a singing religion since the day the Apostle Paul admonished the churches to praise God with psalms, hymns, and spiritual songs. Indeed, Christianity has its roots in a singing tradition. In the Psalms we read, "O sing to the Lord a new song," and through the ages men have done so.

Recently science and technology have ushered in a new age with new problems and challenges to the human spirit. To meet the spiritual needs of modern man, the church has moved toward a deeper theological understanding of the biblical faith and its implications for ecumenicity, education, and social involvement of the Christian community. These far-reaching developments have had important effects upon worship and hymnody.

During the eight years of preparation the Hymnbook Committee has endeavored to produce a hymnal which will retain a great body of Christendom's loftiest hymns, while introducing new texts or adjusting old ones in a manner consistent and helpful to contemporary man. The work of the Committee was facilitated by the appearance of several new and excellent hymnals in the Protestant tradition. All major hymnals, new and old, were examined for materials, as were sources for hymns not yet appearing in any hymnal. The most notable of such sources is the Hymn Society of America, whose material was generously made available to the Committee.

Particular attention was directed toward including a number of hymns which are generally common to all, a "classic" hymnody without which no hymnal can be reckoned complete. Increasing concern was given, among other categories, to securing worthy hymns for the city church, the marriage service, and the Lord's Supper.

The selection of tunes for the *Hymnbook* followed the same general procedure. Although some tunes and texts are wedded by common use, the Committee was mindful that a weak tune can emasculate a strong text, and the possibility of including superior tunes was continually kept in mind. Sources of tunes run the gamut. Included are plainsong melodies, chorales, contemporary and early American tunes, tunes from the Genevan Psalter, and from many nationalities. Every effort has been made to insure ease of congregational singing, including lowering many keys and rendering the makeup of the book as readable as possible.

The presence of several church musicians on the Committee encouraged careful attention to the section devoted to service music. Many choir directors select the bulk of choral responses, and material other than anthems, from the hymnal itself; hence, a large amount was included. No experienced musician would need an admonition, however, to search through the body of hymns as well for choral introits or prayer responses, as much suitable material is contained therein.

It is believed that the proportionately large selection of worship materials will commend itself to pastors and laymen alike. Although the emphasis naturally is on biblical selections, both historic and contemporary material is included. Passages which lend themselves have been arranged for responsive readings, but they may be read in unison.

Extensive effort was made to enter each acknowledgment accurately. Inadvertent omissions will be corrected in subsequent editions.

Members of the Hymnbook Committee were Merrill L. Cadwell, Lloyd V. Channels, John T. Clough, Kenneth L. Cober, Wilbur H. Cramblet, Karl Croel, David M. Evans, Martha Faw, Mary Beth Fulton, Eugene P. Hazlewood, C. Adrian Heaton, Richard Hoiland, Christine Kallstrom, David M. Kellermeyer, Robert E. Keighton, Thomas B. McDormand, Margaret Crain McNeil, W. John Minter, Harold W. Richardson, Victor F. Scalise, Lawrence P. Schreiber, Gentry A. Shelton, John E. Skoglund, Marvin E. Smith, Dorothy Sellers Smotherman, George Oliver Taylor, Edward L. Thompson, Dorothy S. Tolley, Jet E. Turner, Arthur N. Wake, Orville W. Wake, Keith Watkins, David V. Williams, Ellwood S. Wolf, Darrell K. Wolfe, and Robert Young.

This *Hymnbook* is offered to the churches in the name of the Father, the Son, and the Holy Spirit, in the hope that its use will lead congregations into closer communion with God, and into a more vital Christian fellowship one with another.

Charles Huddleston Heaton
Editor

John Paul Pack
Chairman, Christian Church
(Disciples of Christ)

Edward Hughes Pruden
Chairman, American Baptist Convention

Contents

Hymns

Service Music

The Written Word

Acknowledgments

Indexes

Hymns

Joyful, Joyful, We Adore Thee

1

Henry van Dyke, 1852-1933

HYMN TO JOY 8.7.8.7.D.
Arr. from Ludwig van Beethoven, 1770-1827

1 Joy - ful, joy - ful, we a - dore thee, God of glo - ry, Lord of love;
2 All thy works with joy sur - round thee, Earth and heaven re - flect thy rays,
3 Thou art giv - ing and for - giv - ing, Ev - er bless - ing, ev - er blest,
4 Mor - tals, join the hap - py cho - rus Which the morn - ing stars be - gan;

Hearts un - fold like flowers be - fore thee, Open - ing to the sun a - bove.
Stars and an - gels sing a - round thee, Cen - ter of un - bro - ken praise.
Well - spring of the joy of liv - ing, O - cean depth of hap - py rest!
Fa - ther love is reign - ing o'er us, Broth - er love binds man to man.

Melt the clouds of sin and sad - ness, Drive the dark of doubt a - way;
Field and for - est, vale and moun - tain, Flow - ery mead - ow, flash - ing sea,
Thou our Fa - ther, Christ our Broth - er, All who live in love are thine;
Ev - er sing - ing, march we on - ward, Vic - tors in the midst of strife,

Giv - er of im - mor - tal glad - ness, Fill us with the light of day.
Chant - ing bird and flow - ing foun - tain, Call us to re - joice in thee.
Teach us how to love each oth - er, Lift us to the joy di - vine.
Joy - ful mu - sic leads us sun - ward In the tri - umph song of life. A - men.

HIS WORKS IN CREATION

All Things Bright and Beautiful

Cecil F. Alexander, 1818-1895

ROYAL OAK 7.6.7.6. with Refrain
Traditional English Melody
Adapt. Martin Shaw, 1875-1958

All things bright and beau-ti - ful, All crea-tures great and small,

All things wise and won - der - ful, The Lord God made them all.

1 Each lit - tle flower that o - pens, Each lit - tle bird that sings,
2 The pur - ple-head - ed moun-tain, The riv - er run-ning by,
3 The cold wind in the win - ter, The pleas-ant sum-mer sun,

HIS WORKS IN CREATION

He made their glow-ing col - ors, He made their tin - y wings.
The sun - set, and the morn - ing That bright-ens up the sky.
The ripe fruits in the gar - den, He made them ev - ery one.

Let Us with a Gladsome Mind

3

Based on Psalm 136
John Milton, 1608-1674, alt.

INNOCENTS 7.7.7.7.
The Parish Choir, 1850

1 Let us with a glad - some mind Praise the
2 He, with all com - mand - ing might, Filled the
3 All things liv - ing he doth feed; His full
4 Let us with a glad - some mind Praise the

Lord, for he is kind; For his mer - cies aye en -
new - made world with light;
hand sup - plies their need;
Lord, for he is kind;

dure, Ev - er faith - ful, ev - er sure. A - men.

HIS WORKS IN CREATION

We Sing the Mighty Power of God

4

Isaac Watts, 1674-1748, alt.

ELLACOMBE C.M.D.
Gesangbuch, Wirtemberg, 1784

1 We sing the might-y power of God, That made the moun-tains rise,
2 We sing the good-ness of the Lord, That filled the earth with food;
3 There's not a plant or flower be-low, But makes thy glo-ries known;

That spread the flow-ing seas a-broad, And built the loft-y skies.
He formed the crea-tures with his word, And then pro-nounced them good.
And clouds a-rise, and tem-pests blow, By or-der from thy throne.

We sing the wis-dom that or-dained The sun to rule the day.
Lord, how thy won-ders are dis-played, Wher-e'er we turn our eyes:
While all that bor-rows life from thee Is ev-er in thy care,

The moon shines full at his com-mand, And all the stars o-bey.
If we sur-vey the ground we tread, Or gaze up-on the skies.
And ev-ery-where that man can be, Thou, God, art pres-ent there. A-men.

HIS WORKS IN CREATION

This Is My Father's World   5

Maltbie D. Babcock, 1858-1901, alt.

TERRA BEATA S.M.D.
Traditional English Melody
Adapt. Franklin L. Sheppard, 1852-1930

1 This is my Fa-ther's world; And to my lis-tening ears, All
2 This is my Fa-ther's world; The birds their car-ols raise, The
3 This is my Fa-ther's world; Oh, let me ne'er for-get That

na - ture sings, and round me rings The mu - sic of the spheres.
morn - ing light, the lil - y white, De - clare their Mak - er's praise.
though the wrong seems oft so strong, God is the rul - er yet.

This is my Fa-ther's world; I rest me in the thought Of
This is my Fa-ther's world; He shines in all that's fair; In the
This is my Fa-ther's world; Why should my heart be sad? The

rocks and trees, of skies and seas, His hand the won - ders wrought.
rus - tling grass I hear him pass; He speaks to me ev-ery-where.
Lord is King; let the heav-ens ring. God reigns; let earth be glad.

HIS WORKS IN CREATION

6 *The Spacious Firmament on High*

Joseph Addison, 1672-1719

CREATION L.M.D.
Franz Joseph Haydn, 1732-1809

1 The spa-cious fir-ma-ment on high, With all the blue e-the-real sky, And span-gled heavens, a shin-ing frame, Their great O-rig-i-nal pro-claim. The un-wear-ied sun, from day to day, Does his cre-a-tor's power dis-play, And pub-lish-

2 Soon as the eve-ning shades pre-vail, The moon takes up the won-drous tale; And night-ly, to the lis-ten-ing earth, Re-peats the sto-ry of her birth; Whilst all the stars that round her burn, And all the plan-ets in their turn, Con-firm the

3 What though, in sol-emn sil-ence, all Move round the dark ter-res-trial ball? What though no re-al voice nor sound A-midst their ra-diant orbs be found? In rea-son's ear they all re-joice, And ut-ter forth a glo-rious voice; For-ev-er

HIS WORKS IN CREATION

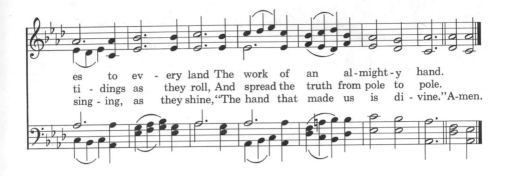

es to ev - ery land The work of an al - might - y hand.
ti - dings as they roll, And spread the truth from pole to pole.
sing - ing, as they shine, "The hand that made us is di - vine." A-men.

For the Beauty of the Earth 7

Folliott S. Pierpoint, 1835-1917, alt.

DIX 7.7.7.7.7.7.
Abridged from a chorale by
Conrad Kocher, 1786-1872

1 For the beau - ty of the earth, For the glo - ry of the skies,
2 For the beau - ty of each hour Of the day and of the night,
3 For the joy of ear and eye, For the heart and mind's de - light,
4 For the joy of hu - man love, Broth-er, sis - ter, par - ent, child,
5 For thy Church that ev - er - more Lift - eth ho - ly hands a - bove,

For the love which from our birth O - ver and a - round us lies,
Hill and vale, and tree and flower, Sun and moon, and stars of light,
For the mys - tic har - mo - ny Link - ing sense to sound and sight,
Friends on earth, and friends a - bove, For all gen - tle thoughts and mild,
Of - fering up on ev - ery shore Her pure sa - cri - fice of love,

Lord of all, to thee we raise This our hymn of grate - ful praise. A-men.

Words by permission of the Estate of the late F. S. Pierpoint
and Oxford University Press.

HIS WORKS IN CREATION

8   *Men and Children Everywhere*

John J. Moment, 1875-1959

ROCK OF AGES 7.7.7.7.5.7.4.7.
Ancient Hebrew Melody

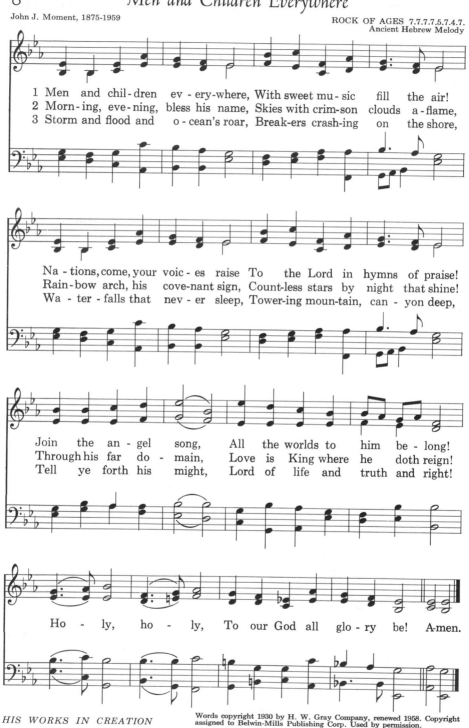

1 Men and chil-dren ev-ery-where, With sweet mu-sic fill the air!
2 Morn-ing, eve-ning, bless his name, Skies with crim-son clouds a-flame,
3 Storm and flood and o-cean's roar, Break-ers crash-ing on the shore,

Na-tions, come, your voic-es raise To the Lord in hymns of praise!
Rain-bow arch, his cove-nant sign, Count-less stars by night that shine!
Wa-ter-falls that nev-er sleep, Tower-ing moun-tain, can-yon deep,

Join the an-gel song, All the worlds to him be-long!
Through his far do-main, Love is King where he doth reign!
Tell ye forth his might, Lord of life and truth and right!

Ho-ly, ho-ly, To our God all glo-ry be! A-men.

HIS WORKS IN CREATION

O God, Thy Great Creation

9

Edward E. Chipman, 1901-

MUNICH 7.6.7.6.D.
Adapt. from *Gesangbuch*, Meiningen, 1693
Harm. adapt. from Felix Mendelssohn, 1809-1847

1 O God, thy great Cre - a - tion Calls forth our hearts' glad praise!
2 The ev - er - cir - cling plan - ets Their cos - mic cours - es run;
3 O God, Cre - a - tive Spir - it, Great Gov - er - nor of Life,

The earth in mute nar - ra - tion Re - veals its Mak - er's ways;
And a - toms in their or - bits Con - vey thy un - i - son.
Help us thy grace to mer - it, To wrest our peace from strife.

The heav - en's spa - cious gran - deur, The rest - less o - cean's span,
With e'er re - turn - ing sea - sons These tell thine or - dered plan,
So guide our minds' in - ten - tions, So fill our souls with awe,

And om - ni - pres - ent ver - dure Pro - claim thy love to man.
And mul - ti - ply the rea - sons For gra - ti - tude in man.
That we and our in - ven - tions Shall serve thy Will and Law. A - men.

HIS WORKS IN CREATION

10

My Shepherd Will Supply My Need

Psalm 23
Para. Isaac Watts, 1674-1748

RESIGNATION C.M.D.
Southern Harmony, 1855

1 My shep - herd will sup - ply my need; Je - ho - vah
2 When I walk through the shades of death Thy pres - ence
3 The sure pro - vi - sions of my God At - tend me

is his name: In pas - tures fresh he makes me feed, Be -
is my stay; One word of thy sup - port - ing breath Drives
all my days; O may thy house be my a - bode, And

side the liv - ing stream. He brings my wand - ering spir - it
all my fears a - way. Thy hand, in sight of all my
all my work be praise. There would I find a set - tled

back, When I for - sake his ways; And leads me,
foes, Doth still my ta - ble spread; My cup with
rest, While oth - ers go and come; No more a

HIS LOVE

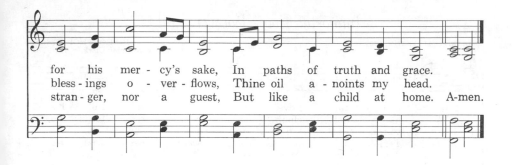

for his mer - cy's sake, In paths of truth and grace.
bless - ings o - ver - flows, Thine oil a - noints my head.
stran - ger, nor a guest, But like a child at home. A-men.

I Sought the Lord, and Afterward I Knew   11

Unknown
The Pilgrim Hymnal, 1904

PEACE 10.10.10.6.
The Revivalist, 1869
Adapt. George Brandon, 1924-

In unison

1 I sought the Lord, and af - ter-ward I knew He moved my
2 Thou didst reach forth thy hand and mine en - fold; I walked and
3 I find, I walk, I love, but O the whole Of love is

soul to seek him, seek - ing me; It was not I that
sank not on the storm-vexed sea; 'Twas not so much that
but my an - swer, Lord, to thee! For thou wert long be -

found, O Sav - ior true; No, I was found of thee.
I on thee took hold As thou, dear Lord, on me.
fore - hand with my soul; Al - ways thou lov - edst me. A-men.

HIS LOVE

Immortal Love, Forever Full

John Greenleaf Whittier, 1807-1892

BISHOPTHORPE C.M.
Att. to Jeremiah Clark, c. 1670-1707

1 Im - mor - tal Love, for - ev - er full, For -
2 We may not climb the heaven - ly steeps To
3 But warm, sweet, ten - der, e - ven yet A
4 The heal - ing of his seam - less dress Is
5 O Lord and Mas - ter of us all, What

ev - er flow - ing free, For - ev - er shared, for -
bring the Lord Christ down; In vain we search the
pres - ent help is he; And faith has still its
by our beds of pain; We touch him in life's
e'er our name or sign, We own thy sway, we

ev - er whole, A nev - er ebb - ing sea!
low - est deeps, For him no depths can drown:
O - liv - et, And love its Ga - li - lee.
throng and press And we are whole a - gain,
hear thy call, We test our lives by thine. A-men.

13

There's a Wideness in God's Mercy

Frederick W. Faber, 1814-1863

WELLESLEY 8.7.8.7.
Lizzie S. Tourjée, 1858-1913

1 There's a wide-ness in God's mer-cy, Like the wide-ness of the sea;
2 There is no place where earth's sor-rows Are more felt than up in heaven;
3 For the love of God is broad-er Than the meas-ure of man's mind;
4 If our love were but more sim-ple, We should take him at his word;

HIS LOVE

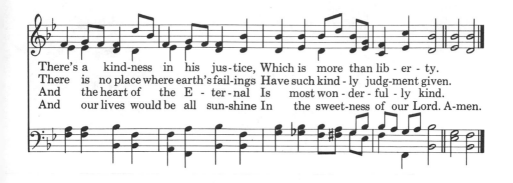

There's a kind-ness in his jus-tice, Which is more than lib - er - ty.
There is no place where earth's fail-ings Have such kind - ly judg-ment given.
And the heart of the E - ter-nal Is most won - der - ful - ly kind.
And our lives would be all sun-shine In the sweet-ness of our Lord. A-men.

Great Is Thy Faithfulness 14

Thomas O. Chisholm, 1866-1960

FAITHFULNESS 11.10.11.10.
William M. Runyan, 1870-1957

1 Great is thy faith - ful-ness, O God my Fa - ther, There is no
2 Sum - mer and win - ter, and spring-time and har - vest, Sun, moon and
3 Par - don for sin and a peace that en - dur - eth, Thy own dear
4 Great is thy faith - ful-ness, O God my Fa - ther, Morn-ing by

shad - ow of turn-ing with thee; Thou chang-est not, thy com - pas-sions, they
stars in their cours-es a - bove, Join with all na - ture in man - i - fold
pres - ence to cheer and to guide; Strength for to - day and bright hope for to -
morn-ing new mer - cies I see. All I have need - ed thy hand hath pro-

fail not; As thou hast been thou for - ev - er wilt be.
wit - ness To thy great faith - ful-ness, mer - cy and love.
mor - row, Bless-ings all mine, with ten thou-sand be - side!
vid - ed; Great is thy faith - ful-ness, Lord, un - to me! A-men.

HIS LOVE

15

Strong Son of God

Alfred Tennyson, 1809-1892

DEO GRACIAS L.M.
The Agincourt Song, 15th century
Arr. for *The Hymnal,* 1933

1 Strong Son of God, im-mor-tal Love, Whom we, that have not seen thy face, By faith, and faith a-lone, em-brace, Be-liev-ing where we can-not prove;

2 Our lit-tle sys-tems have their day; They have their day and cease to be; They are but bro-ken lights of thee, And thou, O Lord, art more than they.

3 We have but faith: we can-not know, For know-ledge is of things we see; And yet we trust it comes from thee, A beam in dark-ness: let it grow.

4 Let know-ledge grow from more to more, But more of rev-erence in us dwell; That mind and soul, ac-cord-ing well, May make one mu-sic as be-fore. A-men.

HIS LOVE

O Love of God, How Strong and True

16

Horatius Bonar, 1808-1889

EISENACH L.M.
Melody by Johann H. Schein, 1586-1630

1 O love of God, how strong and true,
2 O wide em - brac - ing, won - drous love,
3 We read thee best in him who came
4 We read thy power to bless and save

E - ter - nal and yet ev - er new;
We read thee in the sky a - bove;
To bear for us the cross of shame,
E'en in the dark - ness of the grave;

Un - com - pre - hend - ed and un - bought,
We read thee in the earth be - low,
Sent by the Fa - ther from on high,
Still more in res - ur - rec - tion light

Be - yond all know - ledge and all thought.
In seas that swell and streams that flow.
Our life to live, our death to die.
We read the full - ness of thy might. A - men.

HIS LOVE

17

O Love That Wilt Not Let Me Go

George Matheson, 1842-1906

ST. MARGARET 8.8.8.8.6.
Albert L. Peace, 1844-1912

1 O Love that wilt not let me go,
2 O Light that fol-lowest all my way,
3 O Joy that seek-est me through pain,
4 O Cross that lift-est up my head,

I rest my wea-ry soul in thee;
I yield my flick-ering torch to thee;
I can-not close my heart to thee;
I dare not ask to fly from thee;

I give thee back the life I owe,
My heart re-stores its bor-rowed ray,
I trace the rain-bow through the rain,
I lay in dust life's glo-ry dead,

That in thine o-cean depths its flow May rich-er, full-er be.
That in thy sun-shine's blaze its day May bright-er, fair-er be.
And feel the prom-ise is not vain That morn shall tear-less be.
And from the ground there blos-soms red Life that shall end-less be. A-men.

HIS LOVE

O God Whose Love Compels Us

18

Daniel B. Merrick, Jr., 1926-

ROCKPORT 7.6.7.6.D.
T. Tertius Noble, 1867-1953

1 O   God whose love com - pels   us To   be   thy   light and   way,
2 Thy   chil-dren of   this plan - et Are weak, and   lured by   sin.
3 So   let thy love con - trol   us With wis - dom, faith and power,

To   stand in per - fect   free - dom And   yet thy   will   o - bey;
Cruel blood-shed stalks the   na - tions Grim hun - ger   grows with - in.
That   we   may be   thy   ser - vants In   this de - ci - sive hour.

A   trou-bled   world lies   wait - ing, We   seek no oth - er   choice
Man   walks in   deep re - bel - lion In   shame-ful pride and   greed.
O   give thy   church new cour - age; Re - new her heart and   mind,

But   be   our Lord's true serv - ants In   heart and   deed and   voice.
Make sen - si - tive our   spir - its, With love, to   in - ter - cede.
That flames of love's com - pul - sion May kin - dle   all   man-kind. A-men.

HIS LOVE

19

O Father Above Us

Percy Dearmer, 1867-1936

MADDERMARKET 11.11.11.9.
Martin Shaw, 1875-1958

1 O Fa - ther a - bove us, our fa - ther in might, All
2 In thee move the in - fi - nite stars on their rounds, The
3 O Fa - ther in heav - en, our fa - ther on earth, Thou
4 We praise thee, O Fa - ther of in - fi - nite might, We

live by thy love, as the flowers in the light; Our fa - ther and moth-er and
plan - ets, the sun, and the moon in their bounds, As they kin - dle and glit - ter and
mak - est new life in each seed and each birth; The in - ven - tor, de - sign - er and
thank thee for life and for love and for light, We pray thee thy treas-ure on

mak - er art thou. For - ward! For-ward ev - er, for - ward now!
spar - kle and glow: On - ward! On-ward ev - er, on - ward go!
ar - tist art thou. For - ward! For-ward ev - er, for - ward now!
all to be-stow: On - ward! On-ward ev - er, on - ward go!

HIS LOVE From *Songs of Praise for Boys and Girls* by permission of Oxford University Press.

All My Hope on God Is Founded

Joachim Neander, 1650-1680
Para. Robert Bridges, 1844-1930

NEANDER 8.7.8.7.6.7.
From Chorale *Unser Herrscher,*
by Joachim Neander, 1650-1680

1 All my hope on God is found - ed; He doth still my
2 Pride of man and earth - ly glo - ry, Sword and crown be -
3 God's great good - ness aye en - dur - eth, Deep his wis - dom,

trust re - new. Me through change and chance he guid - eth,
tray his trust; What with care and toil he build - eth,
pass - ing thought; Splen - dor, light and life at - tend him,

On - ly good and on - ly true. God un - known,
Tower and tem - ple fall to dust. But God's power,
Beau - ty spring - eth out of nought. Ev - er - more,

he a - lone Calls my heart to be his own.
hour by hour, Is my tem - ple and my tower.
from his store New - born worlds rise and a - dore. A - men.

HIS PROVIDENCE

Unto the Hills Around Do I Lift Up

From Psalm 121.
John Campbell, Duke of Argyll, 1845-1914

SANDON 10.4.10.4.10.10.
Charles H. Purday, 1799-1885

1 Un - to the hills a - round do I lift up My long - ing eyes;
2 He will not suf - fer that thy foot be moved: Safe shalt thou be.
3 Je - ho - vah is him - self thy keep - er true, Thy change - less shade;
4 From ev - ery e - vil shall he keep thy soul, From ev - ery sin;

O whence for me shall my sal - va - tion come, From whence a - rise?
No care - less slum - ber shall his eye - lids close, Who keep - eth thee.
Je - ho - vah thy de - fense on thy right hand Him - self hath made.
Je - ho - vah shall pre - serve thy go - ing out, Thy com - ing in.

From God the Lord doth come my cer - tain aid,
Be - hold, he sleep - eth not, he slum - bereth ne'er,
And thee no sun by day shall ev - er smite;
A - bove thee watch - ing; he whom we a - dore

From God the Lord who heaven and earth hath made.
Who keep - eth Is - rael in his ho - ly care.
No moon shall harm thee in the si - lent night.
Shall keep thee hence - forth, yea, for - ev - er more. A-men.

HIS PROVIDENCE

God of Our Fathers, Whose Almighty Hand

22

Daniel C. Roberts, 1841-1907

NATIONAL HYMN 10.10.10.10.
George W. Warren, 1828-1902

Trumpets, before each stanza
(optional)

1 God of our fathers, whose al-might-y hand
2 Thy love di-vine hath led us in the past;
3 From war's a-larms, from dead-ly pes-ti-lence,
4 Re-fresh thy peo-ple on their toil-some way;

Leads forth in beau-ty all the star-ry band
In this free land by thee our lot is cast;
Be thy strong arm our ev-er sure de-fense;
Lead us from night to nev-er-end-ing day;

Of shin-ing worlds in splen-dor through the skies,
Be thou our rul-er, guard-ian, guide, and stay,
Thy true re-li-gion in our hearts in-crease;
Fill all our lives with love and grace di-vine,

Our grate-ful songs be-fore thy throne a-rise.
Thy word our law, thy paths our cho-sen way.
Thy boun-teous good-ness nour-ish us in peace.
And glo-ry, laud, and praise be ev-er thine. A-men.

HIS PROVIDENCE

23   O God, Our Help in Ages Past

Based on Psalm 90
Isaac Watts, 1674-1748

ST. ANNE C.M.
William Croft, 1678-1727

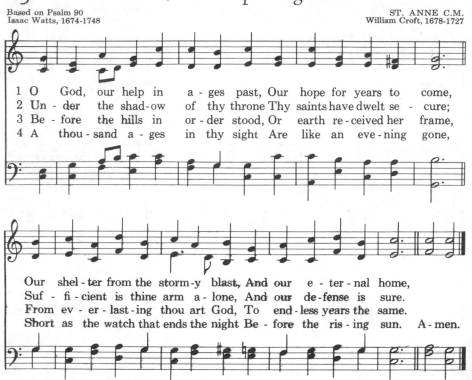

1 O God, our help in a - ges past, Our hope for years to come,
2 Un - der the shad-ow of thy throne Thy saints have dwelt se - cure;
3 Be - fore the hills in or - der stood, Or earth re - ceived her frame,
4 A thou - sand a - ges in thy sight Are like an eve - ning gone,

Our shel - ter from the storm-y blast, And our e - ter - nal home,
Suf - fi - cient is thine arm a - lone, And our de - fense is sure.
From ev - er - last-ing thou art God, To end - less years the same.
Short as the watch that ends the night Be - fore the ris - ing sun. A - men.

5 Time, like an ever-rolling stream,
  Bears all its sons away;
  They fly, forgotten, as a dream
  Dies at the opening day.

6 O God, our help in ages past,
  Our hope for years to come,
  Be thou our guard while troubles last,
  And our eternal home.

24   As the Sun Doth Daily Rise

Latin: Matutinus altiora
Tr. O. B. C. alt.

INNOCENTS 7.7.7.7.
The Parish Choir, 1850

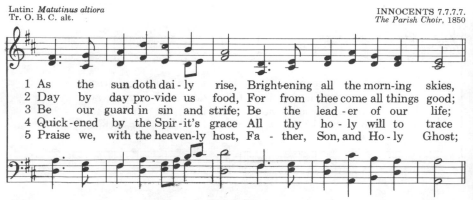

1 As the sun doth dai - ly rise, Bright-ening all the morn-ing skies,
2 Day by day pro-vide us food, For from thee come all things good;
3 Be our guard in sin and strife; Be the lead - er of our life;
4 Quick-ened by the Spir-it's grace All thy ho - ly will to trace
5 Praise we, with the heaven-ly host, Fa - ther, Son, and Ho - ly Ghost;

HIS PROVIDENCE

So to thee with one ac-cord Lift we up our hearts, O Lord!
Strength un-to our souls af-ford From thy liv-ing Bread, O Lord!
Lest from thee we stray a-broad, Stay our way-ward feet, O Lord!
While we dai-ly search thy Word, Wis-dom true im-part, O Lord!
Thee would we with one ac-cord Praise and mag-ni-fy, O Lord! A-men.

Through All the Changing Scenes

25

Based on Psalm 34
New Version, 1696

CONSOLATION C.M.
John Wyeth's *Repository of
Sacred Music, Part Second*, 1813

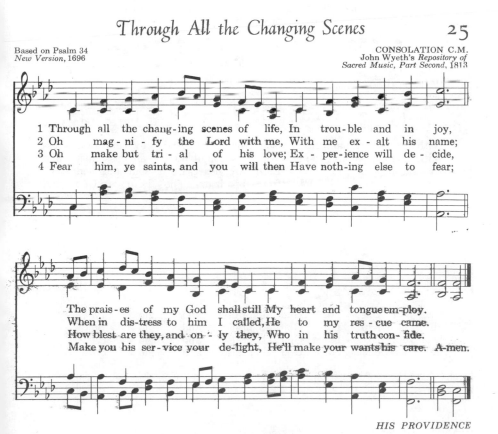

1 Through all the chang-ing scenes of life, In trou-ble and in joy,
2 Oh mag-ni-fy the Lord with me, With me ex-alt his name;
3 Oh make but tri-al of his love; Ex-per-ience will de-cide,
4 Fear him, ye saints, and you will then Have noth-ing else to fear;

The prais-es of my God shall still My heart and tongue em-ploy.
When in dis-tress to him I called, He to my res-cue came.
How blest are they, and on-ly they, Who in his truth con-fide.
Make you his ser-vice your de-light, He'll make your wants his care. A-men.

HIS PROVIDENCE

Sing Praise to God

Johann J. Schütz, 1640-1690
Tr. Frances E. Cox, 1812-1897

MIT FREUDEN ZART 8.7.8.7.8.8.7.
Bohemian Brethren's *Kirchengesänge*, 1566

1 Sing praise to God who reigns a-bove, The God of all cre - a - tion,
2 What God's al-might-y power hath made, His gra-cious mer - cy keep-eth;
3 Then all my glad-some way a - long, I sing a - loud thy prais-es,
4 O ye who name Christ's ho - ly name, Give God all praise and glo - ry;

The God of power, the God of love, The God of our sal - va - tion;
By morn-ing glow or eve-ning shade His watch-ful eye ne'er sleep - eth;
That men may hear the grate-ful song My voice un - wea - ried rais - es;
All ye who own his power, pro-claim A - loud the won - drous sto - ry!

With heal-ing balm my soul he fills, And ev - ery faith - less
With - in the king-dom of his might, Lo! all is just and
Be joy - ful in the Lord, my heart, Both soul and bod - y
Cast each false i - dol from his throne, The Lord is God, and

mur - mur stills: To God all praise and glo - ry.
all is right: To God all praise and glo - ry.
bear your part: To God all praise and glo - ry.
he a - lone: To God all praise and glo - ry. A - men.

HIS PROVIDENCE

Golden Breaks the Dawn

T. C. Chao, 1888-
Tr. Frank W. Price, 1895-

LE P'ING 5.5.5.5.D.
Chinese Folk Melody
Adapt. Hu Te-ngai c. 1900
Arr. Paul E. Koch, 1929-

1 Gold-en breaks the dawn, Comes the east-ern sun Like a man of
2 Give me dai-ly bread While I do my part; Bright skies o-ver

brawn Set his course to run. Birds a-bove me fly, Flow-ers bloom be-
head, Glad-ness in my heart. Sim-ple wants pro-vide, E-vil let me

low; Through the earth and sky God's great mer-cies flow.
shun, Je-sus at my side Till the day is done. A-men.

HIS PROVIDENCE

28 God of Our Life, Through All the Circling Years

Hugh T. Kerr, 1872-1950, alt.

SANDON 10.4.10.4.10.10.
Charles H. Purday, 1799-1885

1 God of our life, through all the cir - cling years, We trust in thee;
2 God of the past, our times are in thy hand; With us a - bide.
3 God of the com - ing years, through paths un-known We fol - low thee;

In all the past, through all our hopes and fears, Thy hand we see.
Lead us by faith to hope's true prom-ised land; Be thou our guide.
When we are strong, Lord, leave us not a - lone; Our ref - uge be.

With each new day, when morn - ing lifts the veil,
With thee to bless, the dark - ness shines as light,
Be thou for us in life our dai - ly bread,

We own thy mer - cies, Lord, which nev - er fail.
And faith's fair vi - sion chan - ges in - to sight.
Our heart's true home when all our years have sped. A-men.

HIS PROVIDENCE

God Moves in a Mysterious Way

William Cowper, 1731-1800

DUNDEE C.M.
Scottish Psalter, 1615

1 God moves in a mys - te - rious way His won-ders to per - form;
2 Ye fear - ful saints, fresh cour-age take; The clouds ye so much dread
3 Judge not the Lord by fee - ble sense, But trust him for his grace;
4 Blind un - be - lief is sure to err, And scan his work in vain;

He plants his foot-steps in the sea And rides up - on the storm.
Are big with mer - cy, and shall break In bless - ings on your head.
Be - hind a frown-ing prov - i - dence He hides a smil-ing face.
God is his own in - ter - pret - er, And he will make it plain. A-men.

Children of the Heavenly Father

30

Caroline V. Sandell Berg, 1832-1903
Tr. Ernest William Olson, 1870-1958

SANDELL L.M.
(TRYGGARE KAN INGEN VARA)
Swedish Melody

1 Chil - dren of the heaven-ly Fa - ther Safe - ly in his bos-om gath - er;
2 God his own doth tend and nour-ish, In his ho - ly courts they flour-ish.
3 Neith - er life nor death shall ev - er From the Lord his chil-dren sev - er;
4 Though he giv - eth or he tak-eth, God his chil-dren ne'er for - sak - eth,

Nest-ling bird nor star in heav-en Such a ref - uge e'er was giv - en.
From all e - vil things he spares them, In his might - y arms he bears them.
Un - to them his grace he show-eth, And their sor - rows all he know-eth.
His the lov - ing pur-pose sole-ly To pre-serve them pure and ho - ly.

From *The Lutheran Service Book and Hymnal*, by permission of the Commission on the Liturgy and Hymnal.

HIS ABIDING PRESENCE

A Mighty Fortress

Martin Luther, 1483-1546
Trans. Frederic Henry Hedge, 1805-1890

EIN' FESTE BURG 8.7.8.7.6.6.6.6.7.
Martin Luther, 1483-1546

1 A might-y for-tress is our God, A bul-wark nev-er fail - ing;
2 Did we in our own strength con-fide, Our striv-ing would be los - ing,
3 And though this world, with dev - ils filled, Should threat-en to un - do us,
4 That word a - bove all earth-ly powers, No thanks to them, a - bid - eth;

Our help - er he a - mid the flood Of mor - tal ills pre - vail - ing.
Were not the right man on our side, The man of God's own choos - ing.
We will not fear, for God hath willed His truth to tri-umph through us.
The Spir - it and the gifts are ours Through him who with us sid - eth.

For still our an - cient foe Doth seek to work us woe; His craft and power are
Dost ask who that may be? Christ Je - sus, it is he; Lord Sab - a - oth his
The prince of dark - ness grim, We trem-ble not for him; His rage we can en -
Let goods and kin - dred go, This mor - tal life al - so; The bod - y they may

great; And armed with cru - el hate, On earth is not his e - qual.
name, From age to age the same, And he must win the bat - tle.
dure, For lo, his doom is sure: One lit - tle word shall fell him.
kill; God's truth a - bid -eth still, His king-dom is for - ev - er. A-men.

HIS ABIDING PRESENCE

Come, My Soul, Thou Must Be Waking

32

Seele, du musst munter werden
Friedrich von Canitz, 1654-1699
Tr. Henry J. Buckoll, 1803- 1871, alt.

RICHTER 8.4.7.8.4.7.
J. A. Freylinghausen's
Geistreiches Gesang-Buch, 1704

1 Come, my soul, thou must be wak - ing. Now is break - ing O'er the earth an - oth - er day: Come, to him who made this splen - dor See thou ren - der All thy fee - ble strength can pay.

2 Glad - ly hail the sun re - turn - ing, Read - y burn - ing Be the in - cense of thy powers; For the night is safe - ly end - ed, God hath tend - ed With his care thy help - less hours.

3 Pray that he may pros - per ev - er Each en - deav - or, When thine aim is good and true; But that he may ev - er thwart thee, And con - vert thee, When thou e - vil wouldst pur - sue.

4 On - ly God's free gifts a - buse not, Light re - fuse not, But his Spir - it's voice o - bey; Thou with him shalt dwell, be - hold - ing Light en - fold - ing All things in un - cloud - ed day. A - men.

HIS ABIDING PRESENCE

God the Omnipotent

Sts. 1,2: Henry F. Chorley, 1808-1872, alt.
St. 3: John Ellerton, 1826-1893, alt.

RUSSIAN HYMN 11.10.11.9.
Alexis Lvov, 1799-1870

1 God the om - nip - o - tent! King, who or - dain - est
2 God the all mer - ci - ful! Earth hath for - sak - en
3 God the all right - eous One! Man hath de - fied thee;

Thun - der thy clar - ion, the light - ning thy sword,
Thy ways all ho - ly, and slight - ed thy word;
Yet to e - ter - ni - ty stand - eth thy word;

Show forth thy pit - y on high where thou reign - est;
Bid not thy wrath in its ter - rors a - wak - en:
False - hood and wrong shall not tar - ry be - side thee:

Give to us peace in our time, O Lord.
Give to us peace in our time, O Lord.
Give to us peace in our time, O Lord. A - men.

HIS ABIDING PRESENCE

God Hath Spoken

34

George Wallace Briggs, 1875-1959

HYMN TO JOY 8.7.8.7.D.
Arr. from Ludwig van Beethoven, 1770-1827

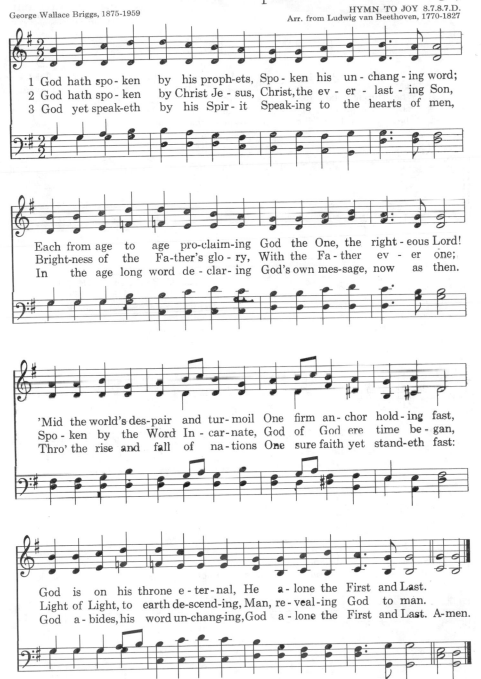

1 God hath spo-ken by his proph-ets, Spo-ken his un-chang-ing word;
2 God hath spo-ken by Christ Je-sus, Christ, the ev-er-last-ing Son,
3 God yet speak-eth by his Spir-it Speak-ing to the hearts of men,

Each from age to age pro-claim-ing God the One, the right-eous Lord!
Bright-ness of the Fa-ther's glo-ry, With the Fa-ther ev-er one;
In the age long word de-clar-ing God's own mes-sage, now as then.

'Mid the world's des-pair and tur-moil One firm an-chor hold-ing fast,
Spo-ken by the Word In-car-nate, God of God ere time be-gan,
Thro' the rise and fall of na-tions One sure faith yet stand-eth fast:

God is on his throne e-ter-nal, He a-lone the First and Last.
Light of Light, to earth de-scend-ing, Man, re-veal-ing God to man.
God a-bides, his word un-chang-ing, God a-lone the First and Last. A-men.

Words from *Ten New Hymns on the Bible* © 1953 by the Hymn Society of America; used by permission.

HIS ABIDING PRESENCE

How Firm a Foundation

"K" in John Rippon's *Selection*
of Hymns, 1787, alt.

FOUNDATION 11.11.11.11.
Early American Melody
Harm. Charles H. Heaton, 1928-

1 How firm a foun - da - tion, ye saints of the Lord,
2 "Fear not, I am with thee, oh, be not dis - mayed,
3 "When through the deep wa - ters I call thee to go,
4 "When through fi - ery tri - als thy path - way shall lie,
5 "The soul that on Je - sus hath leaned for re - pose,

Is laid for your faith in his ex - cel - lent word!
For I am thy God, and will still give thee aid.
The riv - ers of woe shall not thee o - ver - flow;
My grace, all suf - fi - cient, shall be thy sup - ply.
I will not, I will not de - sert to his foes;

What more can he say than to you he hath said,
I'll strength - en thee, help thee, and cause thee to stand,
For I will be near thee, thy trou - bles to bless,
The flame shall not hurt thee; I on - ly de - sign
That soul, though all hell should en - deav - or to shake,

HIS ABIDING PRESENCE

To you who for ref - uge to Je - sus have fled?
Up - held by my right - eous, om - nip - o - tent hand.
And sanc - ti - fy to thee thy deep - est dis - tress.
Thy dross to con - sume, and thy gold to re - fine.
I'll nev - er, no nev - er, no nev - er for - sake!" A-men.

Father, Lead Me Day by Day

36

John P. Hopps, 1834-1912

ORIENTIS PARTIBUS 7.7.7.7.
Adapted from? Pierre de Corbeil, d. 1222

1 Fa - ther, lead me day by day, Ev - er in thine own strong way;
2 When in dan - ger, make me brave, Make me know that thou canst save;
3 When I'm tempt-ed to do wrong, Make me stead - fast, wise and strong;

Teach me to be pure and true, Show me what I ought to do.
Keep me safe - ly by thy side; Let me in thy love a - bide.
And when all a - lone I stand, Shield me with thy might - y hand. A-men.

HIS ABIDING PRESENCE

37

God of the Moving Years

Kenneth Morse, 1913-

CENTRALIA 6.6.12.6.6.6.6.6.6.4.
George Brandon, 1924-, based on a tune in
The Christian Psalmist, revised (1854)

1 God of the mov-ing years, God of the march-ing
2 God of e-ter-nal peace, God of un-dy-ing

days, Thy mu-sic on our ears shall turn our fears to
life, Thy mer-cy will not cease to bring re-lease from

praise; God of each sing-ing heart, God of each
strife. God of each hun-ger-ing soul, God of each

HIS ABIDING PRESENCE

si - lent voice, Thy beau - ty stands a - part, a - bove, be-
search-ing mind, Thy laws a - lone con - trol the power to

yond all art. Ac - cept the song we raise; let
make us whole. Thou art the light of life for

men re - joice.
all man - kind! A - men.

Unison or Harmony

A - men.

HIS ABIDING PRESENCE

38 The Day Thou Gavest, Lord, Is Ended

First Tune

John Ellerton, 1826-1893

ST. CLEMENT 9.8.9.8.
Clement C. Scholefield, 1839-1904

1 The day thou gav - est, Lord, is end - ed,
2 We thank thee that thy Church, un - sleep - ing,
3 As o'er each con - ti - nent and is - land
4 So be it, Lord; thy throne shall nev - er,

The dark - ness falls at thy be - hest;
While earth rolls on - ward in - to light,
The dawn leads on an - oth - er day,
Like earth's proud em - pires, pass a - way;

To thee our morn - ing hymns as - cend - ed
Through all the world her watch is keep - ing,
The voice of prayer is nev - er si - lent,
Thy king - dom stands, and grows for - ev - er,

Thy praise shall sanc - ti - fy our rest.
And rests not now by day or night.
Nor dies the strain of praise a - way.
Till all thy crea - tures own thy sway. A - men.

HIS ABIDING PRESENCE

The Day Thou Gavest, Lord, Is Ended

Second Tune

39

John Ellerton, 1826-1893

LES COMMANDEMENS DE DIEU 9.8.9.8.
Attr. to Louis Bourgeois, c. 1510-c. 1561
Genevan Psalter, 1547

1 The day thou gav - est, Lord, is end - ed,
2 We thank thee that thy Church, un - sleep - ing
3 As o'er each con - ti - nent and is - land
4 So be it, Lord; thy throne shall nev - er,

The dark - ness falls at thy be - hest;
While earth rolls on - ward in - to light,
The dawn leads on an - oth - er day,
Like earth's proud em - pires, pass a - way;

To thee our morn - ing hymns as - cend - ed,
Through all the world her watch is keep - ing,
The voice of prayer is nev - er si - lent,
Thy king - dom stands, and grows for - ev - er,

Thy praise shall sanc - ti - fy our rest.
And rests not now by day or night.
Nor dies the strain of praise a - way.
Till all thy crea - tures own thy sway. A - men.

HIS ABIDING PRESENCE

The Lord's My Shepherd

First Tune

40

CRIMOND C.M.

Based on Psalm 23.
Scottish Psalter, 1650, alt.

Melody by Jessie S. Irvine, 1836-1887

1 The Lord's my shep - herd, I'll not want; He makes me down to lie
2 My soul he doth re - store a - gain. And me to walk doth make
3 Yea, though I walk in death's dark vale, Yet will I fear no ill,
4 My ta - ble thou hast fur - nish - ed In pres - ence of my foes;
5 Good-ness and mer - cy all my life Shall sure - ly fol - low me;

In pas - tures green; he lead - eth me The qui - et wa - ters by;
With - in the paths of right-eous-ness, E'en for his own name's sake.
For thou art with me, and thy rod And staff me com-fort still.
My head thou dost with oil a - noint, And my cup o - ver - flows.
And in God's house for ev - er - more My dwell - ing place shall be. A - men.

The Lord's My Shepherd

Second Tune

41

EVAN C.M.

Based on Psalm 23
Scottish Psalter, 1650, alt.

William H. Havergal, 1793-1870

1 The Lord's my shep - herd, I'll not want; He makes me down to lie
2 My soul he doth re - store a - gain. And me to walk doth make
3 Yea, though I walk in death's dark vale, Yet will I fear no ill,
4 My ta - ble thou hast fur - nish - ed In pres - ence of my foes;
5 Good - ness and mer - cy all my life Shall sure - ly fol - low me;

In pas - tures green; he lead-eth me The qui - et wa - ters by;
With - in the paths of right-eous-ness, E'en for his own name's sake.
For thou art with me, and thy rod And staff me com - fort still.
My head thou dost with oil a - noint, And my cup o - ver - flows.
And in God's house for ev - er - more My dwell - ing place shall be.

HIS ABIDING PRESENCE

O God, in Whom We Live and Move

George Wallace Briggs, 1875-1959

42

SALVATION C.M.D.
Ananias Davisson's *Kentucky Harmony, c.* 1815

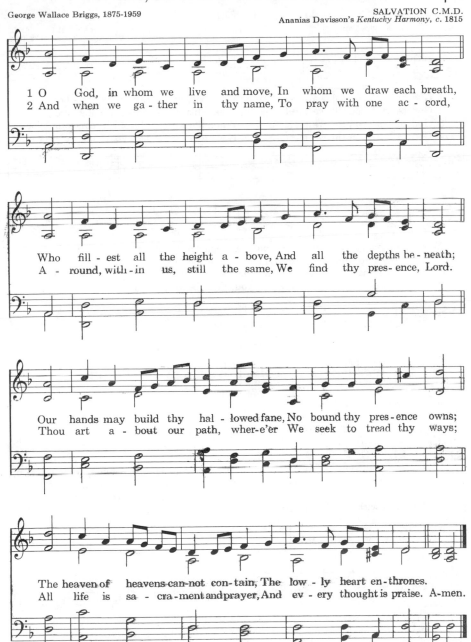

1 O God, in whom we live and move, In whom we draw each breath,
2 And when we ga-ther in thy name, To pray with one ac-cord,

Who fill-est all the height a-bove, And all the depths be-neath;
A-round, with-in us, still the same, We find thy pres-ence, Lord.

Our hands may build thy hal-lowed fane, No bound thy pres-ence owns;
Thou art a-bout our path, wher-e'er We seek to tread thy ways;

The heaven of heavens can-not con-tain, The low-ly heart en-thrones.
All life is sa-cra-ment and prayer, And ev-ery thought is praise. A-men.

Words from *Enlarged Songs of Praise* by permission of Oxford University Press.

HIS ABIDING PRESENCE

43

God Be with You Till We Meet Again
First Tune

Jeremiah E. Rankin, 1828-1904

RANDOLPH 9.8.8.9.
R. Vaughan Williams, 1872-1958

1 God be with you till we meet a-gain; By his coun-sels guide, up-hold you,
2 God be with you till we meet a-gain; 'Neath his wings pro-tect-ing hide you,
3 God be with you till we meet a-gain; When life's per-ils thick con-found you,
4 God be with you till we meet a-gain; Keep love's ban-ner float-ing o'er you,

With his sheep se-cure-ly fold you: God be with you till we meet a-gain.
Dai-ly man-na still pro-vide you: God be with you till we meet a-gain.
Put his arms un-fail-ing round you: God be with you till we meet a-gain.
Smite death's threat-ening wave be-fore you: God be with you till we meet a-gain. A-men.

Music from *The English Hymnal* by permission of Oxford University Press.

44

God Be with You Till We Meet Again
Second Tune

Jeremiah E. Rankin, 1828-1904

GOD BE WITH YOU 9.8.8.9.
William G. Tomer, 1832-1896

1 God be with you till we meet a-gain; By his coun-sels guide, up-hold you,
2 God be with you till we meet a-gain; 'Neath his wings pro-tect-ing hide you,
3 God be with you till we meet a-gain; When life's per-ils thick con-found you,
4 God be with you till we meet a-gain; Keep love's ban-ner float-ing o'er you,

With his sheep se-cure-ly fold you: God be with you till we meet a-gain.
Dai-ly man-na still pro-vide you: God be with you till we meet a-gain.
Put his arms un-fail-ing round you: God be with you till we meet a-gain.
Smite death's threat-ening wave be-fore you: God be with you till we meet a-gain. A-men.

HIS ABIDING PRESENCE

He Leadeth Me, O Blessed Thought

Joseph H. Gilmore, 1834-1918

HE LEADETH ME L.M. with Refrain
William B. Bradbury, 1816-1868

1 He   lead-eth me, O bless-ed thought! O words with heaven-ly com-fort fraught!
2 Lord, I would clasp thy hand in mine, Nor ev - er mur - mur nor re - pine;
3 And when my task on earth is done, When, by thy grace, the vic-tory's won,

What-e'er I do, wher-e'er I be, Still 'tis God's hand that lead - eth me.
Con - tent, what-ev - er lot I see, Since 'tis my God that lead - eth me.
E'en death's cold wave I will not flee, Since God through Jor-dan lead - eth me.

He lead-eth me, he lead-eth me, By his own hand he lead-eth me;

His faith-ful fol-lower I would be, For by his hand he lead-eth me. A-men.

HIS ABIDING PRESENCE

Lead, Kindly Light

John H. Newman, 1801-1890

SANDON 10.4.10.4.10.10.
Charles H. Purday, 1799-1885

1 Lead, kind-ly Light, a - mid the en-cir - cling gloom, Lead thou me on;
2 I was not ev - er thus, nor prayed that thou Shouldst lead me on;
3 So long thy power hath blest me, sure it still Will lead me on

The night is dark, and I am far from home; Lead thou me on!
I loved to choose and see my path, but now Lead thou me on.
O'er moor and fen, o'er crag and tor - rent, till The night is gone;

Keep thou my feet; I do not ask to see The
I loved the gar - ish day, and, spite of fears, Pride
And with the morn those an - gel fa - ces smile Which

dis - tant scene: one step e - nough for me.
ruled my will: re - mem - ber not past years.
I have loved long since, and lost a - while. A - men.

HIS ABIDING PRESENCE

Abide with Me

Henry F. Lyte, 1793-1847, alt.

EVENTIDE 10.10.10.10.
William H. Monk, 1823-1889

1 A - bide with me; fast falls the e - ven - tide;
2 I need thy pres - ence ev - ery pass - ing hour;
3 I fear no foe, with thee at hand to bless;
4 Hold thou thy cross be - fore my clos - ing eyes;

The dark - ness deep - ens, Lord, with me a - bide;
What but thy grace can foil the temp - ter's power?
Ills have no weight, and tears no bit - ter - ness;
Shine through the gloom, and point me to the skies;

When oth - er help - ers fail, and com - forts flee,
Who like thy - self my guide and stay can be?
Where is death's sting? where, grave, thy vic - to - ry?
Heaven's morn - ing breaks, and earth's vain shad - ows flee;

Help of the help - less, O a - bide with me.
Through cloud and sun - shine, O a - bide with me.
I tri - umph still if thou a - bide with me.
In life, in death, O Lord, a - bide with me. A-men.

HIS ABIDING PRESENCE

Before Jehovah's Aweful Throne

Based on Psalm 100
Isaac Watts, 1674-1748
Alt. by John Wesley, 1703-1791

WINCHESTER NEW L.M.
Adapted from
Musicalisches Handbuch, Hamburg, 1690

1 Be - fore Je - ho - vah's awe - ful throne, Ye
2 His sov - ereign power with - out our aid, Made
3 We are his peo - ple, we his care, Our
4 We'll crowd thy gates with thank - ful songs, High
5 Wide as the world is thy com - mand, Vast

na - tions bow with sa - cred joy; Know that the Lord is
us of clay, and formed us men; And when, like wan - dering
souls, and all our mor - tal frame; What last - ing hon - ors
as the heavens our voic - es raise; And earth, with her ten
as e - ter - ni - ty thy love; Firm as a rock thy

God a - lone, He can cre - ate, and he de - stroy.
sheep, we strayed, He brought us to his fold a - gain.
shall we rear, Al - might - y Mak - er, to thy name?
thou-sand tongues, Shall fill thy courts with sound - ing praise.
truth must stand, When roll - ing years shall cease to move. A - men.

HIS ABIDING PRESENCE

The King of Love My Shepherd Is

Based on Psalm 23
Henry W. Baker, 1821-1877

DOMINUS REGIT ME 8.7.8.7.
John B. Dykes, 1823-1876

49

1 The King of love my shep-herd is, Whose
2 Where streams of liv-ing wa-ter flow, My
3 Per-verse and fool-ish oft I strayed, But
4 In death's dark vale I fear no ill, With

good-ness fail-eth nev-er; I noth-ing lack if
ran-somed soul he lead-eth, And where the ver-dant
yet in love he sought me, And on his shoul-der
thee, dear Lord, be-side me: Thy rod and staff my

I am his, And he is mine for-ev-er.
pas-tures grow, With food ce-les-tial feed-eth.
gen-tly laid, And home re-joic-ing brought me.
com-fort still, Thy cross be-fore to guide me. A-men.

5 Thou spread'st a table in my sight,
Thy unction grace bestoweth,
And O what transport of delight
From thy pure chalice floweth!

6 And so through all the length of days
Thy goodness faileth never;
Good Shepherd, may I sing thy praise
Within thy house forever.

HIS ABIDING PRESENCE

With Broken Heart and Contrite Sigh

Cornelius Elven, 1797-1873

BABYLON'S STREAMS L.M.
Thomas Campian, 1567-1620

1 With bro - ken heart and con - trite sigh,
2 Far off I stand with tear - ful eyes,
3 Nor alms, nor deeds that I have done,

A trem - bling sin - ner, Lord, I cry:
Nor dare up - lift them to the skies;
Can for a sin - gle sin a - tone;

Thy par - d'ning grace is rich and free;
But thou dost all my an - guish see:
To Cal - va - ry a - lone I flee:

O God, be mer - ci - ful to me. A - men.

HIS FORGIVENESS

If Thou but Suffer God to Guide Thee

Wer nur den lieben Gott lässt walten
Georg Neumark, 1621-1681
Tr. Catherine Winkworth, 1827-1878

WER NUR DEN LIEBEN GOTT 9.8.9.8.8.8.
Georg Neumark, 1621-1681

1 If thou but suf - fer God to guide thee, And hope in
2 On - ly be still, and wait his lei - sure In cheer - ful
3 Sing, pray, and keep his ways un - swerv - ing; So do thine

him through all thy ways, He'll give thee strength, what-e'er be - tide thee,
hope, with heart con - tent To take what-e'er thy Fa - ther's pleas-ure
own part faith - ful - ly, And trust his word, though un - de - serv-ing;

And bear thee through the e - vil days; Who trusts in God's un-
And all de - serv - ing love have sent; Nor doubt our in - most
Thou yet shalt find it true for thee; God nev - er yet for-

chang - ing love Builds on the rock that nought can move.
wants are known To him who chose us for his own.
sook at need The soul that trust - ed him in - deed. A-men.

HIS FORGIVENESS

Depth of Mercy

Charles Wesley, 1707-1788

HEINLEIN 7.7.7.7.
Attr. to Martin Herbst, 1654-1681

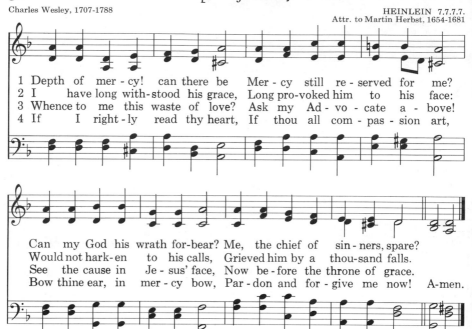

1 Depth of mer - cy! can there be Mer - cy still re - served for me?
2 I have long with-stood his grace, Long pro-voked him to his face:
3 Whence to me this waste of love? Ask my Ad - vo - cate a - bove!
4 If I right-ly read thy heart, If thou all com - pas - sion art,

Can my God his wrath for-bear? Me, the chief of sin - ners, spare?
Would not hark-en to his calls, Grieved him by a thou-sand falls.
See the cause in Je - sus' face, Now be - fore the throne of grace.
Bow thine ear, in mer - cy bow, Par - don and for - give me now! A-men.

Day Is Dying in the West

Mary A. Lathbury, 1841-1913

CHAUTAUQUA 7.7.7.7.4. with Refrain
William F. Sherwin, 1826-1888

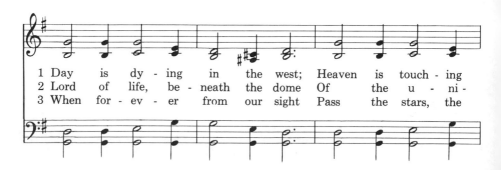

1 Day is dy - ing in the west; Heaven is touch - ing
2 Lord of life, be - neath the dome Of the u - ni -
3 When for - ev - er from our sight Pass the stars, the

earth with rest; Wait and wor - ship while the night
verse, thy home, Gath - er us who seek thy face
day, the night, Lord of an - gels, on our eyes

Sets her eve - ning lamps a - light Through all the sky.
To the fold of thy em - brace, For thou art nigh.
Let e - ter - nal morn - ing rise, And shad - ows end.

Ho - ly, ho - ly, ho - ly, Lord God of Hosts! Heaven and earth are full of thee!

Heaven and earth are prais - ing thee, O Lord most high! A - men.

ADORATION AND PRAISE

54 All Creatures of Our God and King

St. Francis of Assisi, 1182-1226
Tr. William H. Draper, 1855-1933

LASST UNS ERFREUEN 8.8.4.4.8.8. with Alleluias
Melody from *Geistliche Kirchengesäng*, Cologne, 1623
Harm. and arr. R. Vaughan Williams, 1872-1958

1 All crea-tures of our God and King, Lift up your voice and with us
2 Thou rush-ing wind that art so strong, Ye clouds that sail in heaven a -
3 Thou flow-ing wa - ter, pure and clear, Make mus - ic for thy Lord to
4 And all ye men of ten - der heart, For - giv-ing oth-ers, take your

sing Al - le - lu - ia, Al - le - lu - ia! Thou burn-ing sun with gold-en
long, O praise him, Al - le - lu - ia! Thou ris - ing morn, in praise re -
hear, Al - le - lu - ia, Al - le - lu - ia! Thou fire so mas-ter-ful and
part, O sing ye, Al - le - lu - ia! Ye who long pain and sor-row

beam, Thou sil - ver moon with soft-er gleam, O praise him,
joice, Ye lights of eve-ning, find a voice, O praise him,
bright, That giv - est man both warmth and light, O praise him,
bear, Praise God and on him cast your care. O praise him,

ADORATION AND PRAISE

O praise him, Al - le - lu - ia, Al - le - lu - ia, Al - le - lu - ia!

O God, We Praise Thee, and Confess 55

Based on *Te Deum Laudamus*, 5th century?
A Supplement to the New Version, 1700, alt.

TALLIS' ORDINAL C.M.
Thomas Tallis, c. 1505-1585

1 O God, we praise thee, and con - fess That thou the on - ly Lord
2 To thee all an - gels cry a - loud; To thee the powers on high,
3 O ho - ly, ho - ly, ho - ly Lord, Whom heaven-ly hosts o - bey,
4 The a-pos - tles' glo-rious com - pa - ny, And proph-ets crowned with light,
5 The ho-ly Church through-out the world, O Lord, con - fess - es thee,

And ev - er - last-ing Fa - ther art, By all the earth a - dored.
Both cher - u - bim and ser - a-phim, Con - tin - ual - ly do cry:
The world is with the glo - ry filled Of thy ma - jes - tic sway!
With all the mar - tyrs' no - ble host, Thy con-stant praise re-cite.
That thou e - ter - nal Fa - ther art, Of bound-less maj - es - ty. A - men.

ADORATION AND PRAISE

56 Praise the Lord, His Glories Show

Henry F. Lyte, 1793-1847

GWALCHMAI 7.7.7.7. with Alleluias
Joseph D. Jones, 1827-1870

1 Praise the Lord, his glo - ries show, Al - le - lu - ia!
2 Earth to heaven, and heaven to earth, Al - le - lu - ia!
3 Praise the Lord, his mer - cies trace, Al - le - lu - ia!

Saints with - in his courts be - low, Al - le - lu - ia!
Tell his won - ders, sing his worth, Al - le - lu - ia!
Praise his prov - i - dence and grace, Al - le - lu - ia!

An - gels round his throne a - bove, Al - le - lu - ia!
Age to age, and shore to shore, Al - le - lu - ia!
All that he for man hath done, Al - le - lu - ia!

All that see and share his love, Al - le - lu - ia!
Praise him, praise him ev - er - more! Al - le - lu - ia!
All he sends us through his Son. Al - le - lu - ia! A-men.

ADORATION AND PRAISE

Praise to the Lord, the Almighty

Joachim Neander, 1650-1680
Tr. Catherine Winkworth, 1827-1878, alt.

LOBE DEN HERREN 14.14.4.7.8.
Stralsund Gesangbuch, 1665

1 Praise to the Lord, the Al-might-y, the King of cre - a - tion;
2 Praise to the Lord, who o'er all things so won-drous-ly reign - eth,
3 Praise to the Lord, who doth pros-per thy work and de - fend thee;
4 Praise to the Lord, O let all that is in me a - dore him;

O my soul, praise him, for he is thy health and sal - va - tion;
Who, as on wings of an ea - gle up - lift - ed, sus - tain - eth.
Sure - ly his good-ness and mer - cy here dai - ly at - tend thee.
All that hath life and breath, come now with prais-es be - fore him.

Join the great throng, Psal - ter - y, or - gan, and song,
Hast thou not seen? All that is need - ful hath been
Pon - der a - new What the Al - might - y can do,
Let the A - men Sound from his peo - ple a - gain;

Sound - ing in glad ad - o - ra - tion.
Grant - ed in what he or - dain - eth.
Who with his love doth be - friend thee.
Glad - ly for aye we a - dore him. A - men.

ADORATION AND PRAISE

58　All Glory Be to God on High

Allein Gott in der Höh' sei Ehr'
Nikolaus Decius, d. 1541
Tr. Catherine Winkworth, 1827-1878, alt.

ALLEIN GOTT IN DER HÖH' 8.7.8.7.8.8.7.
Geistliche Lieder, Leipzig, 1539
Harm. Hieronymus Praetorius, 1560-1629

1 All glo-ry be to God on high, Who hath our race be-friend-ed! To us no harm shall now come nigh, The strife at last is end-ed; God show-eth his good-will to men, And peace shall reign on earth a-gain;

2 We praise, we wor-ship thee, we trust And give thee thanks for ev-er, O Fa-ther, that thy rule is just And wise, and chang-es nev-er; Thy bound-less power o'er all things reigns, Thou dost what-e'er thy will or-dains;

3 O Je-sus Christ, our bless-ed Lord, Be-got-ten of the Fa-ther, O thou who hast our peace re-stored, And thy lost sheep dost gath-er, Thou Lamb of God, en-throned on high, Be-hold our need and hear our cry;

4 O Ho-ly Spir-it, pre-cious gift, Thou Com-fort-er un-fail-ing, Do thou our trou-bled souls up-lift, A-gainst the foe pre-vail-ing; A-vert our woes and calm our dread: For us the Sav-ior's blood was shed;

ADORATION AND PRAISE

O thank him for his good - ness!
'Tis well thou art our rul - er!
Have mer - cy on us, Je - sus!
Do thou in faith sus - tain us! A - men.

All Praise to Thee, for Thou, O King Divine   59

F. Bland Tucker, 1895-

NATIONAL CITY 10.10.10. with Alleluia
Lawrence P. Schreiber, 1933-

1 All praise to thee, for thou, O King di - vine, Didst
2 Thou cam'st to us in low - li - ness of thought; By
3 Let this mind be in us which was in thee, Who
4 Let ev - ery tongue con - fess with one ac - cord In

yield the glo - ry that of right was thine, That
thee the out - cast and the poor were sought, And
wast a ser - vant that we might be free, Then
heaven and earth that Je - sus Christ is Lord; And

in our dark-ened hearts thy grace might shine. Al - le - lu - ia!
by thy death was God's sal - va - tion wrought. Al - le - lu - ia!
hum-bling thy-self to death on Cal - va - ry. Al - le - lu - ia!
God the Fa-ther be by all a - dored. Al - le - lu - ia! A-men.

Words by permission of The Church Pension Fund; music copyright © 1967 by The Bethany Press.

ADORATION AND PRAISE

60
Come, O Come, in Pious Lays

George Wither, 1588-1667, alt.

ALLE MENSCHEN 7.7.7.7.D.
Jakob Hintze, 1622-1702
Harm. J. S. Bach, 1685-1750

1 Come, O come, in pi - ous lays Sound we God Al-might-y's praise;
2 Come, ye sons of hu - man race, In this cho - rus take a place;
3 So this huge wide orb we see Shall one choir, one tem - ple be;

Hith - er bring in one con - sent Heart, and voice, and in - stru - ment.
And, a - mid the mor - tal throng, Be you mas - ters of the song.
Where in such a praise - ful tone We will sing what he hath done,

Sound the trum - pet, touch the lute, Let no tongue nor string be mute,
Let, in praise of God, the sound Run a nev - er - end - ing round,
That our song shall ov - er - climb All the bounds of place and time;

Nor a crea-ture dumb be found, That hath ei - ther voice or sound.
That our songs of praise may be Ev - er - last-ing, as is he.
Come, then, come, in pi - ous lays Sound we God Al-might-y's praise. A-men.

ADORATION AND PRAISE

God Himself Is with Us

61

Gerhard Tersteegen, 1697-1769
Tr. Frederick W. Foster, 1760-1835
and John Miller, 1756-1810; alt., 1932

ARNSBERG 6.6.8.D.3.3.6.6.
Joachim Neander's *Bundes-Lieder*, 1680

1 God him-self is with us: Let us now a - dore him, And with awe ap-
2 God him-self is with us: Hear the harps re - sound-ing! See the crowds the
3 O thou Fount of bless-ing, Pu - ri - fy my spir - it: Trust-ing on-ly

pear be - fore him. God is in his tem - ple, All with - in keep
throne sur - round-ing! "Ho - ly, ho - ly, ho - ly" Hear the hymn as-
in thy mer - it, Like the ho - ly an - gels Who be - hold thy

si - lence, Pros-trate lie with deep-est rev-erence. Him a - lone God we own,
cend - ing, An-gels, saints, their voic-es blend-ing! Bow thine ear To us here:
glo - ry, May I cease-less-ly a - dore thee, And in all, Great and small,

Him, our God and Sav - ior; Praise his Name for - ev - er.
Hear, O Christ, the prais - es That thy church now rais - es.
Seek to do most near - ly What thou lov - est dear - ly. A-men.

ADORATION AND PRAISE

62 Father, We Praise Thee, Now the Night Is Over

Latin: *Nocte surgentes*
Attr. to Gregory the Great, 540-604
Tr. Percy Dearmer, 1867-1936

CHRISTE SANCTORUM 11.11.11.5.
La Feillée's *Méthode du Plain-chant*, 1781

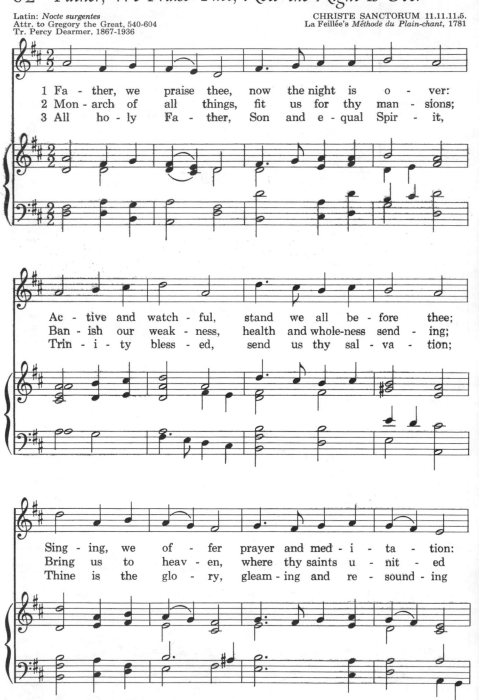

1 Fa - ther, we   praise thee, now   the night is   o - ver:
2 Mon - arch of   all   things, fit   us for thy   man - sions;
3 All   ho - ly   Fa - ther,   Son   and e - qual Spir - it,

Ac - tive and   watch - ful,   stand we all be - fore   thee;
Ban - ish our   weak - ness,   health and whole-ness send - ing;
Trin - i - ty   bless - ed,   send   us thy sal - va - tion;

Sing - ing, we   of - fer   prayer and med - i - ta - tion:
Bring   us   to   heav - en,   where thy saints u - nit - ed
Thine   is   the   glo - ry,   gleam - ing and re - sound - ing

ADORATION AND PRAISE

Thus we a - dore thee.
Joy with - out end - ing.
Through all cre - a - tion. A - men.

Sing to the Lord a Joyful Song 63

John Samuel Bewley Monsell, 1811-1875

SCHÜTZ 81 L.M.
Heinrich Schütz, 1585-1672

1 Sing to the Lord a joy - ful song, Lift up your
2 For life and love, for rest and food, For dai - ly
3 For joys un - told, that from a - bove Cheer those who

hearts, your voic - es raise; To us his gra - cious gifts be -
help and night - ly care, Sing to the Lord, for he is
love his sweet em - ploy, Sing to our God, for he is

long, To him our songs of love and praise.
good, And praise his name, for it is fair.
love, Ex - alt his name, for it is joy. A-men.

ADORATION AND PRAISE

Come, Thou Almighty King

Anonymous, c. 1757

ITALIAN HYMN 6.6.4.6.6.6.4.
Felice de Giardini, 1716-1796

1 Come, thou al - might - y King, Help us thy name to sing; Help us to praise: Fa - ther, all glo - ri - ous, O'er all vic - to - ri - ous, Come, and reign o - ver us, An - cient of Days.

2 Come, thou in - car - nate Word, Gird on thy might - y sword; Our prayer at - tend: Come, and thy peo - ple bless, And give thy word suc - cess; Spir - it of ho - li - ness, On us de - scend.

3 Come, ho - ly Com - fort - er, Thy sa - cred wit - ness bear In this glad hour! Thou who al - might - y art, Now rule in ev - ery heart, And ne'er from us de - part, Spir - it of power.

4 To thee, great One in Three E - ter - nal prais - es be Hence ev - er - more! His sov - ereign maj - es - ty May we in glo - ry see, And to e - ter - ni - ty Love and a - dore. A - men.

ADORATION AND PRAISE

It Is Good to Sing Thy Praises

From Psalm 92
The Psalter, 1912

HASTINGS-ON-HUDSON 8.7.8.7.D.
Harold W. Friedell, 1905-1958

1 It is good to sing thy prais-es And to thank thee, O Most High,
2 Thou hast filled my heart with glad-ness Thro' the works thy hands have wrought;
3 But the good shall live be-fore thee, Plant-ed in thy dwell-ing place,

Show-ing forth thy lov-ing kind-ness When the morn-ing lights the sky.
Thou hast made my life vic-to-rious, Great thy works and deep thy thought.
Fruit-ful trees and ev-er ver-dant, Nour-ished by thy bound-less grace.

It is good when night is fall-ing Of thy faith-ful-ness to tell,
Thou, O Lord, on high ex-alt-ed, Reign-est ev-er-more in might;
In his good-ness to the right-eous, God his right-eous-ness dis-plays;

While with sweet, mel-o-dious prais-es Songs of ad-o-ra-tion swell.
All thy en-e-mies shall per-ish, Sin be ban-ished from thy sight.
God my rock, my strength and refuge, Just and true are all his ways. A-men.

Music from *Hymns for Children and Grownups*. Used by permission of Mrs. Harold
W. Friedell and Lee H. Bristol, Jr.

ADORATION AND PRAISE

Glad Hymns and Songs Will I Recite

Author unknown, 13th century
Tr. from the Hebrew by Alice Lucas

OMNOM KAYN L.M.
Traditional Hebrew Melody

1 Glad hymns and songs will I re - cite
2 How doth my soul with - in me yearn
3 O may my words of bless - ing rise
4 My med - i - ta - tion day and night,

To sing of thee, by day and night,
Be - neath thy shad - ow to re - turn,
To thee, who throned a - bove the skies,
May it be pleas - ant in thy sight,

Of thee, who art my soul's de - light,
Thy se - cret mys - ter - ies to learn,
Art just and might - y, great and wise!
For thou art all my soul's de - light,

Of thee, who art my soul's de - light.
Thy se - cret mys - ter - ies to learn.
Art just and might - y, great and wise!
For thou art all my soul's de - light. A - men.

ADORATION AND PRAISE From *Union Hymnal* copyright 1932 by the Central Conference of American Rabbis. Used by permission.

O Worship the King

ADORATION AND PRAISE

68 All Praise to Thee, My God

Thomas Ken, 1637-1711, alt.

TALLIS' CANON L.M.
Thomas Tallis, c. 1505-1585

1 All praise to thee, my God, this night, For all the bless-ings of the light! Keep me, O keep me, King of kings, Be - neath thine own al - might - y wings!

2 For - give me, Lord, for thy dear Son, The ill that I this day have done, That with the world, my-self, and thee, I, ere I sleep, at peace may be.

3 O may my soul on thee re - pose, And with sweet sleep mine eye - lids close, Sleep that shall me more vig - orous make To serve my God when I a - wake.

4 Praise God, from whom all bless - ings flow; Praise him, all crea - tures here be - low; Praise him a - bove, ye heaven-ly host; Praise Fa - ther, Son, and Ho - ly Ghost. A - men.

ADORATION AND PRAISE

Holy God, Thy Name We Bless

Attr. to Ignaz Franz, 1719-1790
Tr. R. Birch Hoyle, 1875-1939
Stanza 2 tr. Clarence Walworth, 1820-1900

GROSSER GOTT, WIR LOBEN DICH 7.8.7.8.7.7.
Katholisches Gesangbuch, Vienna, *c.* 1774

69

1 Ho - ly God, thy Name we bless, All thy prais - es cel - e - bra - ting, And for our un - worth - i - ness Thy for - give - ness sup - pli - ca - ting. With the an - gels thus we bring Ad - o - ra - tion to our King.

2 Hark, the glad ce - les - tial hymn, An - gel choirs a - bove are rais - ing; Cher - u - bim and ser - a - phim, In un - ceas - ing cho - rus prais - ing, Fill the heavens with sweet ac - cord; Ho - ly, ho - ly, ho - ly Lord.

3 From the earth's re - mot - est bounds Great and small u - nite to hymn thee: Fa - ther God, thy praise re - sounds Where thy Church de - lights to sing thee: With thy sole be - got - ten Son Reign - ing with thee on thy Throne. A - men.

ADORATION AND PRAISE

Holy, Holy, Holy! Lord God Almighty

Reginald Heber, 1783-1826

NICAEA 11.12.12.10.
John B. Dykes, 1823-1876

1 Ho - ly, ho - ly, ho - ly! Lord God Al - might - y!
2 Ho - ly, ho - ly, ho - ly! all the saints a - dore thee,
3 Ho - ly, ho - ly, ho - ly! though the dark - ness hide thee,
4 Ho - ly, ho - ly, ho - ly! Lord God Al - might - y!

Ear - ly in the morn - ing our song shall rise to thee;
Cast - ing down their gold - en crowns a - round the glass - y sea;
Though the eye of sin - ful man thy glo - ry may not see;
All thy works shall praise thy name in earth and sky and sea;

Ho - ly, ho - ly, ho - ly! mer - ci - ful and might - y;
Cher - u - bim and ser - a - phim fall - ing down be - fore thee,
On - ly thou art ho - ly; there is none be - side thee,
Ho - ly, ho - ly, ho - ly! mer - ci - ful and might - y;

God in three per - sons, bless - ed Trin - i - ty!
Which wert, and art, and ev - er - more shalt be.
Per - fect in power, in love, and pur - i - ty.
God in three per - sons, bless - ed Trin - i - ty! A - men.

ADORATION AND PRAISE

All People That on Earth Do Dwell

Paraphrase of Psalm 100
William Kethe, d. 1593

OLD HUNDREDTH L.M.
Genevan Psalter, 1551

1 All peo-ple that on earth do dwell, Sing to the Lord with cheer-ful voice;
2 The Lord ye know is God in-deed; With-out our aid he did us make;
3 O en-ter then his gates with praise, Ap-proach with joy his courts un - to;
4 For why? the Lord our God is good, His mer-cy is for - ev - er sure;

Him serve with mirth, his praise forth tell; Come ye be-fore him and re - joice.
We are his folk, he doth us feed, And for his sheep he doth us take.
Praise, laud, and bless his name al-ways, For it is seem-ly so to do.
His truth at all times firm-ly stood; And shall from age to age en - dure. A men.

O for a Thousand Tongues to Sing

72

Charles Wesley, 1707-1788

AZMON C.M.
Carl G. Gläser, 1784-1829
Mason's *Modern Psalmody*, 1839

1 O for a thou-sand tongues to sing My great Re-deem - er's praise,
2 My gra-cious Mas - ter and my God, As - sist me to pro-claim,
3 Glo - ry to God and praise and love Be ev - er, ev - er given

The glo-ries of my God and King, The tri-umphs of his grace!
To spread through all the earth a-broad The hon-ors of thy name.
By saints be-low and saints a-bove, The Church in earth and heaven. A-men.

Praise, My Soul, the King of Heaven

Based on Psalm 103
Henry Francis Lyte, 1793-1847, alt.

PRAISE MY SOUL 8.7.8.7.8.7.
John Goss, 1800-1880

1 Praise, my soul, the King of heav - en, To his feet thy
2 Praise him for his grace and fa - vor To our fa - thers
3 Fa - ther - like, he tends and spares us; Well our fee - ble
4 An - gels, help us to a - dore him, Ye be - hold him

trib - ute bring; Ran - somed, healed, re - stored, for - giv - en,
in dis - tress; Praise him, still the same for - ev - er,
frame he knows; In his hands he gen - tly bears us,
face to face; Sun and moon, bow down be - fore him;

Who, like me, his praise should sing? Praise him! praise him!
Slow to chide, and swift to bless. Praise him! praise him!
Res - cues us from all our foes. Praise him! praise him!
Dwell - ers all in time and space, Praise him! praise him!

Praise him! praise him! Praise the ev - er - last - ing King!
Praise him! praise him! Glo - rious in his faith - ful - ness!
Praise him! praise him! Wide - ly yet his mer - cy flows!
Praise him! praise him! Praise with us the God of grace! A - men.

ADORATION AND PRAISE

I'll Praise My Maker While I've Breath

74

Psalm 146
Isaac Watts, 1674-1748
Alt. by John Wesley, 1703-1791

OLD 113TH 8.8.8.8.8.8.
Strassburger Kirchenamt, 1525
Probably by Matthäus Greiter, *c.* 1500-1552
Harm. V. Earle Copes, 1921-

Unison

1 I'll praise my Mak - er while I've breath; And when my voice
2 Hap - py the man whose hopes re - ly On Is - rael's God;
3 The Lord pours eye - sight on the blind; The Lord sup - ports
4 I'll praise him while he lends me breath; And when my voice

is lost in death, Praise shall em - ploy my no - bler powers.
he made the sky And earth and seas, with all their train.
the faint - ing mind; He sends the la - boring con-science peace.
is lost in death, Praise shall em - ploy my no - bler powers.

My days of praise shall ne'er be past, While life, and thought,
His truth for - ev - er stands se - cure, He saves th'op-pressed
He helps the stran - ger in dis - tress, The wid - ow and
My days of praise shall ne'er be past, While life, and thought,

and be - ing last, Or im - mor - tal - i - ty en - dures.
he feeds the poor, And none shall find his prom - ise vain.
the fa - ther - less, And grants the pris-oner sweet re - lease.
and be - ing last, Or im - mor - tal - i - ty en - dures. A-men.

ADORATION AND PRAISE

75 Immortal, Invisible, God Only Wise

Walter Chalmers Smith, 1824-1908, alt.

ST. DENIO 11.11.11.11.
Welsh hymn melody
John Roberts' *Caniadau y Cyssegr*, 1839

1 Im - mor - tal, in - vis - i - ble, God on - ly wise,
2 Un - rest - ing, un - hast - ing, and si - lent as light,
3 To all, life thou giv - est, to both great and small;
4 Great Fa - ther of glo - ry, pure Fa - ther of light,

In light in - ac - ces - si - ble hid from our eyes,
Nor want - ing, nor wast - ing, thou rul - est in might;
In all life thou liv - est, the true life of all;
Thine an - gels a - dore thee, all veil - ing their sight;

Most bless - ed, most glo - rious, the An - cient of Days,
Thy jus - tice like moun-tains high soar - ing a - bove
We blos - som and flour - ish as leaves on the tree,
All praise we would ren - der; O help us to see

Al - might - y, vic - to - rious, thy great name we praise.
Thy clouds which are foun-tains of good - ness and love.
And with - er and per - ish, but naught chang-eth thee.
'Tis on - ly the splen-dor of light hid - eth thee. A-men.

ADORATION AND PRAISE

Ye Servants of God, Your Master Proclaim 76

Charles Wesley, 1707-1788

HANOVER 10.10.11.11.
William Croft, 1678-1727

1 Ye serv - ants of God, your Mas - ter pro - claim,
2 God rul - eth on high, al - might - y to save,
3 Sal - va - tion to God who sits on the throne!
4 Then let us a - dore and give him his right,

And pub - lish a - broad his won - der - ful name.
And still he is nigh, his pres - ence we have;
Let all cry a - loud and hon - or the Son;
All glo - ry and power, all wis - dom and might,

The name, all vic - to - rious, of Je - sus ex - tol;
The great con - gre - ga - tion his tri - umph shall sing,
The prais - es of Je - sus the an - gels pro - claim,
All hon - or and bless - ing with an - gels a - bove,

His king - dom is glo - rious, he rules o - ver all.
As - crib - ing sal - va - tion to Je - sus, our King.
Fall down on their fa - ces and wor - ship the Lamb.
And thanks nev - er ceas - ing and in - fi - nite love. A - men.

ADORATION AND PRAISE

O Be Joyful in the Lord!

77

Based on Psalm 100
Curtis Beach, 1914-

FINLAY 7.7.7.7.5.7.6.7.
Harold W. Friedell, 1905-1958

1 O be joy - ful in the Lord! Sing be - fore him, all the earth!
2 Know ye that the Lord is King! All his works his wis - dom prove!
3 En - ter now his ho - ly gate; Let our bur-dened hearts be still;
4 For the Lord our God is kind, And his love shall con - stant be;

Praise him with a glad ac - cord And with lives of no - blest worth.
By his might the heav-ens ring; In his love we live and move.
In the sa - cred si - lence wait, As we seek to know his will.
In his will our peace we find; In his ser-vice, lib - er - ty.

Sons of ev - ery land, Hum - bly now be - fore him stand!
By him we are made, So we trust him un - a - fraid.
Let our lives ex - press Our a - bun-dant thank-ful - ness;
Yea, his law is sure; In his light we walk se - cure;

ADORATION AND PRAISE

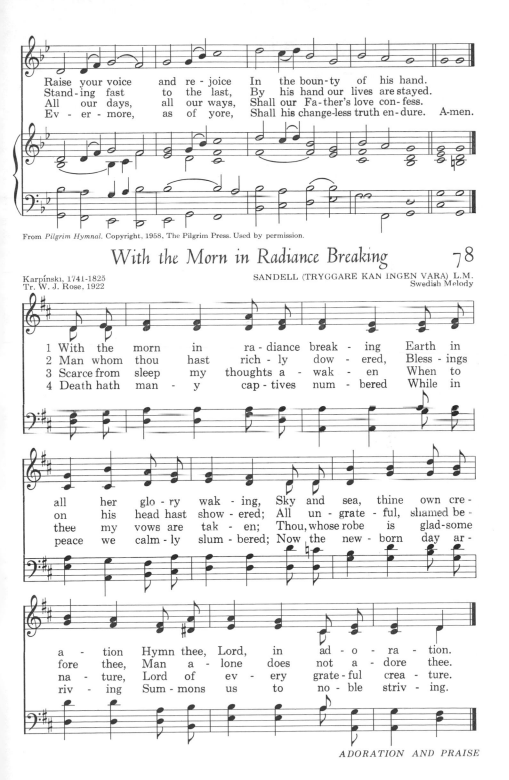

Raise your voice and re-joice In the boun-ty of his hand.
Stand-ing fast to the last, By his hand our lives are stayed.
All our days, all our ways, Shall our Fa-ther's love con-fess.
Ev - er - more, as of yore, Shall his change-less truth en-dure. A-men.

With the Morn in Radiance Breaking 78

Karpínski, 1741-1825
Tr. W. J. Rose, 1922

SANDELL (TRYGGARE KAN INGEN VARA) L.M.
Swedish Melody

1 With the morn in ra-diance break - ing Earth in
2 Man whom thou hast rich - ly dow - ered, Bless - ings
3 Scarce from sleep my thoughts a - wak - en When to
4 Death hath man - y cap - tives num - bered While in

all her glo - ry wak - ing, Sky and sea, thine own cre -
on his head hast show - ered; All un - grate - ful, shamed be -
thee my vows are tak - en; Thou, whose robe is glad-some
peace we calm - ly slum - bered; Now the new - born day ar -

a - tion Hymn thee, Lord, in ad - o - ra - tion.
fore thee, Man a - lone does not a - dore thee.
na - ture, Lord of ev - ery grate - ful crea - ture.
riv - ing Sum - mons us to no - ble striv - ing.

ADORATION AND PRAISE

79

Praise the Lord! Ye Heavens

Based on Psalm 148
Stanzas 1, 2. Foundling Hospital Collection, c. 1801
Stanza 3: Edward Osler, 1798-1863

HYFRYDOL 8.7.8.7.D.
Rowland Hugh Prichard, 1811-1887

1 Praise the Lord! ye heavens, a - dore him; Praise him, an - gels, in the height. Sun and moon, re - joice be - fore him; Praise him, all ye stars of light. Praise the Lord! for he hath spo - ken; Worlds his might - y voice o - beyed; Laws which nev - er

2 Praise the Lord! for he is glo - rious; Nev - er shall his prom - ise fail; God hath made his saints vic - to - rious; Sin and death shall not pre - vail. Praise the God of our sal - va - tion! Hosts on high, his power pro - claim: Heaven, and earth, and

3 Wor - ship, hon - or, glo - ry, bless - ing, Lord, we of - fer un - to thee; Young and old, thy praise ex - press - ing, In glad hom - age bend the knee. All the saints in heaven a - dore thee. We would bow be - fore thy throne; As thine an - gels

shall be bro - ken For their guid - ance he hath made.
all cre - a - tion, Laud and mag - ni - fy his name.
serve be - fore thee, So on earth thy will be done. A-men.

As Pants the Hart 80

Based on Psalm 42
A New Version of the Psalms, 1696, alt.

IRISH C.M.
Hymns and Sacred Poems, Dublin, 1749

1 As pants the hart for cool - ing streams When
2 For thee, my God, the liv - ing God, My
3 Why rest - less, why cast down, my soul? Hope

heat - ed in the chase, So longs my soul, O
thirst - y soul doth pine. O when shall I be -
still, and thou shalt sing The praise of him who

God, for thee, And thy re - fresh - ing grace.
hold thy face, Thou maj - es - ty di - vine?
is thy God, Thy health's e - ter - nal spring. A - men.

ADORATION AND PRAISE

81   *The God of Abraham Praise*

Yigdal elohim chay veyishtabach
Daniel ben Judah Dayyan, c. 1400
Tr. Max Landsberg, 1845-1928 and
Newton Mann, 1836-1926

LEONI 6.6.8.4.D.
Hebrew Tradition, 17th century?
Transcribed by Meyer Lyon, 1751-1797

1 The God of A-braham praise, All prais-ed be his name,
2 His spir-it flow-eth free, High surg-ing where it will;
3 He hath e-ter-nal life Im-plant-ed in the soul;

Who was, and is, and is to be, For aye the same!
In proph-et's word he spoke of old He speak-eth still.
His love shall be our strength and stay, While a-ges roll.

The one e-ter-nal God, Ere aught that now ap-pears;
Es-tab-lished is his law, And change-less it shall stand,
Praise to the liv-ing God! All prais-ed be his name

The First, the Last: be-yond all thought His time-less years!
Deep writ up-on the hu-man heart, On sea, or land.
Who was, and is, and is to be, For aye the same! A-men.

ADORATION AND PRAISE

Savior, Again to Thy Dear Name

John Ellerton, 1826-1893

ELLERS 10.10.10.10.
Edward J. Hopkins, 1818-1901

1 Sav - ior, a - gain to thy dear name we raise With one ac - cord our
2 Grant us thy peace up - on our home-ward way; With thee be - gan, with
3 Grant us thy peace, Lord, through the com-ing night; Turn thou for us its
4 Grant us thy peace through-out our earth-ly life, Our balm in sor - row,

part - ing hymn of praise; We stand to bless thee ere our wor - ship cease,
thee shall end the day; Guard thou the lips from sin, the hearts from shame,
dark-ness in - to light; From harm and dan - ger keep thy chil - dren free,
and our stay in strife; Then, when thy voice shall bid our con - flict cease,

Then, low - ly kneel - ing, wait thy word of peace.
That in this house have called up - on thy name.
For dark and light are both a - like to thee.
Call us, O Lord, to thine e - ter - nal peace. A - men.

ADORATION AND PRAISE

83 Let All the World in Every Corner Sing

George Herbert, 1593-1632

ALL THE WORLD 10.4.6.6.6.6.10.4.
Robert G. McCutchan, 1877-1958

1 Let all the world in ev-ery cor-ner sing: My God and King!
2 Let all the world in ev-ery cor-ner sing: My God and King!

The heavens are not too high, His praise may thith-er fly; The
The church with psalms must shout, No door can keep them out; But,

earth is not too low, His prais-es there may grow. Let
a - bove all, the heart Must bear the long-est part. Let

ADORATION AND PRAISE

all the world in ev-ery cor-ner sing: My God and King!
all the world in ev-ery cor-ner sing: My God and King! A-men.

My God, I Love Thee

84

No me mueve, mi Dios
Attr. to Francis Xavier, 1506-1552
Tr. Edward Caswall, 1814-1878, alt.

ABBEY C.M.
Scottish Psalter, 1615

1 My God, I love thee: not be-cause I hope for heaven there-by,
2 Not with the hope of gain-ing aught; Not seek-ing a re-ward;
3 E'en so I love thee, and will love, And in thy praise will sing,

Nor yet be-cause who love thee not Are lost e-ter-nal-ly.
But as thy-self hast lov-ed me, O ev-er-lov-ing Lord,
Sole-ly be-cause thou art my God, And my e-ter-nal King. A-men.

CONFESSION AND COMMITMENT

Dear Lord and Father of Mankind

First Tune

John Greenleaf Whittier, 1807-1892

SALVATION 8.6.8.8.6.
Ananias Davisson's *Kentucky Harmony*, c. 1815, adapted

1 Dear Lord and Fa - ther of man-kind, For - give our fool - ish ways!
2 In sim - ple trust like theirs who heard, Be - side the Syr - ian sea,
3 O Sab - bath rest by Gal - i - lee! O calm of hills a - bove,
4 Drop thy still dews of qui - et - ness, Till all our striv-ings cease;
5 Breathe through the heats of our de - sire Thy cool - ness and thy balm;

Re - clothe us in our right - ful mind, In pur - er lives thy
The gra - cious call - ing of the Lord, Let us, like them, with -
Where Je - sus knelt to share with thee The si - lence of e -
Take from our souls the strain and stress, And let our or - dered
Let sense be dumb, let flesh re - tire; Speak through the earth - quake,

ser - vice find, In deep - er rev - erence, praise.
out a word, Rise up and fol - low thee.
ter - ni - ty, In - ter - pret-ed by love!
lives con - fess The beau - ty of thy peace.
wind, and fire, O still, small voice of calm. A - men.

CONFESSION AND COMMITMENT

Music from *Hymnal for Colleges and Schools*; used by permission of Yale University Press.

Dear Lord and Father of Mankind

Second Tune

John Greenleaf Whittier, 1807-1892

REST 8.6.8.8.6.
Frederick C. Maker, 1844-1927

1 Dear Lord and Fa-ther of man-kind, For-give our fool-ish ways!
2 In sim-ple trust like theirs who heard, Be-side the Syr-ian sea,
3 O Sab-bath rest by Gal-i-lee! O calm of hills a-bove,
4 Drop thy still dews of qui-et-ness, Till all our striv-ings cease;
5 Breathe through the heats of our de-sire Thy cool-ness and thy balm;

Re-clothe us in our right-ful mind, In pur-er lives thy
The gra-cious call-ing of the Lord, Let us, like them, with-
Where Je-sus knelt to share with thee The si-lence of e-
Take from our souls the strain and stress, And let our or-dered
Let sense be dumb, let flesh re-tire; Speak through the earth-quake,

ser-vice find, In deep-er rev-erence, praise.
out a word, Rise up and fol-low thee.
ter-ni-ty, In-ter-pret-ed by love!
lives con-fess The beau-ty of thy peace.
wind, and fire, O still, small voice of calm. A-men.

CONFESSION AND COMMITMENT

Declare, O Heavens, the Lord of Space

Robert Lansing Edwards, 1915-

LASST UNS ERFREUEN 8.8.4.4.8.8. with Alleluias
Melody from *Geistliche Kirchengesäng*, Cologne, 1623
Harm. and arr. Ralph Vaughan Williams, 1872-1958

1 De - clare, O heavens, the Lord of space,
2 Launch forth, O man, and bold - ly rise,
3 O Lord, whose power all space ex - tols,

Re - ply broad lands in ev - ery place,
Be - yond our plan - et pierce the skies,
Draw near our lives, en - large our souls,

Tell his splen - dor! Al - le - lu - ia!
Bound - less ven - ture! Al - le - lu - ia!
Dwell with - in us! Al - le - lu - ia!

CONFESSION AND COMMITMENT

New   realms   we   find   he   first   hath   made,
No   soar - ing   flight can   e'er   out - run
Stir   deeds   of   grace   to   serve   thy   plan,

All   be - ing   is   his power dis - played;   Al - le - lu - ia!
Truth   God   has shown us   in   his   Son;   Al - le - lu - ia!
Wake   joy   the morn-ing stars be - gan;   Al - le - lu - ia!

Al - le - lu - ia! Al - le - lu - ia! Al - le - lu - ia! Al - le - lu - ia!

CONFESSION AND COMMITMENT

88 Creator of the Universe

J. Donald Hughes, 1932–

WEYMOUTH C.M.D.
Theodore P. Ferris, 1908–

1 Cre - a - tor of the u - ni - verse, We lift our minds to thee;
2 Let not the love of eas - y ways Leave deep - er truth un - known;

En - light - en them and lead our thought In fear - less lib - er - ty.
Teach us that power to learn and grow Is found in thee a - lone.

Let not our search for truth in things From thee our souls di - vide;
Let sci - ence find in thee its truth; Tech - nol - o - gy, its Goal;

Thou art the liv - ing Lord of truth; Thy Spir - it be our guide!
Phi - los - o - phy, its no - blest thought: Thy light makes know - ledge whole! A - men.

CONFESSION AND COMMITMENT

Words from *Five New Youth Hymns* copyright 1955 by the
Hymn Society of America; used by permission. Music by
permission of The Church Pension Fund.

Out of the Depths I Cry to Thee

Aus tiefer Not schrei ich zu dir
Martin Luther, 1483-1546
Tr. Catherine Winkworth, 1827-1878

AUS TIEFER NOT 8.7.8.7.8.8.7.
Martin Luther? 1483-1546
Harm. J. S. Bach, 1685-1750

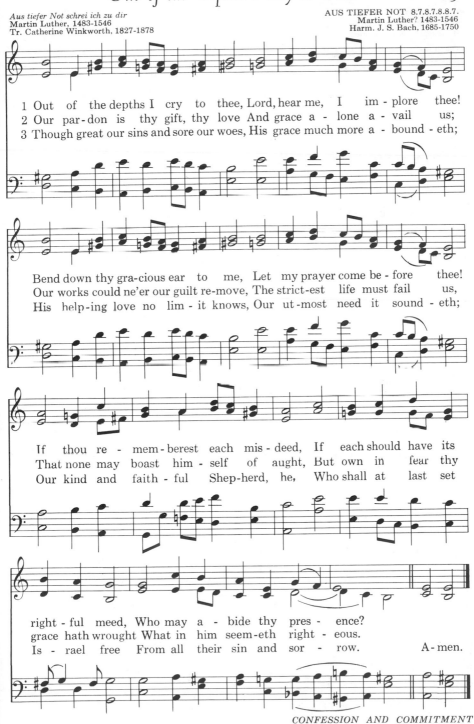

1 Out of the depths I cry to thee, Lord, hear me, I im-plore thee!
2 Our par-don is thy gift, thy love And grace a-lone a-vail us;
3 Though great our sins and sore our woes, His grace much more a-bound-eth;

Bend down thy gra-cious ear to me, Let my prayer come be-fore thee!
Our works could ne'er our guilt re-move, The strict-est life must fail us,
His help-ing love no lim-it knows, Our ut-most need it sound-eth;

If thou re-mem-berest each mis-deed, If each should have its
That none may boast him-self of aught, But own in fear thy
Our kind and faith-ful Shep-herd, he, Who shall at last set

right-ful meed, Who may a-bide thy pres-ence?
grace hath wrought What in him seem-eth right-eous.
Is-rael free From all their sin and sor-row. A-men.

CONFESSION AND COMMITMENT

Be Thou My Vision, O Lord of My Heart

Rob tu mo bhoile, a Comdi cride
Irish text, 8th cent.?
Tr. Mary Elizabeth Byrne, 1880-1931
Versified by Eleanor Henrietta Hull, 1860-1935

SLANE 10.10.9.10.
Trad. Irish melody
Harm. David Evans, 1874-1948

1 Be thou my vi - sion, O Lord of my heart;
2 Be thou my wis - dom, and thou my true word;
3 Rich - es I heed not, nor man's emp - ty praise,
4 High King of heav - en, my vic - to - ry won,

Naught be all else to me, save that thou art
I ev - er with thee and thou with me, Lord;
Thou mine in - her - i - tance, now and al - ways:
May I reach heav - en's joys, O bright heaven's Sun!

Thou my best thought, by day or by night,
Thou my great Fa - ther, I thy true son;
Thou and thou on - ly, first in my heart,
Heart of my own heart, what - ev - er be - fall,

CONFESSION AND COMMITMENT

Wak - ing   or   sleep - ing,   thy   pre - sence   my   light.
Thou   in   me   dwell - ing,   and   I   with   thee   one.
High   King   of   heav - en,   my   trea - sure   thou   art.
Still   be   my   vi - sion,   O   Ru - ler   of   all.   A - men.

On This Day, the First of Days 91

Die parente temporum
Breviary of Le Mans, 1748
Tr. Henry W. Baker, 1821-1877

SCHÜTZ 19 7.7.7.7.
Heinrich Schütz, 1585-1672

1 On   this day, the   first of days, God   the Fa - ther's   name we praise,
2 On   this day the e - ter - nal Son   O - ver death his   tri - umph won;
3 Fa - ther, who didst   fash - ion me   Im - age of   thy - self   to   be,
4 Thou who dost all   gifts im - part,   Shine, good Spir - it,   in   my heart;

Who, cre - a - tion's Lord and spring, Did the world from dark - ness bring.
On   this day the   Spir - it came   With his gifts of   liv - ing flame.
Fill   me with thy   love di - vine;   Let my ev - ery   thought be thine.
Best   of gifts, thy - self be - stow;   Make me burn thy   love to know. A - men.

CONFESSION AND COMMITMENT

92 Take Thou Our Minds

William H. Foulkes, 1877-1961

HALL 10.10.10.10.
Calvin W. Laufer, 1874-1938

1 Take thou our minds, dear Lord, we hum - bly pray;
2 Take thou our hearts, O Christ, they are thine own;
3 Take thou our wills, Most High! Hold thou full sway;
4 Take thou our - selves, O Lord, heart, mind, and will;

Give us the mind of Christ each pass - ing day;
Come thou with - in our souls and claim thy throne;
Have in our in - most souls thy per - fect way;
Through our sur - ren - dered souls thy plans ful - fill.

Teach us to know the truth that sets us free;
Help us to shed a - broad thy death - less love;
Guard thou each sa - cred hour from self - ish ease;
We yield our - selves to thee — time, tal - ents, all;

Grant us in all our thoughts to hon - or thee.
Use us to make the earth like heaven a - bove.
Guide thou our or - dered lives as thou dost please.
We hear, and hence - forth heed, thy sov - ereign call. A - men.

CONFESSION AND COMMITMENT

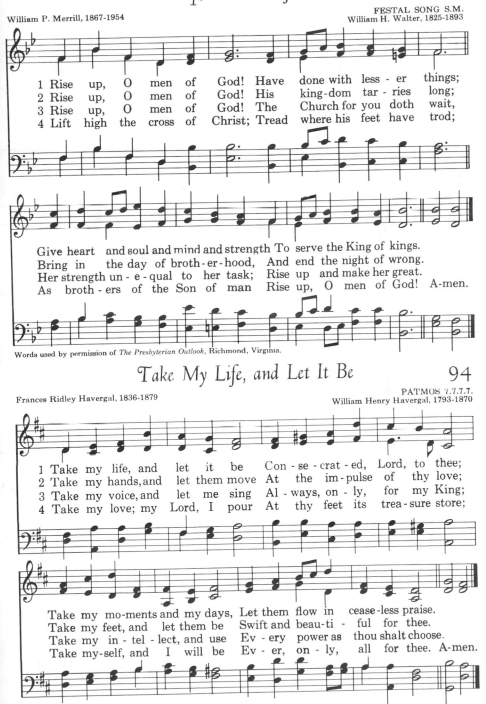

Rise Up, O Men of God!

William P. Merrill, 1867-1954

FESTAL SONG S.M.
William H. Walter, 1825-1893

1 Rise up, O men of God! Have done with less-er things;
2 Rise up, O men of God! His king-dom tar-ries long;
3 Rise up, O men of God! The Church for you doth wait,
4 Lift high the cross of Christ; Tread where his feet have trod;

Give heart and soul and mind and strength To serve the King of kings.
Bring in the day of broth-er-hood, And end the night of wrong.
Her strength un-e-qual to her task; Rise up and make her great.
As broth-ers of the Son of man Rise up, O men of God! A-men.

Words used by permission of *The Presbyterian Outlook*, Richmond, Virginia.

Take My Life, and Let It Be 94

Frances Ridley Havergal, 1836-1879

PATMOS 7.7.7.7.
William Henry Havergal, 1793-1870

1 Take my life, and let it be Con-se-crat-ed, Lord, to thee;
2 Take my hands, and let them move At the im-pulse of thy love;
3 Take my voice, and let me sing Al-ways, on-ly, for my King;
4 Take my love; my Lord, I pour At thy feet its trea-sure store;

Take my mo-ments and my days, Let them flow in cease-less praise.
Take my feet, and let them be Swift and beau-ti-ful for thee.
Take my in-tel-lect, and use Ev-ery power as thou shalt choose.
Take my-self, and I will be Ev-er, on-ly, all for thee. A-men.

CONFESSION AND COMMITMENT

95 Praise to God, Immortal Praise

Anna Laetitia Barbauld, 1743-1825, alt.

DIX 7.7.7.7.7.7.
Adapted from a chorale by
Conrad Kocher, 1786-1872

1 Praise to God, im - mor-tal praise, For the love that crowns our days;
2 All the plen - ty sum-mer pours; Au-tumn's rich o'er - flow - ing stores;
3 As thy pros-p'ring land hath blest, May we give thee of our best;

Boun - teous source of ev - ery joy, Let thy praise our tongues em - ploy:
Flocks that whi - ten all the plain; Yel - low sheaves of rip - ened grain:
And by deeds of kind - ly love For thy mer - cies grate - ful prove;

All to thee, our God, we owe, Source whence all our bless-ings flow.
Lord, for these our souls shall raise Grate-ful vows and sol - emn praise.
Sing-ing thus through all our days Praise to God, im - mor - tal praise. A-men.

96 When Thy Heart with Joy O'erflowing

Theodore C. Williams, 1855-1915

BULLINGER 8.5.8.3.
Ethelbert W. Bullinger, 1837-1913

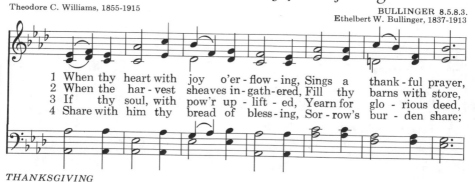

1 When thy heart with joy o'er - flow - ing, Sings a thank - ful prayer,
2 When the har - vest sheaves in-gath-ered, Fill thy barns with store,
3 If thy soul, with pow'r up - lift - ed, Yearn for glo - rious deed,
4 Share with him thy bread of bless-ing, Sor - row's bur - den share;

THANKSGIVING

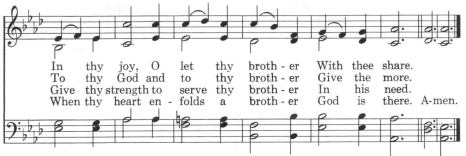

In thy joy, O let thy broth-er With thee share.
To thy God and to thy broth-er Give the more.
Give thy strength to serve thy broth-er In his need.
When thy heart en-folds a broth-er God is there. A-men.

Rejoice, Ye Pure in Heart

Edward H. Plumptre, 1821-1891

MARION S.M. with Refrain
Arthur H. Messiter, 1834-1916

1 Re - joice, ye pure in heart; Re - joice, give thanks and sing;
2 With voice as full and strong As o - cean's surg - ing praise,
3 Then on through life's long path, Still chant - ing as ye go,
4 Still lift your stand-ard high, Still march in firm ar - ray,

Your fes - tal ban - ner wave on high, The cross of Christ your King!
Send forth the hymns our fa - thers loved, The psalms of an - cient days.
From youth to age, by night and day, In glad-ness and in woe.
As war - riors through the dark-ness toil Till dawns the gold - en day!

Re - joice, re - joice, Re - joice, give thanks and sing. A-men.

Re - joice, re - joice,

THANKSGIVING

98 As Men of Old Their First Fruits Brought

Frank von Christierson, 1900-

FOREST GREEN C.M.D.
English melody
Arr. R. Vaughan Williams, 1872-1958

1 As men of old their first fruits brought Of orch - ard, flock, and field
2 A world in need now sum - mons us To la - bor, love and give;
3 In gra - ti - tude and hum - ble trust We bring our best to thee

To God the Giv - er of all good, The Source of boun-teous yield;
To make our life an of - fer - ing To God, that man may live;
To serve thy cause and share thy love With all hu - man - i - ty.

So we to - day first fruits would bring The wealth of this good land,
The Church of Christ is call - ing us To make the dream come true:
O thou who gav - est us thy - self In Je - sus Christ thy Son,

Of farm and mar - ket, shop and home, Of mind, and heart, and hand.
A world re-deemed by Christ-like love; All life in Christ made new.
Teach us to give our - selves each day Un - til life's work is done. A-men.

THANKSGIVING

First Tune

Nun danket alle Gott
Martin Rinckart, 1586-1649
Tr. Catherine Winkworth, 1827-1878

NUN DANKET 6.7.6.7.6.6.6.6.
Melody by Johann Crüger, 1598-1662

1 Now thank we all our God With heart and hands and voic - es,
2 O may this boun - teous God Through all our life be near us,
3 All praise and thanks to God The Fa - ther now be giv - en,

Who won-drous things hath done, In whom his world re - joic - es,
With ev - er joy - ful hearts And bless-ed peace to cheer us,
The Son, and him who reigns With them in high-est heav - en,

Who, from our moth-ers' arms, Hath blessed us on our way
And keep us in his grace, And guide us when per - plexed,
The one e - ter - nal God, Whom earth and heaven a - dore,

With count-less gifts of love, And still is ours to - day.
And free us from all ills In this world and the next.
For thus it was, is now, And shall be ev - er - more. A - men.

Now Thank We All Our God

Second Tune

Nun danket alle Gott
Martin Rinckart, 1586-1649
Tr. Catherine Winkworth, 1827-1878

GRACIAS 6.7.6.7.6.6.6.6.
Geoffrey Beaumont, 1903-

1 Now thank we all our God, With hearts and hands and
2 may this boun-teous God Through all our life be
3 praise and thanks to God The Fa-ther now be

voi - ces, Who won-drous things hath done, In
near us, With ev - er joy - ful hearts And
gi - ven, The Son, and him who reigns With

whom his world re - joi - ces; Who, from our
bless - ed peace to cheer us; And keep us
them in high - est hea - ven; The one e -

THANKSGIVING

mo - thers' arms, Hath blessed us on our way With
in his grace, And guide us when per - plexed, And
ter - nal God, Whom earth and heaven a - dore; For

count - less gifts of love, And still is ours to -
free us from all ills In this world and the
thus it was, is now, And shall be ev - er -

vs. 1 and 2 / v. 3

day.
next. 2 O
3 All more.

Music taken from *Three Hymn Tunes* from 20th Century Folk Mass by permission
of the publishers, W. Paxton & Co. Ltd., London, W. 1., England.

THANKSGIVING

101   *Come, Ye Thankful People, Come*

Henry Alford, 1810-1871
Anna L. Barbauld, 1743-1825, and others

ST. GEORGE'S WINDSOR 7.7.7.7.D.
George J. Elvey, 1816-1893

1 Come, ye thank-ful peo - ple, come, Raise the song of har - vest home;
2 All the bless-ings of the field, All the stores the gar - dens yield,
3 These to thee, our God, we owe, Source whence all our bless-ings flow;

All is safe - ly gath - ered in, Ere the win - ter storms be - gin;
All the fruits in full sup - ply, Rip - ened 'neath the sum - mer sky,
And for these our souls shall raise Grate-ful vows and sol - emn praise.

God, our Mak - er, doth pro - vide For our wants to be sup - plied;
All that spring with boun-teous hand Scat - ters o'er the smil - ing land,
Come, then, thank-ful peo - ple, come, Raise the song of har - vest home;

Come to God's own tem - ple, come, Raise the song of har - vest home.
All that lib - eral au-tumn pours From her rich o'er - flow - ing stores,
Come to God's own tem - ple, come, Raise the song of har - vest home. A-men.

THANKSGIVING

We Gather Together

Wilt heden nu treden
Anonymous, 16th cent.
Tr. Theodore Baker, 1851-1934

KREMSER 12.11.12.11.
Nederlandtsche Gedenckclanck, 1626
Arr. Edward Kremser, 1838-1914

1 We gath - er to - geth - er to ask the Lord's bless - ing;
2 Be - side us to guide us, our God with us join - ing,
3 We all do ex - tol thee, thou lead - er tri - um-phant

He chast - ens and hast - ens his will to make known;
Or - dain - ing, main - tain - ing his king - dom di - vine;
And pray that thou still our de - fend - er wilt be.

The wick - ed op - press - ing now cease from dis - tress - ing:
So from the be - gin - ning the fight we were win - ning:
Let thy con - gre - ga - tion es - cape tri - bu - la - tion;

Sing prais - es to his name; He for - gets not his own.
Thou, Lord, wast at our side: all glo - ry be thine!
Thy name be ev - er praised! O Lord, make us free! A - men.

THANKSGIVING

Creator of the Stars of Night

First Tune

Conditor alme siderum
9th century
Tr. John Mason Neale, 1818-1866, alt.
Version in *The Hymnal 1940*

CONDITOR ALME L.M.
Sarum plainsong, Mode IV
Harm. J. H. Arnold, 1887-1956

1 Cre - a - tor of the stars of night, Thy peo - ple's ev - er - last - ing light, O Christ, thou Sav - ior of us all, We pray thee, hear us when we call.

2 To thee the trav - ail deep was known That made the whole cre - a - tion groan, Till thou, Re - deem - er, should - est free Thine own in glo - rious lib - er - ty.

3 When the old world drew on toward night, Thou cam - est, not in splen - dor bright As mon - arch, but the hum - ble child Of Mar - y, blame - less moth - er mild.

4 At thy great name ex - alt - ed now All knees must bend, all hearts must bow; And things ce - les - tial thee shall own, And things ter - res - trial, Lord a - lone. A - men.

Words by permission of The Church Pension Fund. Music from *Enlarged Songs of Praise* by permission of Oxford University Press.

ADVENT

Second Tune

Conditor alme siderum
9th century
Tr. John Mason Neale, 1818-1866, alt.
Version in *The Hymnal 1940*

PUER NOBIS NASCITUR L.M.
Adapt. Michael Praetorius, 1571-1621
Harm. George R. Woodward, 1848-1934

1 Cre - a - tor of the stars of night, Thy peo - ple's
2 To thee the trav - ail deep was known That made the
3 When the old world drew on toward night, Thou cam - est,
4 At thy great name ex - alt - ed now All knees must

ev - er - last - ing light, O Christ, thou Sav - ior of us
whole cre - a - tion groan, Till thou, Re - deem - er, should - est
not in splen - dor bright As mon - arch, but the hum - ble
bend, all hearts must bow; And things ce - les - tial thee shall

all, We pray thee, hear us when we call.
free Thine own in glo - rious lib - er - ty.
child Of Ma - ry, blame - less moth - er mild.
own, And things ter - res - trial, Lord a - lone. A - men.

Words by permission of The Church Pension Fund. Music by permission of A. R.
Mowbray & Company Ltd.

ADVENT

Lift Up Your Heads, Ye Mighty Gates

Based on Psalm 24
Georg Weissel, 1590-1635
Tr. Catherine Winkworth, 1827-1878, alt.

TRURO L.M.
Psalmodia Evangelica, 1789

1 Lift up your heads, ye might-y gates; Be-hold the King of
2 O blest the land, the cit-y blest, Where Christ the rul-er
3 Fling wide the por-tals of your heart, Make it a tem-ple
4 Re-deem-er, come! with us a-bide: Our hearts to thee we

glo-ry waits! The King of kings is draw-ing
is con-fessed! O hap-py hearts and hap-py
set a-part From earth-ly use for heaven's em-
o-pen wide, Let us thy in-ner pres-ence

near; The Sa-vior of the world is here.
homes To whom this King in tri-umph comes!
ploy, A-dorned with prayer and love and joy.
feel, Thy grace and love in us re-veal. A-men.

106

Come, Thou Long-Expected Jesus

Charles Wesley, 1707-1788

STUTTGART 8.7.8.7.
Christian F. Witt, 1660-1716
Psalmodia Sacra, Gotha, 1715

1 Come, thou long-ex-pect-ed Je-sus, Born to set thy peo-ple free;
2 Is-rael's strength and con-so-la-tion, Hope of all the earth thou art;
3 Born thy peo-ple to de-liv-er, Born a child, and yet a king,
4 By thine own e-ter-nal Spir-it Rule in all our hearts a-lone;

ADVENT

From our fears and sins re-lease us; Let us find our rest in thee.
Dear de-sire of ev-ery na-tion, Joy of ev-ery long-ing heart.
Born to reign in us for-ev-er, Now thy gra-cious king-dom bring.
By thine all-suf-fi-cient mer-it Raise us to thy glo-rious throne. A-men.

Alternate tune No. 294

Ah! Think Not the Lord Delayeth

107

Percy Dearmer, 1867-1936

ALLES IST AN GOTTES SEGEN 8.8.7.D.
Attr. to J. B. König, 1691-1758
Harmonischer Lieder-Schatz, 1738

1 Ah! think not the Lord de-lay-eth; "I am with you," still he say-eth,
2 For e'en now the reign of heav-en Spreads through-out the world like leav-en,
3 Not for us to find the rea-sons, Or to know the times and sea-sons,

"Do you yet not un-der-stand?" Look not back, the past re-gret-ting;
Un-ob-served, and ver-y near, Like the seed when no man know-eth,
Comes the Lord when strikes the hour; Ours to bear the faith-ful wit-ness

On the dawn your hearts be set-ting; Rise, and join the Lord's com-mand.
Like the shel-ter-ing tree that grow-eth, Comes the life e-ter-nal here.
Which can shape the world to fit-ness, Thine, O God, to give the power. A-men.

ADVENT

O Come, O Come, Emmanuel

First Tune

Veni, veni Emmanuel
Psalteriolum Cantionum Catholicarum, Cologne, 1710
Sts. 1,2: Tr. John Mason Neale, 1818-1866, alt.
Sts. 3,4: Henry Sloane Coffin, 1877-1954

VENI EMMANUEL 8.8.8.8.8.8.
Adapted from plainsong phrases
by Thomas Helmore, 1811-1890

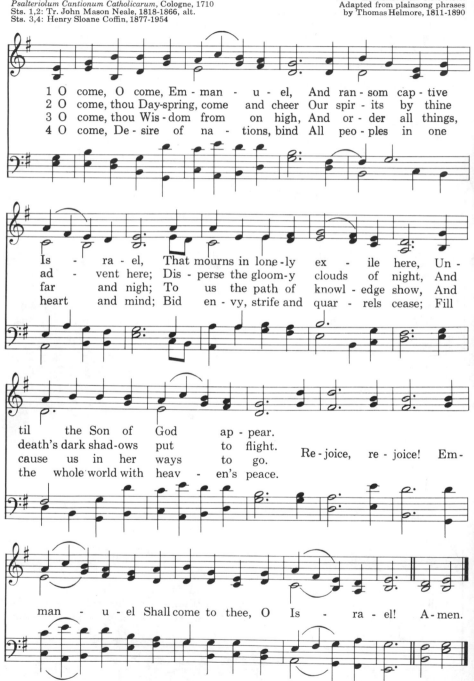

1 O come, O come, Emman - u - el, And ran - som captive Is - ra - el, That mourns in lone - ly ex - ile here, Un - til the Son of God ap - pear.

2 O come, thou Day-spring, come and cheer Our spir - its by thine ad - vent here; Dis - perse the gloom - y clouds of night, And death's dark shad-ows put to flight.

3 O come, thou Wis - dom from on high, And or - der all things, far and nigh; To us the path of knowl - edge show, And cause us in her ways to go.

4 O come, De - sire of na - tions, bind All peo - ples in one heart and mind; Bid en - vy, strife and quar - rels cease; Fill the whole world with heav - en's peace.

Re - joice, re - joice! Em - man - u - el Shall come to thee, O Is - ra - el! A - men.

Words from *Hymns of the Kingdom of God* by Coffin and Vernon. Used by permission of Harper & Row, Publishers.

ADVENT

O Come, O Come, Emmanuel

Second Tune   109

Veni, veni Emmanuel
Psalteriolum Cantionum Catholicarum, Cologne, 1710
Sts. 1,2: Tr. John Mason Neale, 1818-1866, alt.
Sts. 3,4: Henry Sloane Coffin, 1877-1954

VENI EMMANUEL 8.8.8.8.8.8.
Plainsong Melody, Mode I
Arr. by Ernest White, 1899-

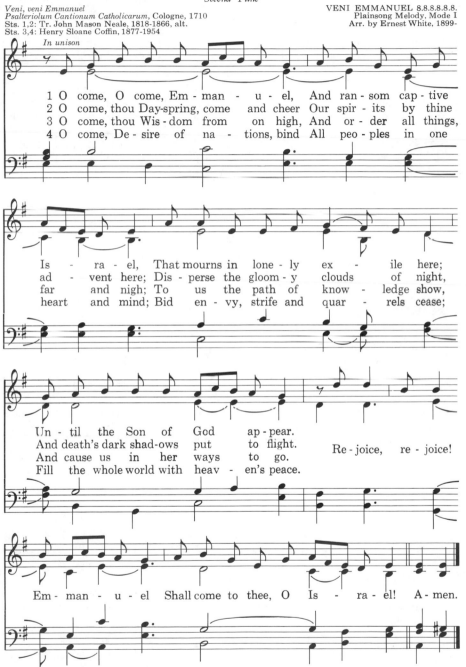

1 O come, O come, Em - man - u - el, And ran - som cap - tive
2 O come, thou Day-spring, come and cheer Our spir - its by thine
3 O come, thou Wis - dom from on high, And or - der all things,
4 O come, De - sire of na - tions, bind All peo - ples in one

Is - ra - el, That mourns in lone - ly ex - ile here;
ad - vent here; Dis - perse the gloom - y clouds of night,
far and nigh; To us the path of know - ledge show,
heart and mind; Bid en - vy, strife and quar - rels cease;

Un - til the Son of God ap - pear.
And death's dark shad-ows put to flight.
And cause us in her ways to go.
Fill the whole world with heav - en's peace.

Re - joice, re - joice!

Em - man - u - el Shall come to thee, O Is - ra - el! A - men.

Words from *Hymns of the Kingdom of God* by Coffin and Vernon. Used by permission of Harper & Row, Publishers. Music from *The Lutheran Service Book and Hymnal* by permission of the Commission on the Liturgy and Hymnal.

ADVENT

Comfort, Comfort Ye My People

Based on Isaiah 40:1-8
Johann Olearius, 1611-1684
Tr. Catherine Winkworth, 1827-1878, alt.

PSALM 42 8.7.8.7.7.7.8.8.
Genevan Psalter, 1551

1 Com - fort, com - fort ye my peo - ple, Speak ye peace, thus saith our God;
2 Hark, the voice of one that cri - eth In the des - ert far and near,
3 Make ye straight what long was crook-ed, Make the rough-er pla - ces plain;

Com - fort those who sit in dark - ness Mourn-ing 'neath their sor - rows' load.
Bid - ding all men to re - pent - ance Since the king-dom now is here.
Let your hearts be true and hum - ble, As be - fits his ho - ly reign.

Speak ye to Je - ru - sa - lem Of the peace that waits for them;
Oh, that warn - ing cry o - bey! Now pre-pare for God a way;
For the glo - ry of the Lord Now o'er earth is shed a - broad;

Tell her that her sins I cov - er, And her war-fare now is o - ver.
Let the val-leys rise to meet him And the hills bow down to greet him.
And all flesh shall see the to - ken That his word is nev-er bro-ken. A-men.

ADVENT

Veiled in Darkness Judah Lay

Douglas LeTell Rights, 1891-1956

111

NICHT SO TRAURIG 7.7.7.7.7.7.
Johann Georg Ebeling, 1637-1676

1 Veiled in dark - ness Ju - dah lay, Wait - ing for the
2 Still the earth in dark - ness lies. Up from death's dark
3 Light of light, we hum - bly pray, Shine up - on thy

prom - ised day, While a - cross the shad - owy night
vale a - rise Voic - es of a world in grief,
world to - day; Break the gloom of our dark night,

Streamed a flood of glo - rious light, Heaven - ly voic - es
Prayers of men who seek re - lief: Now our dark - ness
Fill our souls with love and light, Send thy bless - ed

chant - ing then,
pierce a - gain, "Peace on earth, good - will to men."
word a - gain,

ADVENT

112 Wake, Awake, for Night Is Flying

Wachet auf, ruft uns die Stimme
Philipp Nicolai, 1556-1608
Tr. Catherine Winkworth, 1827-1878, and others

WACHET AUF 8.9.8.8.9.8.6.6.4.8.8.
Philipp Nicolai, 1556-1608
Harm. J. S. Bach, 1685-1750

1 Wake, a-wake, for night is fly - ing; The watch-men on the
2 Zi - on hears the watch-men sing - ing; Her heart with deep de-

heights are cry - ing, A - wake, Je - ru - sa - lem, a - rise!
light is spring - ing, She wakes, she ris - es from her gloom,

Mid-night's sol - emn hour is toll - ing; His char-iot wheels are
For her Lord comes down all glo - rious, In grace ar - rayed, by

near - er roll - ing; He comes! O Church, lift up thine eyes!
truth vic - to - rious; Her star is risen, her light is come!

ADVENT

Rise up, with will-ing feet Go forth, the Bride-groom meet:
Ah, come thou bless-ed One, God's own be-lov-ed Son,

Hal - le - lu - jah! Lo, great and small, we an - swer all;
Hal - le - lu - jah! We haste a - long, an ea - ger throng,

We fol - low where thy voice shall call.
And glad - some join the ad - vent song. A - men.

3 Now let all the heavens adore thee,
   And men and angels sing before thee
      With harp and cymbal's clearest tone;
   Of one pearl each shining portal,
   Where we shall join the choirs immortal
      In praises round thy glorious throne;
   No vision ever brought,
   No ear hath ever caught
      Such great glory!
   Therefore will we, eternally,
   Sing hymns of joy and praise to thee.

113 Hail to the Lord's Anointed

Psalm 72
James Montgomery, 1771-1854

WOODBIRD 7.6.7.6.D.
Traditional German Melody

1 Hail to the Lord's A - noint - ed, Great Da - vid's great-er Son!
2 He comes with suc - cor speed - y To those who suf - fer wrong,
3 He shall come down like show - ers Up - on the fruit - ful earth,
4 Kings shall bow down be - fore him, And gold and in - cense bring;

Hail, in the time ap - point - ed His reign on earth be - gun!
To help the poor and need - y, And bid the weak be strong;
And love, joy, hope, like flow - ers, Spring in his path to birth:
All na - tions shall a - dore him, His praise all peo - ple sing;

He comes to break op - pres - sion, To set the cap - tive free;
To give them songs for sigh - ing, Their dark-ness turn to light,
Be - fore him on the moun - tains Shall peace, the her - ald, go;
To him shall prayer un - ceas - ing And dai - ly vows as - cend;

To take a - way trans - gres - sion, And rule in e - qui - ty.
Whose souls, con-demned and dy - ing, Were pre - cious in his sight.
And right-eous-ness in foun - tains From hill to val - ley flow.
His king-dom still in - creas - ing, A king-dom with-out end. A-men.

ADVENT

Let All Mortal Flesh Keep Silence

Σιγησάτω πᾶσα σὰρξ βροτεία
Liturgy of St. James
Tr. Gerard Moultrie, 1829-1885

PICARDY 8.7.8.7.8.7.
Traditional French Carol

114

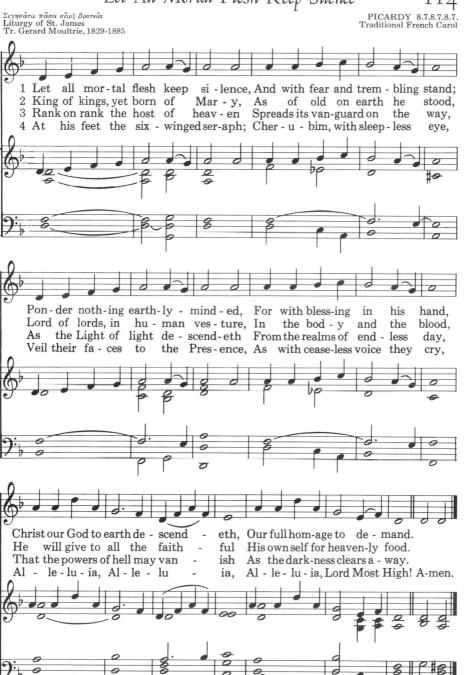

1 Let all mor-tal flesh keep si-lence, And with fear and trem-bling stand;
2 King of kings, yet born of Mar-y, As of old on earth he stood,
3 Rank on rank the host of heav-en Spreads its van-guard on the way,
4 At his feet the six-winged ser-aph; Cher-u-bim, with sleep-less eye,

Pon-der noth-ing earth-ly-mind-ed, For with bless-ing in his hand,
Lord of lords, in hu-man ves-ture, In the bod-y and the blood,
As the Light of light de-scend-eth From the realms of end-less day,
Veil their fa-ces to the Pres-ence, As with cease-less voice they cry,

Christ our God to earth de-scend-eth, Our full hom-age to de-mand.
He will give to all the faith-ful His own self for heaven-ly food.
That the powers of hell may van-ish As the dark-ness clears a-way.
Al-le-lu-ia, Al-le-lu-ia, Al-le-lu-ia, Lord Most High! A-men.

ADVENT

115 *On Jordan's Bank the Baptist's Cry*

Jordanis oras praeira
Charles Coffin, 1676-1749
Tr. Jonn Chandler, 1806-1876, alt.

ALSTONE L.M.
Christopher Edwin Willing, 1830-1904

1 On Jor - dan's bank the Bap - tist's cry
2 Then cleansed be ev - ery breast from sin;
3 For thou art our sal - va - tion, Lord,
4 To him who left the throne of heaven

An - nounc - es that the Lord is nigh;
Make straight the way for God with - in;
Our ref - uge and our great re - ward;
To save man - kind, all praise be given;

Come then and heark - en, for he brings
Pre - pare we in our hearts a home,
With - out thy grace we waste a - way,
Like praise be to the Fa - ther done,

Glad ti - dings from the King of kings.
Where such a might - y guest may come.
Like flowers that with - er and de - cay;
And Ho - ly Spir - it, Three in One. A - men.

ADVENT

Hark! a Thrilling Voice Is Sounding

Vox clara ecce intonat
Latin, c. 6th cent.
Tr. Edward Caswall, 1814-1878, alt.

116

MERTON 8.7.8.7.
William Henry Monk, 1823-1889

1 Hark! a thrill - ing voice is sound - ing;
2 Wak - ened by the sol - emn warn - ing,
3 Lo! the Lamb, so long ex - pect - ed,
4 So when next he comes with glo - ry,
5 Hon - or, glo - ry, might, and bless - ing

"Christ is nigh," it seems to say;
Let the earth - bound soul a - rise;
Comes with par - don down from heaven;
And the world is wrapped in fear,
To the Fa - ther and the Son,

"Cast a - way the works of dark - ness,
Christ, her sun, all sloth dis - pell - ing,
Let us haste, with tears of sor - row,
May he with his mer - cy shield us,
With the ev - er - last - ing Spir - it

O ye chil - dren of the day."
Shines up - on the morn - ing skies.
One and all to be for - given;
And with words of love draw near.
While un - end - ing a - ges run. A - men.

ADVENT

117

The First Nowell

Traditional English Carol

THE FIRST NOWELL Irregular
Traditional English Melody

1 The first Now - ell, the an-gel did say, Was to
2 They look - ed up and saw a star Shin-ing
3 And by the light of that same star Three
4 This star drew nigh to the north - west, O'er
5 Then en - tered in those wise men three, Full

cer-tain poor shep-herds in fields as they lay; In fields where
in the east, be - yond them far, And to the
wise men came from coun - try far; To seek for a
Beth - le - hem it took its rest, And there it
rev - erent-ly up - on their knee, And of fered

they lay keep-ing their sheep, On a cold win - ter's
earth it gave great light, And so it con -
king was their in - tent, And to fol - low the
did both stop and stay, Right o - ver the
there, in his pres - ence, Their gold and

night that was so deep.
tin-ued both day and night.
star wher - ev - er it went. Now - ell, Now - ell, Now-
place where Je - sus lay.
myrrh and frank - in - cense.

BIRTH

ell, Now - ell, Born is the King of Is - ra - el.

Silent Night, Holy Night 118

Stille Nacht, heilige Nacht
Joseph Mohr, 1792-1848
Tr. John F. Young, 1820-1865

STILLE NACHT Irregular
Franz Gruber, 1787-1863

1 Si - lent night, ho - ly night, All is calm, all is bright
2 Si - lent night, ho - ly night, Shep-herds quake at the sight,
3 Si - lent night, ho - ly night, Son of God, love's pure light
4 Si - lent night, ho - ly night, Won-drous star, lend thy light;

Round yon vir - gin moth-er and child, Ho - ly in-fant so ten - der and mild,
Glo - ries stream from heav-en a - far, Heaven-ly hosts sing al - le-lu - ia;
Ra - diant beams from thy ho-ly face, With the dawn of re - deem - ing grace,
With the an - gels let us sing, Al - le-lu - ia to our King;

Sleep in heav - en - ly peace, Sleep in heav - en - ly peace.
Christ, the Sav - ior, is born! Christ, the Sav - ior, is born!
Je - sus, Lord, at thy birth, Je - sus, Lord, at thy birth.
Christ, the Sav - ior, is born, Christ, the Sav - ior, is born.

BIRTH

119 *It Came Upon the Midnight Clear*

Edmund H. Sears, 1810-1876, alt.

CAROL C.M.D.
Richard S. Willis, 1819-1900

1 It came up - on the mid-night clear, That glo - rious song of old,
2 Still through the clo - ven skies they come, With peace-ful wings un - furled,
3 Yet with the woes of sin and strife The world has suf - fered long,
4 And ye, be - neath life's crush-ing load Whose forms are bend-ing low,
5 For lo, the days are hasten-ing on, By proph-et bards fore - told,

From an - gels bend-ing near the earth To touch their harps of gold;
And still their heaven-ly mu - sic floats O'er all the wea - ry world;
Be - neath the an - gel strain have rolled Two thou - sand years of wrong;
Who toil a - long the climb-ing way, With pain - ful steps and slow,
When with the ev - er - cir - cling years Comes round the age of gold;

"Peace on the earth, good will to men, From heaven's all gra - cious King."
A - bove its sad and low - ly plains They bend on hover-ing wing,
And man, at war with man, hears not The love song which they bring:
Look now, for glad and gold - en hours Come swift - ly on the wing;
When peace shall o - ver all the earth Its an - cient splen-dors fling,

The world in sol - emn still-ness lay To hear the an - gels sing.
And ev - er o'er its Ba - bel sounds The bless - ed an - gels sing.
O hush the noise, ye men of strife, And hear the an - gels sing!
O rest be - side the wea - ry road, And hear the an - gels sing!
And the whole world send back the song Which now the an - gels sing.

BIRTH

Phillips Brooks, 1835-1893

ST. LOUIS 8.6.8.6.7.6.8.6.
Lewis H. Redner, 1831-1908

1 O lit-tle town of Beth-le-hem, How still we see thee lie!
2 For Christ is born of Mar - y, And gath-ered all a-bove,
3 How si-lent-ly, how si-lent-ly, The won-drous gift is given!
4 O ho-ly Child of Beth-le-hem! De-scend to us, we pray;

A-bove thy deep and dream-less sleep The si-lent stars go by;
While mor-tals sleep, the an-gels keep Their watch of won-dering love.
So God im-parts to hu-man hearts The bless-ings of his heaven.
Cast out our sin and en-ter in; Be born in us to-day.

Yet in thy dark streets shin-eth The ev-er-last-ing Light;
O morn-ing stars, to-geth-er Pro-claim the ho-ly birth!
No ear may hear his com-ing, But in this world of sin,
We hear the Christ-mas an-gels The great glad ti-dings tell;

The hopes and fears of all the years Are met in thee to-night.
And prais-es sing to God the King, And peace to men on earth.
Where meek souls will re-ceive him, still The dear Christ en-ters in.
O come to us, a-bide with us, Our Lord Em-man-u-el! A-men.

BIRTH

121

O Come, All Ye Faithful

Adeste fideles
John Francis Wade?, *c.* 1711-1786
Tr. Frederick Oakeley, 1802-1880, and others

ADESTE FIDELES Irregular
John Francis Wade?, *c.* 1711-1786

1 O come, all ye faith-ful, joy-ful, and tri-um-phant, O
2 Sing, choirs of an-gels, sing in ex-ul-ta-tion,
3 Child, for us sin-ners poor and in the man-ger,
4 Yea, Lord, we greet thee, born this hap-py morn-ing,

come ye, O come ye to Beth-le-hem;
Sing, all ye cit-i-zens of heaven a-bove!
We would em-brace thee, with love and awe;
Je-sus, to thee be all glo-ry given;

Come and be-hold him, born the King of an-gels;
Glo-ry to God, all glo-ry in the high-est;
Who would not love thee, lov-ing us so dear-ly?
Word of the Fa-ther, now in flesh ap-pear-ing;

O come, let us a-dore him, O come, let us a-dore him,

O come, let us a-dore him, Christ, the Lord! A-men.

BIRTH

Joy to the World! the Lord Is Come

122

Psalm 98
Isaac Watts, 1674-1748

ANTIOCH C.M.
Adapted from G. F. Handel, 1685-1759
Arr. Lowell Mason, 1792-1872

1 Joy to the world! the Lord is come: Let earth re-
2 Joy to the earth! the Sav - ior reigns: Let men their
3 He rules the world with truth and grace, And makes the

ceive her King; Let ev - er - y heart pre - pare him room,
songs em - ploy; While fields and floods, rocks, hills, and plains
na - tions prove The glo - ries of his right - eous - ness,

And heaven and na - ture sing, And heaven and na - ture
Re - peat the sound - ing joy, Re - peat the sound - ing
And won - ders of his love, And won - ders of his

And heaven and na - ture sing, And
Re - peat the sound - ing joy, Re -
And won - ders of his love, And

sing, And heaven, and heaven and na - ture sing.
joy, Re - peat, re - peat the sound - ing joy.
love, And won - ders, won - ders of his love. A - men.

heaven and na - ture sing.
peat the sound - ing joy,
won - ders of his love,

BIRTH

123 Hark! the Herald Angels Sing

Charles Wesley, 1707-1788, alt.

MENDELSSOHN 7.7.7.7.D. with Refrain
Felix Mendelssohn, 1809-1847
Arr. William H. Cummings, 1831-1915

1 Hark! the her - ald an - gels sing, "Glo - ry to the new-born King;
2 Christ, by high - est heaven a - dored; Christ, the ev - er - last - ing Lord!
3 Hail the heaven-born Prince of peace! Hail the Sun of right-eous - ness!

Peace on earth, and mer - cy mild, God and sin - ners rec - on - ciled!"
Late in time be - hold him come, Off - spring of the Vir - gin's womb.
Light and life to all he brings, Risen with heal - ing in his wings,

Joy - ful, all ye na - tions, rise, Join the tri - umph of the skies;
Veiled in flesh the God-head see; Hail the in-car - nate De - i - ty,
Mild he lays his glo - ry by, Born that man no more may die,

With the an-gel - ic host pro - claim, "Christ is born in Beth - le - hem!"
Pleased as man with men to dwell, Je - sus, our Em - man - u - el.
Born to raise the sons of earth, Born to give them sec - ond birth.

BIRTH

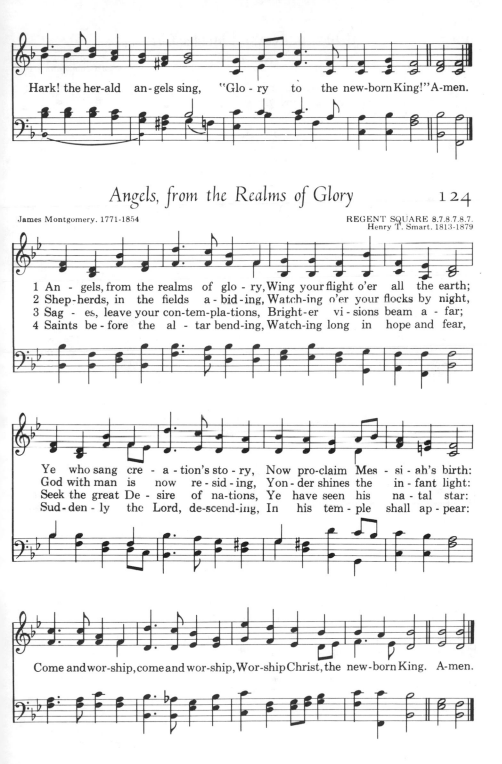

Hark! the her-ald an-gels sing, "Glo - ry to the new-born King!" A-men.

Angels, from the Realms of Glory   124

James Montgomery. 1771-1854

REGENT SQUARE 8.7.8.7.8.7.
Henry T. Smart. 1813-1879

1 An - gels, from the realms of glo - ry, Wing your flight o'er all the earth;
2 Shep-herds, in the fields a - bid - ing, Watch-ing o'er your flocks by night,
3 Sag - es, leave your con-tem-pla-tions, Bright-er vi - sions beam a - far;
4 Saints be - fore the al - tar bend-ing, Watch-ing long in hope and fear,

Ye who sang cre - a - tion's sto - ry, Now pro-claim Mes - si - ah's birth:
God with man is now re - sid - ing, Yon - der shines the in - fant light:
Seek the great De - sire of na-tions, Ye have seen his na - tal star:
Sud - den - ly the Lord, de-scend-ing, In his tem - ple shall ap - pear:

Come and wor-ship, come and wor-ship, Wor-ship Christ, the new-born King. A-men.

BIRTH

125 Once in Royal David's City

Cecil Frances Alexander, 1818-1895

IRBY 8.7.8.7.7.7.
Henry J. Gauntlett, 1805-1876

1 Once in roy - al Da - vid's cit - y Stood a low - ly cat - tle
2 He came down to earth from heav - en Who is God and Lord of
3 Je - sus is our child - hood's pat-tern, Day by day like us he
4 And our eyes at last shall see him, Through his own re - deem - ing

shed, Where a moth - er laid her ba - by In a
all, And his shel - ter was a sta - ble, And his
grew; He was lit - tle, weak, and help - less, Tears and
love; For that child so dear and gen - tle Is our

man - ger for his bed: Ma - ry was that moth - er
cra - dle was a stall: With the poor, and mean, and
smiles like us he knew: And he feel - eth for our
Lord in heaven a - bove, And he leads his chil - dren

mild, Je - sus Christ, her lit - tle child.
low - ly Lived on earth our Sav - ior ho - ly.
sad - ness, And he shar - eth in our glad - ness.
on To the place where he is gone. A - men.

BIRTH

While Shepherds Watched Their Flocks 126

Nahum Tate, 1652-1715

CHRISTMAS C.M.
George Friedrich Handel, 1685-1759

1 While shep-herds watched their flocks by night, All
2 "Fear not," he said for might-y dread Had
3 "To you, in Da-vid's town this day, Is
4 "The heaven-ly Babe you there shall find To

seat-ed on the ground, The an-gel of the Lord came down,
seized their trou-bled mind, "Glad ti-dings of great joy I bring
born of Da-vid's line, A Sav-ior, who is Christ, the Lord,
hu-man view dis-played, All mean-ly wrapped in swath-ing bands,

And glo-ry shone a-round, And glo-ry shone a-round.
To you and all man-kind, To you and all man-kind.
And this shall be the sign: And this shall be the sign:
And in a man-ger laid, And in a man-ger laid."

5 Thus spake the seraph, and forthwith
Appeared a shining throng
Of angels praising God, who thus
Addressed their joyful song:

6 "All glory be to God on high
And on the earth be peace;
Good will henceforth from heaven to men
Begin and never cease."

BIRTH

127 On This Day Earth Shall Ring

Piae Cantiones, 1582
Tr. Jane M. Joseph, c. 1894-1929

PERSONENT HODIE 6.6.6.6.6. with Refrain
Piae Cantiones, 1582
Arr. Gustav T. Holst, 1874-1934

1 On this day earth shall ring With the song
2 His the doom, ours the mirth; When he came
3 God's bright star, o'er his head, Wise men three
4 On this day an-gels sing; With their song

chil-dren sing To the Lord, Christ our King, Born on earth to
down to earth, Beth-le-hem saw his birth; Ox and ass be-
to him led, Kneel-ing low by his bed, Lay their gifts be-
earth shall ring, Prais-ing Christ, heav-en's King, Born on earth to

REFRAIN

save us; Him the Fa-ther gave us.
side him From the cold would hide him.
fore him, Praise him and a-dore him. Id-e-o - o - o,
save us. Peace and love he gave us.

R.H.

R.H. L.H.

BIRTH

Id-e-o - o - o, Id-e-o glo-ri-a in ex-cel-sis De-o!

Away in a Manger   128

Anonymous

CRADLE SONG 11.11.11.11.
W. J. Kirkpatrick, 1838-1921

1 A - way in a man-ger, no crib for a bed, The lit - tle Lord
2 The cat - tle are low-ing, the ba - by a - wakes, But lit - tle Lord

Je - sus laid down his sweet head. The stars in the bright sky looked
Je - sus, no cry-ing he makes. I love thee, Lord Je - sus, look

down where he lay, The lit - tle Lord Je - sus, a - sleep on the hay.
down from the sky, And stay by my cra - dle till morn-ing is nigh.

BIRTH

129   *Angels We Have Heard on High*

French carol

GLORIA 7.7.7.7. with Refrain
French carol

1 An - gels we have heard on high   Sweet - ly sing - ing o'er the plains.
2 Shep-herds, why this ju - bi - lee?   Why these songs of hap - py cheer?
3 Come to Beth - le - hem and see   Him whose birth the an - gels sing;

And the moun-tains in re - ply   Ech - o - ing their joy - ous strains.
What great bright-ness did you see?   What glad ti - dings did you hear?
Come, a - dore on bend - ed knee,   Christ, the Lord, the new - born King.

Glo - - - - - - - ri - a

in ex - cel - sis De - o.   De - o.

BIRTH

Words for stanza two from *The New Church Hymnal* by permission of the Fleming Revell Co.

Come Hither, Ye Children

Christian Schmidt
Tr. Anonymous

IHR KINDERLEIN KOMMET 11.11.11.11.
Johann A. P. Schulz, 1747-1800

130

1 Come hith - er, ye chil - dren, O come one and all,
To Beth - le - hem has - ten, in man - ger so small,
God's Son for a gift has been sent you this night
To be your Re - deem - er, your joy and de - light.

2 On hay and on straw in the man - ger he lies,
Both Ma - ry and Jos - eph, with fond lov - ing eyes,
Are gaz - ing up - on him, and shep - herds draw near,
And ju - bi - lant an - gels from heav - en ap - pear.

3 O kneel with the shep - herds in wor - ship - ful prayer,
And join the dear an - gels who al - so are there,
Sing glo - ry to God in the heav - en a - bove,
And praise him for Je - sus, the gift of his love. A - men.

BIRTH

131 Break Forth, O Beauteous Heavenly Light

St. 1, Johann Rist, 1607-1667
Tr. John Troutbeck, 1832-1899
St. 2 Arthur Tozer Russell, 1806-1874

ERMUNTRE DICH, MEIN SCHWACHER GEIST 8.7.8.7.8.8.7.7.
Johann Schop, c. 1590-1664
Harm. J. S. Bach, 1685-1750

1 Break forth, O beau-teous heaven-ly light, And ush - er in the
2 All bless - ing, thanks and praise to thee, Lord Je - sus Christ, be

morn - ing; Ye shep - herds, shrink not with af - fright, But
giv - en; Thou hast our broth-er deigned to be, Our

hear the an - gels' warn - ing. This child, now weak in
foes a - sun - der riv - en. O grant us through our

in - fan - cy, Our con - fi - dence and joy shall be, The
day of grace With con - stant praise to seek thy face; Grant

BIRTH

power of Sa - tan break - ing, Our peace e - ter - nal mak - ing.
us ere long in glo - ry With prais-es to a - dore thee.

From Heaven Above to Earth I Come   132

Vom Himmel Hoch
Martin Luther, 1483-1546
Tr. Catherine Winkworth, 1827-1878

VOM HIMMEL HOCH L.M.
Valentin Schumann's *Geistliche Leider*, 1539

1 From heaven a - bove to earth I come To bear good news to
2 To you this night is born a child Of Ma - ry, cho - sen
3 Ah, dear - est Je - sus, ho - ly Child, Make thee a bed, soft,
4 Glo - ry to God in high - est heaven, Who un - to man his

ev - ery home; Glad ti - dings of great joy I bring, Where-
moth-er mild; This lit - tle child, of low - ly birth, Shall
un - de - filed, With - in my heart, that it may be A
Son hath given, While an - gels sing with pi - ous mirth A

of I now will say and sing.
be the joy of all the earth.
qui - et cham - ber kept for thee.
glad new year to all the earth.

BIRTH

133 *What Child Is This*

William Chatterton Dix, 1837-1898

GREENSLEEVES 8.7.8.7. with Refrain
English Folk Song

1 What Child is this who, laid to rest, On Ma - ry's lap is sleep - ing?
2 Why lies he in such mean es - tate Where ox and ass are feed - ing?
3 So bring him in - cense, gold, and myrrh, Come, pea - sant, king, to own him,

Whom an - gels greet with an - thems sweet, While shep - herds watch are keep - ing?
Good Christ - ian, fear: for sin - ners here The si - lent Word is plead - ing.
The King of kings sal - va - tion brings, Let lov - ing hearts en - throne him.

This, this is Christ the King, Whom shep - herds guard and an - gels sing:

BIRTH

Haste, haste to bring him laud, The Babe, the Son of Ma - ry.

Love Came Down at Christmas

134

Christina G. Rossetti, 1830-1894

GARTAN 6.7.6.7.
Irish Traditional Air
Harm. David Evans, 1874-1948

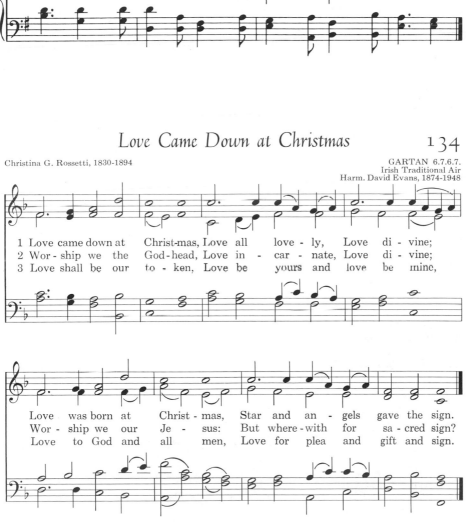

1 Love came down at Christ-mas, Love all love - ly, Love di - vine;
2 Wor - ship we the God-head, Love in - car - nate, Love di - vine;
3 Love shall be our to - ken, Love be yours and love be mine,

Love was born at Christ - mas, Star and an - gels gave the sign.
Wor - ship we our Je - sus: But where-with for sa - cred sign?
Love to God and all men, Love for plea and gift and sign.

BIRTH

In the Bleak Midwinter

Christina G. Rossetti, 1830-1894, alt.

CRANHAM Irregular
Gustav T. Holst, 1874-1934

1   In   the bleak mid - win - ter,   Frost - y wind made moan,
2 Our God, heaven can-not hold him,   Nor   earth sus - tain;
3   An - gels and arch - an - gels   May have gath - ered there,
4   What   can   I   give him,   Poor   as   I   am?

Earth stood hard as i - - ron,   Wa - ter like   a   stone;
Heaven and earth shall flee a - way   When he comes to   reign;
Cher - u - bim and ser - a - phim Throng-ed the   air;
If   I   were a shep - herd, I   would bring a lamb;

Snow had fall - en, snow on snow, Snow   on   snow,
In   the bleak mid - win - ter   A sta - ble place suf - ficed   The
But his moth - er   on - ly,   In her maid - en   bliss,
If   I   were a wise   man,   I   would do my part; Yet

In   the bleak mid - win - ter,   Long   a - go.
Lord   God   al - might - y, Je -   sus   Christ.
Wor-shipped the be - lov - ed   With   a   kiss.
what I   can   I   give him— Give   my   heart.

BIRTH

Infant Holy, Infant Lowly

From the Polish
Para. Edith M. G. Reed, 1885-1933

W ZLOBIE LEZY 4.4.7.4.4.7.4.4.4.4.7.
Polish Carol
Harm. David Hugh Jones, 1900-

1 In - fant ho - ly, In - fant low - ly, For his bed a cat - tle stall;
2 Flocks were sleep-ing; Shep-herds keep-ing Vig - il till the morn-ing new

Ox - en low - ing, Lit - tle know-ing Christ the Babe is Lord of all.
Saw the glo - ry, Heard the sto - ry, Ti - dings of a gos - pel true.

Swift are wing - ing An - gels sing - ing, No - els ring - ing,
Thus re - joic - ing, Free from sor - row, Prais - es voic - ing

Tid - ings bring - ing: Christ the Babe is Lord of all.
Greet the mor - row: Christ the Babe was born for you. A - men.

BIRTH

137 Good Christian Men, Rejoice

Latin, 14th century
Tr. John Mason Neale, 1818-1866

IN DULCI JUBILO 6.6.7.7.7.8.5.5.
14th Century Melody

1 Good Chris-tian men, re - joice, With heart and soul and voice;
2 Good Chris-tian men, re - joice, With heart and soul and voice;
3 Good Chris-tian men, re - joice, With heart and soul and voice;

Give ye heed to what we say: Je - sus Christ is born to - day;
Now ye hear of end - less bliss; Je - sus Christ was born for this!
Now ye need not fear the grave; Je - sus Christ was born to save!

Ox and ass be - fore him bow, And he is in the man - ger now.
He hath oped the heaven-ly door, And man is bless - ed ev - er - more.
Calls you one and calls you all, To gain his ev - er - last - ing hall.

Christ is born to - day! Christ is born to - day!
Christ was born for this! Christ was born for this!
Christ was born to save! Christ was born to save!

BIRTH

Let All Together Praise Our God

138

Lobt Gott, ihr Christen allzugleich
Nikolaus Herman, c. 1485-1561
Tr. Arthur Tozer Russell, 1806-1874

LOBT GOTT, IHR CHRISTEN C.M.
Nikolaus Herman, c. 1485-1561
Harm. J. S. Bach, 1685-1750

1 Let all to - geth - er praise our God Up -
2 He lays a - side his maj - es - ty And
3 Be - hold the won - der - ful ex - change Our

on his loft - y throne; For he un - clos - es
seems as noth - ing worth, And takes on him a
Lord with us doth make! Lo, he as - sumes our

heaven to - day And gives to us his
ser - vant's form, Who made the heaven and
flesh and blood, And we of heaven par -

Son, And gives to us his Son.
earth, Who made the heaven and earth.
take, And we of heaven par - take. A - men.

BIRTH

139

Of the Father's Love Begotten

Corde natus ex Parentis
Aurelius Clemens Prudentius, 348-c. 413
Tr. John Mason Neale, 1818-1866
and Henry W. Baker, 1821-1877

DIVINUM MYSTERIUM 8.7.8.7.8.7.7.
13th century plainsong Mode V
Harm. Winfred Douglas, 1867-1944

1 Of the Fa-ther's love be - got - ten, Ere the worlds be - gan to be,
2 O ye heights of heaven a - dore him; An - gel hosts, his prais - es sing;
3 Christ, to thee with God the Fa - ther, And, O Ho - ly Ghost, to thee,

He is Al - pha and O - me - ga, He the source, the end - ing he;
Powers, do-min-ions, bow be - fore him, And ex - tol our God and King;
Hymn and chant and high thanks-giv - ing, And un - wea - ried prais - es be:

Of the things that are, that have been, And that
Let no tongue on earth be si - lent, Ev - ery
Hon - or, glo - ry, and do - min - ion, And e -

BIRTH

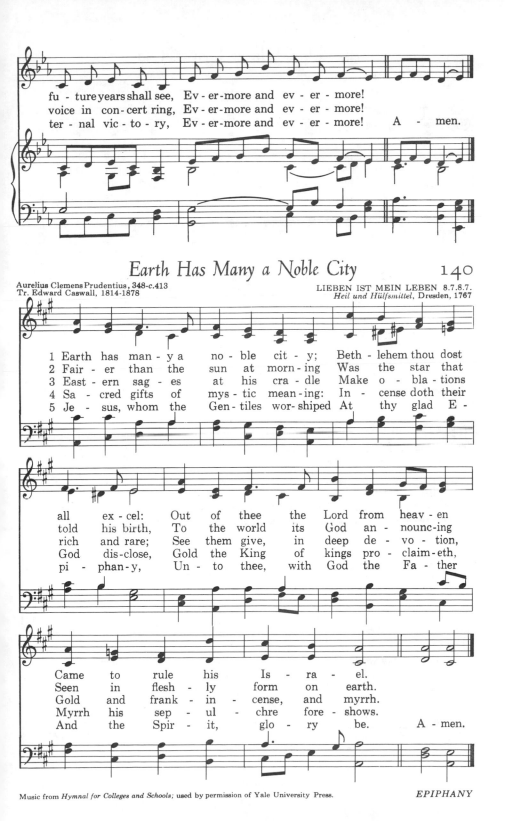

Earth Has Many a Noble City   140

Music from *Hymnal for Colleges and Schools*; used by permission of Yale University Press.

EPIPHANY

As with Gladness Men of Old

William C. Dix, 1837-1898, alt.

DIX 7.7.7.7.7.7.
Abridged from a chorale by
Conrad Kocher, 1786-1872

1 As with glad - ness men of old Did the guid - ing
2 As with joy - ful steps they sped To that low - ly
3 As they of - fered gifts most rare, At the man - ger
4 Ho - ly Je - sus, ev - ery day Keep us in the

star be - hold; As with joy they hailed its light,
man - ger bed, There to bend the knee be - fore
rude and bare, So may we with ho - ly joy,
nar - row way; And, when earth - ly things are past,

Lead - ing on - ward, beam - ing bright; So, most gra - cious
Him whom heaven and earth a - dore; So may we with
Pure and free from sin's al - loy, All our cost - liest
Bring our ran - somed souls at last Where they need no

Lord, may we Ev - er - more be led to thee.
will - ing feet Ev - er seek thy mer - cy seat.
treas - ures bring, Christ, to thee, our heaven - ly King.
star to guide, Where no clouds thy glo - ry hide. A - men.

EPIPHANY

What Star Is This, with Beams So Bright   142

Charles Coffin, 1676-1749
Tr. John Chandler, 1806-1876, alt.

PUER NOBIS NASCITUR L.M.
Adapt. Michael Praetorius, 1571-1621
Harm. George R. Woodward, 1848-1934

1 What star is this, with beams so bright, More love - ly
2 'Tis now ful - filled what God de - creed, "From Ja - cob
3 O Je - sus, while the star of grace Im - pels us
4 To God the Fa - ther, heaven - ly Light, To Christ, re -

than the noon - day light? 'Tis sent to announce a new - born
shall a star pro - ceed"; And lo! the east - ern sa - ges
on to seek thy face, Let not our sloth - ful hearts re -
vealed in earth - ly night, To God the Ho - ly Ghost we

king, Glad ti - dings of our God to bring.
stand, To read in heaven the Lord's com - mand.
fuse The guid - ance of thy light to use.
raise An end - less song of thank - ful praise! A - men.

Music used by permission of A. R. Mowbray and Company Ltd.

EPIPHANY

143 Our Faith Is in the Christ Who Walks

Thomas Curtis Clark, 1877-1953

WAREHAM L.M.
William Knapp, 1698?-1768

1 Our faith is in the Christ who walks
2 His gos - pel calls for liv - ing men,
3 We serve no God whose work is done,
4 God was and is and e'er shall be;

With men to - day, in street and mart;
With sing - ing blood and minds a - lert;
Who rests with - in his firm - a - ment;
Christ lived and loved and loves us still;

The con - stant Friend who thinks and talks
Strong men, who fall to rise a - gain,
Our God, his la - bor but be - gun,
And man goes for - ward, proud and free,

With those who seek him with the heart.
Who strive and bleed, with cour - age girt.
Toils ev - er - more, with power un - spent.
God's pres - ent pur - pose to ful - fill. A - men.

LIFE AND MINISTRY

Words reprinted through permission of First Church of Christ, Scientist, Maywood, Illinois.

Jesus, Friend of Thronging Pilgrims

144

W. Nantlais Williams, 1874-1959

REGENT SQUARE 8.7.8.7.8.7.
Henry T. Smart, 1813-1879

1 Je - sus, Friend of throng - ing pil - grims, As of those who
2 Thou didst know the mar - ket plac - es And the streets in
3 Send thy serv - ants to the high - ways Where are heard the
4 By thy power be streets trans - fig - ured, Haunts of sin be

walk a - lone, Look up - on our crowd - ed cit - ies
days of yore; Thou could'st see be - neath the plea - sures
dole - ful cries; Call a - gain the hun - gry mass - es
pur - i - fied; Rich and poor be found in con - cord,

With com - pas - sion from thy throne; Lov - ing Shep - herd,
Bro - ken hearts and spir - its sore; Gra - cious Heal - er,
To the feast that sat - is - fies; For the sup - per,
Zi - on's courts their hope and pride; Lord of cit - ies,

Lov - ing Shep - herd, Move a - mong us as thine own.
Gra - cious Heal - er, How we need thy touch once more!
For the sup - per Now is spread be - fore their eyes.
Lord of cit - ies, Here make heal - ing peace a - bide. A - men.

Words from *Five City Hymns* copyright 1954 by The Hymn Society of America. Used
by permission.

LIFE AND MINISTRY

145 Lord, Whose Love Through Humble Service

Albert F. Bayly, 1901-

IN BABILONE 8.7.8.7.D.
Oude en Nieuwe Hollantse Boerenlities, c. 1710

1 Lord, whose love through hum-ble serv-ice Bore the weight of hu - man need,
2 Still thy chil-dren wan-der home-less; Still the hun-gry cry for bread;
3 As we wor-ship, grant us vi - sion, Till thy love's re - veal-ing light,
4 Called from wor-ship un-to ser-vice, Forth in thy dear name we go,

Who did'st on the Cross, for-sak-en, Work with mer-cy's per - fect deed;
Still the cap-tives long for free-dom; Still in grief men mourn their dead.
In its height and depth and great-ness Dawns up - on our quick-ened sight,
To the child, the youth, the a - ged, Love in liv - ing deeds to show,

We, thy ser-vants, bring the wor-ship Not of voice a - lone, but heart
As, O Lord, thy deep com-pas-sion Healed the sick and freed the soul,
Mak - ing known the needs and bur-dens Thy com-pas-sion bids us bear,
Hope and health, good will and com-fort, Coun-sel, aid and peace we give,

Con - se - crat-ing to thy pur-pose Ev - ery gift thou dost im-part.
Use the love thy Spir-it kin-dles Still to save and make men whole.
Stir - ring us to tire-less striv-ing Thine a - bun-dant life to share.
That thy chil-dren, Lord, in free-dom May thy mer-cy know and live. A-men.

LIFE AND MINISTRY

O Love, How Deep, How Broad, How High   146

O amor quam ecstaticus
Latin, 15th century
Tr. Benjamin Webb, 1819-1885, alt.

DEO GRACIAS L.M.
Arr. for *The Hymnal* 1933

1 O love, how deep, how broad, how high, How pass - ing
2 For us bap - tized, for us he bore His ho - ly
3 For us he prayed, for us he taught, For us his
4 For us to wick - ed men be - trayed, Scourged, mocked, in
5 For us he rose from death a - gain, For us he

thought and fan - ta - sy, That God, the Son of God, should
fast, and hun-gered sore; For us temp - ta - tions sharp he
dai - ly works he wrought, By words and signs and ac - tions,
pur - ple robe ar - rayed, He bore the shame - ful cross and
went on high to reign; For us he sent his Spir - it

take Our mor - tal form for mor - tals' sake.
knew; For us the temp - ter o - ver - threw.
thus Still seek - ing not him - self, but us.
death; For us gave up his dy - ing breath.
here To guide, to strength - en, and to cheer. A - men.

LIFE AND MINISTRY

147 O Son of Man, Our Hero Strong and Tender

Frank Fletcher, 1870-1954

CHARTERHOUSE 11.10.11.10.
David Evans, 1874-1948

1 O Son of man, our he - ro strong and ten - der,
2 O feet so strong to climb the path of dut - y,
3 Lov - er of chil - dren, boy-hood's in - spir - a - tion,
4 Not in our fail - ures on - ly and our sad - ness

Whose ser - vants are the brave in all the earth,
O lips di - vine that taught the words of truth,
Of all man - kind the ser - vant and the King;
We seek thy pre - sence, Com - fort - er and Friend;

Our liv - ing sac - ri - fice to thee we ren - der,
Kind eyes that marked the li - lies in their beau - ty,
O Lord of joy and hope and con - so - la - tion,
O rich man's guest, be with us in our glad - ness,

LIFE AND MINISTRY

Who shar - est all our sor - rows, all our mirth.
And heart that kin - dled at the zeal of youth.
To thee our fears and joys and hopes we bring.
O poor man's mate, our low - liest tasks at - tend. A - men.

Words by permission of Oxford University Press. Music from *The Revised Church Hymnary* by permission of Oxford University Press.

Jesus, with Thy Church Abide   148

Thomas B. Pollock, 1836-1896

ST. KATRINE 7.7.7.6.
J. Williamson, 1868-1947

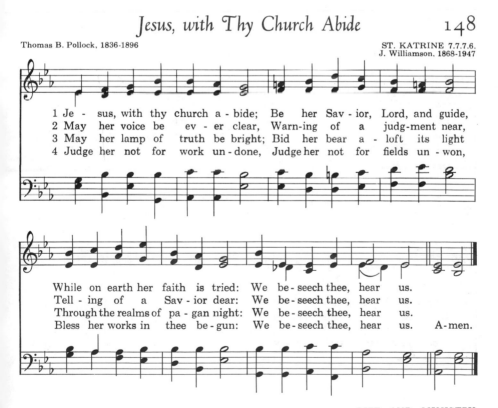

1 Je - sus, with thy church a - bide; Be her Sav - ior, Lord, and guide,
2 May her voice be ev - er clear, Warn - ing of a judg - ment near,
3 May her lamp of truth be bright; Bid her bear a - loft its light
4 Judge her not for work un - done, Judge her not for fields un - won,

While on earth her faith is tried: We be - seech thee, hear us.
Tell - ing of a Sav - ior dear: We be - seech thee, hear us.
Through the realms of pa - gan night: We be - seech thee, hear us.
Bless her works in thee be - gun: We be - seech thee, hear us. A - men.

LIFE AND MINISTRY

149 *The Son of God, Our Christ*

Edward M. Blumenfeld, 1927-

TOULON 10.10.10.10.
Abridged from *Genevan Psalter*, 1551

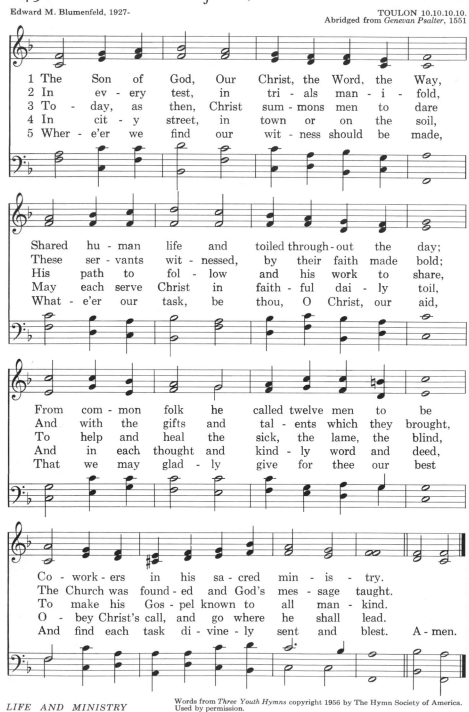

1 The Son of God, Our Christ, the Word, the Way,
2 In ev-ery test, in tri-als man-i-fold,
3 To-day, as then, Christ sum-mons men to dare
4 In cit-y street, in town or on the soil,
5 Wher-e'er we find our wit-ness should be made,

Shared hu-man life and toiled through-out the day;
These ser-vants wit-nessed, by their faith made bold;
His path to fol-low and his work to share,
May each serve Christ in faith-ful dai-ly toil,
What-e'er our task, be thou, O Christ, our aid,

From com-mon folk he called twelve men to be
And with the gifts and tal-ents which they brought,
To help and heal the sick, the lame, the blind,
And in each thought and kind-ly word and deed,
That we may glad-ly give for thee our best

Co-work-ers in his sa-cred min-is-try.
The Church was found-ed and God's mes-sage taught.
To make his Gos-pel known to all man-kind.
O-bey Christ's call, and go where he shall lead.
And find each task di-vine-ly sent and blest. A-men.

LIFE AND MINISTRY

Words from *Three Youth Hymns* copyright 1956 by The Hymn Society of America. Used by permission.

Thou Didst Leave Thy Throne

Emily E. S. Elliott, 1836-1897, alt.

MARGARET Irregular
Timothy R. Matthews, 1826-1910

1 Thou didst leave thy throne and thy king - ly crown When thou cam - est to earth for me, But in Beth - le - hem's home there was found no room For thy ho - ly na - tiv - i - ty. O come to my heart, Lord Je - sus; There is room in my heart for thee!

2 Heav - en's arch - es rang when the an - gels sang, Pro - claim - ing thy roy - al de - gree, But in low - ly birth didst thou come to earth, And in great hu - mil - i - ty. O come to my heart, Lord Je - sus; There is room in my heart for thee!

3 Thou didst come, O Lord, with the liv - ing word That should set thy peo - ple free, But with mock - ing scorn and with crown of thorn They bore thee to Cal - va - ry. O come to my heart, Lord Je - sus; There is room in my heart for thee!

4 When the heavens shall ring and the an - gels sing At thy com - ing to vic - to - ry, Let thy voice call me home, say - ing, "Yet there is room, There is room at my side for thee." And my heart shall re - joice, Lord Je - sus; When thou com - est and call - est me. A - men.

LIFE AND MINISTRY

151

Take Up Thy Cross

Charles W. Everest, 1814-1877

DISTRESS L.M.
William Walker's *Southern Harmony*, 1835

1 Take up thy cross, the Sav - ior said, If
2 Take up thy cross; let not its weight Fill
3 Take up thy cross, nor heed the shame, Nor
4 Take up thy cross, and fol - low Christ, Nor

thou wouldst my dis - ci - ple be; De - ny thy - self, the
thy weak spir - it with a - larm; His strength shall bear thy
let thy fool - ish pride re - bel; Thy Lord for thee the
think till death to lay it down; For on - ly he who

world for - sake, And hum - bly fol - low af - ter me.
spir - it up, And brace thy heart, and nerve thine arm.
cross en - dured And fought the powers of death and hell.
bears the cross May hope to wear the glo - rious crown. A - men.

152

My Master Was So Very Poor

Harry Lee, 1875-1942

HERRNHUT L.M.
Bartholomaeus Gesius, c. 1555-c. 1613

1 My Mas - ter was so ver - y poor, A man - ger was his crad - ling place;
2 My Mas - ter was so ver - y poor, And with the poor he broke the bread;
3 My Mas - ter was so ver - y poor, They nailed him na - ked to a cross;

LIFE AND MINISTRY

So ver-y rich my Mas-ter was, Kings came from far to gain his grace.
So ver-y rich my Mas-ter was, That mul-ti-tudes by him were fed.
So ver-y rich my Mas-ter was, He gave his all and knew no loss. A-men.

Most Wondrous Is of All on Earth
153

N. F. S. Grundtvig, 1783-1872
Tr. Jean Fraser, 1951

8.7.8.7.
Danish Folk Song

1 Most won-drous is of all on earth The
2 As breath of wind in - vis - i - ble, Its
3 Its se - cret: God's al - might - y word Which
4 The tempt - er by his e - vil power The
5 Its glo - rious King is he who died Up -

king-dom Je - sus found - ed, Its glo - ry, peace and
signs are yet re - vealed: A cit - y set up -
heaven and earth cre - a - ted, The val - leys when his
king-dom is dis - tress - ing, God crowns in his ap -
on the Cross to save us, New joy un - to the

pre-cious worth No tongue has ev - er sound - ed.
on a hill From men is not con - ceal - ed.
voice they heard Were filled, the floods a - bat - ed.
point-ed hour With joy and fruit - ful bless - ing.
world to bring His ver - y life he gave us. A - men.

LIFE AND MINISTRY

154 *Draw Nigh to Thy Jerusalem*

Jeremy Taylor, 1613-1667, alt.

FARLEY CASTLE 10.10.10.10.
Henry Lawes, 1596-1662

1 Draw nigh to thy Je - ru - sa - lem, O Lord,
2 Thy road is read - y; and thy paths, made straight
3 Ho - san - na! wel - come to our hearts! for here

Thy faith - ful peo - ple cry with one ac - cord:
With long - ing ex - pec - ta - tion, seem to wait
Thou hast a tem - ple, too, as Zi - on dear;

Ride on in tri - umph; Lord, be - hold we lay
The con - se - cra - tion of thy beau - teous feet,
O en - ter in, dear Lord, un - bar the door

Our pas - sions, lusts, and proud wills in thy way.
And si - lent - ly thy prom - ised ad - vent greet.
And in that tem - ple dwell for - ev - er - more. A - men.

TRIUMPHAL ENTRY

Music from *Hymnal for Colleges and Schools*, edited by E. Harold Geer. Used by permission of Yale University Press.

All Glory, Laud, and Honor

155

Gloria, laus, et honor
Theodulph of Orleans, c. 760-c. 821
Tr. John M, Neale, 1818-1866

ST. THEODULPH 7.6.7.6.D.
Melchior Teschner, 1584-1635

1 All glo - ry, laud, and hon - or, To thee, Re-deem-er, King,
2 The com-pa - ny of an - gels Are prais-ing thee on high,
3 To thee, be-fore thy pas - sion They sang their hymns of praise;

To whom the lips of chil - dren Made sweet ho - san - nas ring.
And mor - tal men and all things Cre - a - ted make re - ply.
To thee, now high ex - alt - ed, Our mel - o - dy we raise.

Thou art the King of Is - rael, Thou Da - vid's roy - al Son,
The peo - ple of the He - brews With palms be - fore thee went;
Thou didst ac - cept their prais - es; Ac - cept the praise we bring,

Who in the Lord's name com - est, The King and Bless-ed One.
Our praise and prayer and an - thems Be - fore thee we pre - sent.
Who in all good de - light - est, Thou good and gra - cious King. A-men.

TRIUMPHAL ENTRY

156 Ride On, Ride On in Majesty!

Henry H. Milman, 1791-1878, alt.

THE KING'S MAJESTY L.M.
Graham George, 1912-

1 Ride on, ride on in ma - - jes - ty! Hark! all the
2 Ride on, ride on in ma - - jes - ty! In low - ly
3 Ride on, ride on in ma - - jes - ty! The wing - ed
4 Ride on, ride on in ma - - jes - ty! Thy last and

tribes ho-san - na cry; Thy hum - ble beast pur - sues his
pomp ride on to die; O Christ, thy tri - umphs now be -
squad - rons of the sky Look down with sad and won-dering
fierc - est strife is nigh; Bow thy meek head to mor - tal

road With palms and scat - tered gar - ments strowed.
gin O'er cap - tive death and con - quered ' sin.
eyes To see the ap - proach - ing sac - ri - fice.
pain, Then take, O Christ, thy power, and reign. A - men.

TRIUMPHAL ENTRY

What Wondrous Love Is This

American Folk Hymn

WONDROUS LOVE 12.9.12.9
Southern Harmony, 1835
Arr. Paul Christiansen, 1914-

157

1 What won-drous love is this, O my soul, O my soul!
2 What won-drous love is this, O my soul, O my soul!

What won-drous love is this, O my soul!
What won-drous love is this, O my soul!

What won-drous love is this that caused the Lord of bliss
What won-drous love is this that caused the Lord of life

To bear the dread-ful curse for my soul.
To lay a-side his crown for my soul. A-men.

PASSION

Into the Woods My Master Went

Sidney Lanier, 1842-1881

RIDGEFIELD Irregular
Harold W. Friedell, 1905-1958

1 In - to the woods my Mas - ter went, Clean for - spent,
2 Out of the woods my Mas - ter went, And he was well con -

for - spent, In - to the woods my Mas - ter came, For -
tent, con - tent, Out of the woods my Mas - ter came, Con -

spent with love and shame. But the o - lives they were not
tent with death and shame. When death and shame would

PASSION

blind to him, The lit - tle gray leaves were kind to him, The
woo him last, From un - der the trees they drew him last, 'Twas

thorn tree had a mind to him, When in - to the woods he came.
on a tree they slew him last, When out of the woods he came.

Music from *New Songs for the Junior Choir* by permission of Concordia Publishing House.

159
Beneath the Cross of Jesus

Elizabeth C. Clephane, 1830-1869

ST. CHRISTOPHER 7.6.8.6.8.6.8.6.
Frederick C. Maker, 1844-1927

1 Be-neath the cross of Je-sus I fain would take my stand,
2 Up-on that cross of Je-sus Mine eye at times can see
3 I take, O cross, thy shad-ow For my a-bid-ing place;

The shad-ow of a might-y rock With-in a wea-ry land;
The ver-y dy-ing form of one Who suf-fered there for me;
I ask no oth-er sun-shine than The sun-shine of his face;

A home with-in the wild-er-ness, A rest up-on the way,
And from my smit-ten heart with tears Two won-ders I con-fess—
Con-tent to let the world go by, To know no gain nor loss,

From the burn-ing of the noon-tide heat, And the bur-den of the day.
The won-ders of his glo-rious love And my un-wor-thi-ness.
My sin-ful self my on-ly shame, My glo-ry all the cross. A-men.

PASSION

Before the Cross of Jesus

Ferdinand Q. Blanchard, 1876-1968

ST. CHRISTOPHER 7.6.8.6.7.6.8.6.
Frederick C. Maker, 1844-1927

1 Be - fore the cross of Je - sus Our lives are judged to - day;
2 The hopes that lead us on - ward, The fears that hold us back,
3 Yet hum - bly, in our striv - ing, O God, we face its test.

The mean - ing of our ea - ger strife Is test - ed by his Way.
Our will to dare great things for God, The cour - age that we lack,
We crave the pow'r to do thy will With him who did it best.

A - cross our rest - less liv - ing The light streams from his cross,
The faith we keep in good - ness, Our love, as low or pure,
On us let now the heal - ing Of his great Spir - it fall,

And by its clear, re - veal - ing beams We meas - ure gain and loss.
On all, the judg - ment of the cross Falls stead - y, clear, and sure.
And make us brave and full of joy To an - swer to his call. A - men.

PASSION

161 Were You There When They Crucified My Lord?

Anonymous

WERE YOU THERE Irregular
Negro Spiritual

1 Were you there when they cru - ci - fied my Lord? _____ Were you
2 Were you there when they nailed him to the tree? _____ Were you
3 Were you there when they laid him in the tomb? _____ Were you

there when they cru - ci - fied my Lord? _____
there when they nailed him to the tree? _____
there when they laid him in the tomb? _____

Oh! _____ Some-times it caus - es me to trem - ble, trem - ble,
Oh! _____ Some-times it caus - es me to trem - ble, trem - ble,
Oh! _____ Some-times it caus - es me to trem - ble, trem - ble,

PASSION

trem - ble.   Were you there when they cru - ci - fied   my   Lord?
trem - ble.   Were you there when they nailed him to   the   tree?
trem - ble.   Were you there when they laid him in   the   tomb?

Ah, Holy Jesus, How Hast Thou Offended   162

Herzliebster Jesu, was hast du verbrochen?
Johann Heerman, 1585-1647
Tr. Robert S. Bridges, 1844-1930

HERZLIEBSTER JESU 11.11.11.5.
Johann Crüger, 1598-1662

1 Ah,   ho - ly   Je - sus,   how hast thou of - fend - ed,
2 Who was the   guilt - y?   Who brought this up - on thee?
3 For   me, kind Je - sus,   was thy in - car - na - tion,
4 There - fore, kind Je - sus, since I can - not pay thee,

That man to judge thee hath in hate pre - tend - ed? By foes de -
A - las, my trea - son, Je - sus, hath un - done thee! 'Twas I, Lord
Thy mor - tal sor - row, and thy life's ob - la - tion; Thy death of
I   do a - dore thee, and will ev - er pray thee, Think on thy

rid - ed, by thine own re - ject - ed, O most af - flict - ed!
Je - sus, I it was de - nied thee; I cru - ci - fied thee.
an - guish and thy bit - ter pas - sion, For my sal - va - tion.
pit - y and thy love un - swerv - ing, Not my de - serv - ing. A-men.

PASSION

163 O Sacred Head, Now Wounded

Based on Latin attributed to Bernard of Clairvaux, 1091-1153
German version Paul Gerhardt, 1607-1676
Tr. James Waddell Alexander, 1804-1859

PASSION CHORALE 7.6.7.6.D.
Hans Leo Hassler, 1564-1612
Harm. J. S. Bach, 1685-1750

1 O sa - cred Head, now wound - ed, With grief and shame weighed down;
2 What thou, my Lord, hast suf - fered Was all for sin - ners' gain:
3 What lan-guage shall I bor - row To thank thee, dear - est Friend,

Now scorn-ful - ly sur - round - ed With thorns, thine on - ly crown;
Mine, mine was the trans-gres - sion, But thine the dead - ly pain.
For this thy dy - ing sor - row, Thy pit - y with - out end?

O sa - cred Head, what glo - ry, What bliss till now was thine!
Lo, here I fall, my Sav - ior! 'Tis I de - serve thy place;
O make me thine for - ev - er; And should I faint - ing be,

Yet, though de - spised and gor - y, I joy to call thee mine.
Look on me with thy fa - vor, Vouch-safe to me thy grace.
Lord, let me nev - er, nev - er Out - live my love to thee. A-men.

PASSION

From the Latin, 13th century
Tr. Louis Fitzgerald Benson, 1855-1930

STABAT MATER 8.8.7.8.8.7.
Mechlin Plainsong, Mode IV

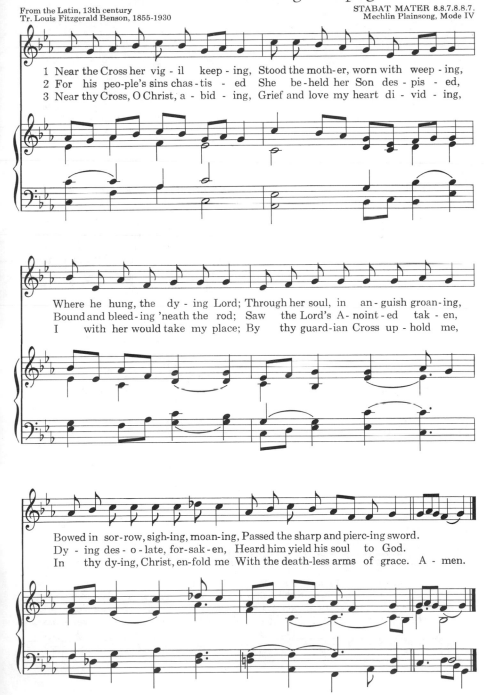

1 Near the Cross her vig - il keep - ing, Stood the moth-er, worn with weep - ing,
2 For his peo-ple's sins chas-tis - ed She be-held her Son des - pis - ed,
3 Near thy Cross, O Christ, a - bid - ing, Grief and love my heart di - vid - ing,

Where he hung, the dy - ing Lord; Through her soul, in an - guish groan-ing,
Bound and bleed-ing 'neath the rod; Saw the Lord's A - noint - ed tak - en,
I with her would take my place; By thy guard-ian Cross up - hold me,

Bowed in sor-row, sigh-ing, moan-ing, Passed the sharp and pierc-ing sword.
Dy - ing des - o - late, for-sak-en, Heard him yield his soul to God.
In thy dy-ing, Christ, en-fold me With the death-less arms of grace. A - men.

PASSION

165   'Tis Midnight, and on Olive's Brow

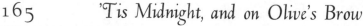

William B. Tappan, 1794-1849, alt.

OLIVE'S BROW L.M.
William B. Bradbury, 1816-1868

1 'Tis mid-night, and on Ol-ive's brow The
2 'Tis mid-night, and, from all re-moved, The
3 'Tis mid-night, and, for oth-ers' guilt, The
4 'Tis mid-night, and from heaven-ly plains Is

star is dimmed that late-ly shone; 'Tis mid-night, in the
Sav-ior wres-tles lone with fears; E'en that dis-ci-ple
Man of Sor-rows weeps in blood; Yet he that hath in
borne the song that an-gels know; Un-heard by mor-tals

gar-den now The suf-fering Sav-ior prays a-lone.
whom he loved Heeds not his Mas-ter's grief and tears.
an-guish knelt Is not for-sak-en by his God.
are the strains That sweet-ly soothe the Sav-ior's woe. A-men.

166   Lord, Who Throughout These Forty Days

Claudia F. Hernaman, 1838-1898

ST. FLAVIAN C.M.
Adapt. from the *English Psalter*, 1562

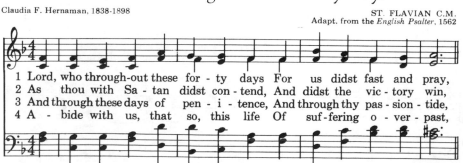

1 Lord, who through-out these for-ty days For us didst fast and pray,
2 As thou with Sa-tan didst con-tend, And didst the vic-tory win,
3 And through these days of pen-i-tence, And through thy pas-sion-tide,
4 A-bide with us, that so, this life Of suf-fering o-ver-past,

PASSION

Teach us with thee to mourn our sins, And close by thee to stay.
O give us strength in thee to fight, In thee to con-quer sin.
Yea, ev-er-more, in life and death, Je-sus! with us a-bide.
An East-er of un-end-ing joy We may at-tain at last! A-men.

Throned Upon the Awful Tree 16₇

John Ellerton, 1826-1893, alt.

ARFON 7.7.7.7.7.7.
Welsh Hymn Melody

1 Throned up-on the aw-ful tree, King of grief, I watch with thee.
2 Si-lent through those three dread hours, Wres-tling with the e-vil powers,
3 Hark, that cry that peals a-loud Up-ward through the whelm-ing cloud!
4 Lord, should fear and an-guish roll Dark-ly o'er my sin-ful soul,

Dark-ness veils thine an-guished face; None its lines of woe can trace;
Left a-lone with hu-man sin, Gloom a-round thee and with-in,
Thou, the Fa-ther's on-ly Son, Thou, his own a-noint-ed one,
Thou, who once wast thus be-reft That thine own might ne'er be left,

None can tell what pangs un-known Hold thee si-lent and a-lone.
Till the ap-point-ed time is nigh, Till the Lamb of God may die.
Thou dost ask him can it be? "Why hast thou for-sak-en me?"
Teach me by that bit-ter cry In the gloom to know thee nigh. A-men.

PASSION

168 *O Come and Mourn with Me Awhile*

Frederick William Faber, 1814-1863

COUTANCES L.M.
French Church Melody,
from the *Rouen Antiphoner*, 1728

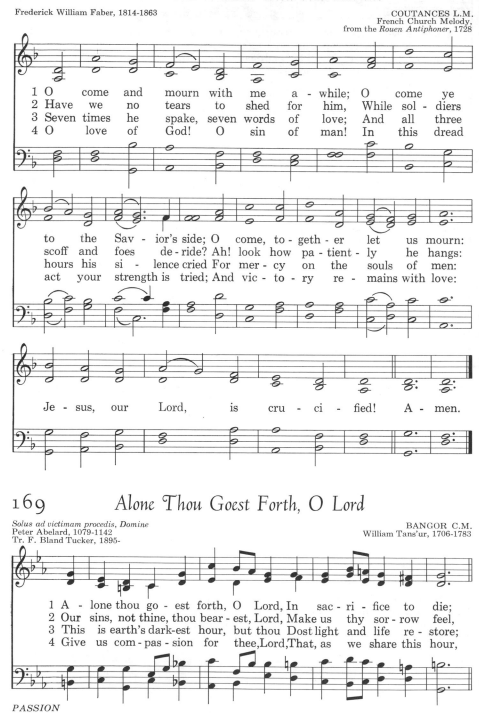

1 O come and mourn with me a - while; O come ye
2 Have we no tears to shed for him, While sol - diers
3 Seven times he spake, seven words of love; And all three
4 O love of God! O sin of man! In this dread

to the Sav - ior's side; O come, to - geth - er let us mourn:
scoff and foes de - ride? Ah! look how pa - tient - ly he hangs:
hours his si - lence cried For mer - cy on the souls of men:
act your strength is tried; And vic - to - ry re - mains with love:

Je - sus, our Lord, is cru - ci - fied! A - men.

169 *Alone Thou Goest Forth, O Lord*

Solus ad victimam procedis, Domine
Peter Abelard, 1079-1142
Tr. F. Bland Tucker, 1895-

BANGOR C.M.
William Tans'ur, 1706-1783

1 A - lone thou go - est forth, O Lord, In sac - ri - fice to die;
2 Our sins, not thine, thou bear - est, Lord, Make us thy sor - row feel,
3 This is earth's dark-est hour, but thou Dost light and life re - store;
4 Give us com - pas - sion for thee, Lord, That, as we share this hour,

PASSION

Is this thy sor-row naught to us Who pass un-heed-ing by?
Till through our pit-y and our shame Love an-swers love's ap-peal.
Then let all praise be giv-en thee Who liv-est ev-er-more.
Thy cross may bring us to thy joy And res-ur-rec-tion power. A-men.

Words by permission of The Church Pension Fund.

Go to Dark Gethsemane 170

James Montgomery, 1771-1854

ARFON 7.7.7.7.7.7.
Welsh Hymn Melody

1 Go to dark Geth-se-ma-ne, Ye that feel the temp-ter's pow'r;
2 Fol-low to the judg-ment hall; View the Lord of life ar-raigned.
3 Cal-v'ry's mourn-ful moun-tain climb; There, a-dor-ing at his feet

Your Re-deem-er's con-flict see, Watch with him one bit-ter hour:
O the worm-wood and the gall! O the pangs his soul sus-tained!
Mark that mir-a-cle of time, God's own sac-ri-fice com-plete:

Turn not from his griefs a-way; Learn of Je-sus Christ to pray.
Shun not suf-f'ring, shame or loss; Learn of him to bear the cross.
"It is fin-ished!" hear him cry; Learn of Je-sus Christ to die. A-men.

PASSION

171   *When I Survey the Wondrous Cross*

Isaac Watts, 1674-1748

HAMBURG L.M.
Arr. Lowell Mason, 1792-1872

1 When I sur - vey the won - drous cross On which the
2 For - bid it, Lord, that I should boast, Save in the
3 See, from his head, his hands, his feet, Sor - row and

Prince of glo - ry died, My rich - est gain I
death of Christ, my God; All the vain things that
love flow min - gled down! Did e'er such love and

count but loss, And pour con - tempt on all my pride.
charm me most I sac - ri - fice them to his blood.
sor - row meet, Or thorns com - pose so rich a crown? A-men.

4 Were the whole realm of nature mine,
   That were a present far too small;
Love so amazing, so divine,
   Demands my soul, my life, my all.

PASSION

Deep Were His Wounds

William Johnson, 1906-

MARLEE 6.6.6.6.8.8.
Leland B. Sateren, 1913-

1 Deep were his wounds, and red, On cru - el Cal - va - ry,
2 He suf-fered shame and scorn, And wretch-ed, dire dis - grace;
3 His life, his all, he gave When he was cru - ci - fied;

As on the Cross he bled In bit - ter ag - o - ny; But they, whom
For-sak- en and for-lorn, He hung there in our place. But such as
Our burd-ened souls to save, What fear - ful death he died! But each of

sin has wound - ed sore, Find heal-ing in the wounds he bore.
would from sin be free Look to his Cross for vic - to - ry.
us, though dead in sin, Through him e-ter - nal life may win. A-men.

Words and music from *The Lutheran Service Book and Hymnal* by permission of the Commission on the Liturgy and Hymnal.

PASSION

173   *Come, Ye Faithful, Raise the Strain*

Attr. to John of Damascus, *c.* 696-*c.* 754
Tr. John M. Neale, 1818-1866, alt.

ST. KEVIN 7.6.7.6.D.
Arthur S. Sullivan, 1842-1900

1 Come, ye faith-ful, raise the strain Of tri-umph-ant glad-ness;
2 'Tis the spring of souls to-day; Christ hath burst his pris-on,
3 Now the queen of sea-sons, bright With the day of splen-dor,

God hath brought his peo-ple forth In - to joy from sad-ness;
And from three days' sleep in death As a sun hath ris-en;
With the roy-al feast of feasts, Comes its joy to ren-der;

Now re-joice, Je-ru-sa-lem, And with true af-fec-tion
All the win-ter of our sins, Long and dark, is fly-ing
Comes to glad Je-ru-sa-lem Who with true af-fec-tion

Wel-come in un-wea-ried strains Je-sus' res-ur-rec-tion.
From his light, to whom we give Laud and praise un-dy-ing.
Wel-comes in un-wea-ried strains Je-sus' res-ur-rec-tion. A-men.

RESURRECTION

Jesus Christ Is Risen Today

174

St. 1: *Surrexit Christus hodie*, 14th century
Tr. in *Lyra Davidica*, 1708
Sts. 2,3: J. Arnold's *Compleat Psalmodist*, 1750, alt.
St. 4: Charles Wesley, 1707-1788

LLANFAIR 7.7.7.7. with Alleluias
Robert Williams, c. 1781-1821
Harm. John Roberts, 1822-1877

1 Je - sus Christ is risen to - day,
2 Hymns of praise then let us sing:
3 But the pains which he en - dured,
4 Sing we to our God a - bove:

Al - le - lu - ia!

Our tri - um - phant ho - ly day,
Un - to Christ, our heaven - ly King,
Our sal - va - tion have pro - cured,
Praise e - ter - nal as his love,

Al - le - lu - ia!

Who did once up - on the cross,
Who en - dured the cross and grave,
Now a - bove the sky he's King,
Praise him, all ye heaven - ly host,

Al - le - lu - ia!

Suf - fer to re - deem our loss.
Sin - ners to re - deem and save.
Where the an - gels ev - er sing:
Fa - ther, Son, and Ho - ly Ghost.

Al - le - lu - ia!

RESURRECTION

175 *Alleluia! Alleluia! Hearts to Heaven and Voices Raise*

Christopher Wordsworth, 1807-1885

IN BABILONE 8.7.8.7.D.
Oude en Nieuwe Hollantse Boerenlities, c. 1710

1 Al - le - lu - ia! Al - le - lu - ia! Hearts to heaven and voic - es raise;
2 Now the i - ron bars are bro - ken, Christ from death to life is born;
3 Al - le - lu - ia! Al - le - lu - ia! Glo - ry be to God on high;

Sing to God a hymn of glad-ness, Sing to God a hymn of praise.
Glo - rious life, and life im - mor - tal On this ho - ly Eas - ter morn;
Al - le - lu - ia! to the Sav - ior Who has won the vic - to - ry;

He who on the cross as Sav - ior For the world's sal - va - tion bled,
Christ has tri-umphed, and we con - quer By his might - y en - ter - prise.
Al - le - lu - ia! to the Spir - it, Fount of love and sanc - ti - ty;

RESURRECTION

Je - sus Christ, the King of glo - ry, Now is ris - en from the dead.
We with him to life e - ter - nal By his re - sur - rec - tion rise.
Al - le - lu - ia! Al - le - lu - ia! To the Tri - une Maj - es - ty. A-men.

Christ the Lord Is Risen Again 176

Christ ist erstanden
Michael Weisse, *c.* 1488-1534
Tr. Catherine Winkworth, 1827-1878

CHRIST IST ERSTANDEN 7.7.7.7.4.
Germany, 12th century

1 Christ the Lord is risen a - gain, Christ hath bro - ken ev - ery chain,
2 He who bore all pain and loss Com - fort - less up - on the cross,
3 He who slum - bered in the grave Is ex - alt - ed now to save;

Hark, the an - gels shout for joy, Sing - ing ev - er - more on high:
Lives in glo - ry now on high, Pleads for us and hears our cry:
Now through Chris - ten - dom it rings That the Lamb is King of kings:

Al - le - lu - ia! A - men.

RESURRECTION

177 Christ Jesus Lay in Death's Strong Bands

Christ lag in Todesbanden
Martin Luther, 1483-1546
Tr. Richard Massie, 1800-1887

CHRIST LAG IN TODESBANDEN 8.7.8.7.7.8.7.4.
Johann Walther's *Geystliche gesangk Buchleyn*, 1524
Harm. Hans Leo Hassler, 1564-1612

1 Christ Je-sus lay in death's strong bands For our of-fens-es giv-en; But now at God's right hand he stands And brings us life from heav-en; Where-fore let us joy-ful be, And sing to God right thank-ful-ly Loud

2 It was a strange and dread-ful strife When life and death con-tend-ed; The vic-to-ry re-mained with life, The reign of death was end-ed; Stripped of power, no more he reigns, An emp-ty form a-lone re-mains; His

3 So let us feast this Eas-ter day On the true Bread of heav-en. The word of grace hath purged a-way The old and wick-ed leav-en; Christ a-lone our souls will feed, He is our meat and drink in-deed, Faith

RESURRECTION

songs of Al - le - lu - ia! Al - le - lu - ia!
sting is lost for - ev - er. Al - le - lu - ia!
lives up - on no oth - er. Al - le - lu - ia! A - men.

Good Christian Men Rejoice and Sing! 178

Cyril A. Alington, 1872-1955

GELOBT SEI GOTT 8.8.8. with Alleluias
Melody by Melchior Vulpius, c. 1560-1616

1 Good Chris - tian men re - joice and sing! Now is the
2 The Lord of life is risen for aye; Bring flowers of
3 Praise we in songs of vic - to - ry That love, that
4 Thy name we bless, O ris - en Lord, And sing to -

tri - umph of our King! To all the world glad
song to strew his way; Let all man - kind re -
life which can - not die, And sing with hearts up -
day with one ac - cord The life laid down, the

news we bring:
joice and say: Al - le - lu - ia! Al - le - lu - ia! Al - le - lu - ia!
lift - ed high:
life re - stored:

RESURRECTION

179 O Sons and Daughters, Let Us Sing

Jean Tisserand, d. 1494
Tr. John M. Neale, 1818-1866, alt.

O FILII ET FILIAE 8.8.8. with Alleluias
French: 15th century?
Airs sur les hymnes sacres, odes et noels, 1623; adapted

Al - le - lu - ia, Al - le - lu - ia, Al - le - lu - ia!

1 O sons and daugh - ters, let us sing! The
2 On Eas - ter morn, at break of day, The
3 An an - gel clad in white they see, Who
4 How blest are they who have not seen, And
5 On this most ho - ly day of days, Our

King of heaven, the glo - rious King, O'er death to - day rose
faith - ful wom - en went their way To seek the tomb where
sat, and spake un - to the three, "Your Lord doth go to
yet whose faith has con - stant been; For they e - ter - nal
hearts and voic - es, Lord, we raise To thee in jub - i -

tri - umph - ing.
Je - sus lay.
Gal - i - lee." Al - le - lu - ia! Al - le - lu - ia!
life shall win.
lee and praise.

RESURRECTION

Christ the Lord Is Risen Today

180

CharlesCharles Wesley, 1707-1788, and others

EASTER HYMN 7.7.7.7. with Alleluias
From *Lyra Davidica*, 1708

1 Christ the Lord is risen to - day,
2 Lives a - gain our glo - rious King,
3 Love's re - deem - ing work is done,
4 Soar we now where Christ has led,

Al - - - le - lu - ia!

Sons of men and an - gels say,
Where, O death, is now thy sting?
Fought the fight, the bat - tle won,
Fol - lowing our ex - alt - ed Head,

Al - - - le - lu - ia!

Raise your joys and tri - umphs high,
Once he died, our souls to save,
Death in vain for - bids him rise,
Made like him, like him we rise,

Al - - - le - lu - ia!

Sing, ye heavens, and earth re - ply,
Where thy vic - to - ry, O grave?
Christ hath o - pened Par - a - dise,
Ours the cross, the grave, the skies,

Al - - - le - lu - ia!

RESURRECTION

181

Thine Is the Glory

Edmond L. Budry, 1854-1932
Tr. R. Birch Hoyle, 1875-1939

MACCABEUS 5.5.6.5.6.5.6.5. with Refrain
George Friedrich Handel, 1685-1759

1 Thine is the glo - ry, Ris - en, con - quering Son,
2 Lo! Je - sus meets thee, Ris - en from the tomb;
3 No more we doubt thee, Glo - rious Prince of life!

End - less is the vic - tory Thou o'er death hast won.
Lov - ing - ly he greets thee, Scat - ters fear and gloom;
Life is nought with - out thee; Aid us in our strife;

An - gels in bright rai - ment Rolled the stone a - way,
Let his church with glad - ness Hymns of tri - umph sing,
Make us more than con - querors, Through thy death - less love.

Kept the fold - ed grave-clothes Where thy bod - y lay.
For her Lord now liv - eth; Death hath lost its sting.
Bring us safe through Jor - dan To thy home a - bove.

RESURRECTION

Thine is the glo - ry, Ris - en, con - quering Son,

End - less is the vic - tory Thou o'er death hast won.

The Strife Is O'er 182

Finita iam sunt praelia
Latin 17th century
Tr. Francis Pott, 1832-1908, alt.

VICTORY 8.8.8. with Alleluia
Arr. from G. P. da Palestrina, 1525-1594
William H. Monk, 1823-1889

1 The strife is o'er, the bat - tle done; The vic - to - ry of life is won;
2 The powers of death have done their worst, But Christ their le - gions hath dis-persed;
3 The three sad days are quick-ly sped, He ris - es glo - rious from the dead;
4 Lord, by the stripes which wound-ed thee, From death's dread sting thy serv-ants free,

The song of tri - umph has be - gun:
Let shouts of ho - ly joy out - burst: Al - le - lu - ia!
All glo - ry to our ris - en Head!
That we may live and sing to thee:

RESURRECTION

183 The Day of Resurrection

'Αναστάσεως ἡμέρα
John of Damascus, c. 696-c. 754
Tr. John M. Neale, 1818-1866, alt.

LANCASHIRE 7.6.7.6.D.
Henry T. Smart, 1813-1879

1 The day of res - ur - rec - tion! Earth, tell it out a - broad;
2 Our hearts be pure from e - vil, That we may see a - right
3 Now let the heavens be joy - ful, Let earth her song be - gin,

The Pass - o - ver of glad - ness, The Pass - o - ver of God.
The Lord in rays e - ter - nal Of res - ur - rec - tion light;
The round world keep high tri - umph, And all that is there - in;

From death to life e - ter - nal, From earth un - to the sky,
And, lis-tening to his ac - cents, May hear so calm and plain
Let all things seen and un - seen Their notes of glad - ness blend,

Our Christ hath brought us o - ver With hymns of vic - to - ry
His own "All hail," and, hear - ing, May raise the vic - tor strain.
For Christ the Lord is ris - en, Our joy that hath no end. A-men.

RESURRECTION

Crown Him with Many Crowns

Matthew Bridges, 1800-1894
Godfrey Thring, 1823-1903, st. 3

DIADEMATA S.M.D.
George J. Elvey, 1816-1893

184

1 Crown him with man - y crowns, The Lamb up - on his throne;
2 Crown him the Lord of love; Be - hold his hands and side,
3 Crown him the Lord of life, Who tri - umphed o'er the grave,
4 Crown him the Lord of years, The po - ten - tate of time,

Hark! how the heaven-ly an - them drowns All mu - sic but its own;
Rich wounds, yet vis - i - ble a - bove, In beau - ty glo - ri - fied;
And rose vic - to - rious in the strife For those he came to save;
Cre - a - tor of the roll - ing spheres, In - eff - a - bly sub - lime.

A - wake, my soul, and sing Of him who died for thee,
No an - gel in the sky Can ful - ly bear that sight,
His glo - ries now we sing Who died and rose on high,
All hail, Re - deem - er, hail! For thou hast died for me;

And hail him as thy match-less King Through all e - ter - ni - ty.
But down-ward bends his burn-ing eye At mys - ter - ies so bright.
Who died, e - ter - nal life to bring, And lives that death may die.
Thy praise shall nev-er, nev - er fail Through-out e - ter - ni - ty. A-men.

ASCENSION AND REIGN

185 Blessing and Honor and Glory and Power

Horatius Bonar, 1808-1889

O QUANTA QUALIA 10.10.10.10.
La Feillée's *Méthode du Plain-chant*, 1808

1 Bless - ing and hon - or and glo - ry and power,
2 Sound - eth the heaven of the heavens with his name;
3 Ev - er as - cend - eth the song and the joy;
4 Give we the glo - ry and praise to the Lamb;

Wis - dom and rich - es and strength ev - er - more
Ring - eth the earth with his glo - ry and fame;
Ev - er de - scend - eth the love from on high;
Take we the robe and the harp and the palm;

Give ye to him who our bat - tle hath won,
O - cean and moun - tain, stream, for - est, and flower
Bless - ing and hon - or and glo - ry and praise,
Sing we the song of the Lamb that was slain,

Whose are the king - dom, the crown, and the throne.
E - cho his prais - es and tell of his power.
This is the theme of the hymns that we raise.
Dy - ing in weak - ness, but ris - ing to reign. A - men.

ASCENSION AND REIGN

Look, Ye Saints, the Sight Is Glorious 186

Thomas Kelly, 1769-1854

CWM RHONDDA 8.7.8.7.8.7.7.
John Hughes, 1873-1932

1 Look, ye saints, the sight is glo - rious, See the Man of Sor - rows now; From the fight re - turned vic - to - rious, Ev - ery knee to him shall bow; Crown him! Crown him! Crown him! Crown him! Crowns be-come the vic-tor's brow; Crowns be - come the vic-tor's brow.

2 Crown the Sav - ior, an - gels, crown him! Rich the tro - phies Je - sus brings; In the seat of power en-throne him While the vault of heav - en rings Crown him! Crown him! Crown him! Crown him! Crown the Sav - ior King of kings; Crown the Sav - ior King of kings.

3 Sin - ners in de - ri - sion crowned him, Mock - ing thus the Sav - ior's claim; Saints and an - gels throng a - round him, Own his ti - tle, praise his Name; Crown him! Crown him! Crown him! Crown him! Spread a-broad the vic-tor's fame; Spread a - broad the vic-tor's fame.

4 Hark, those bursts of ac - cla - ma - tion, Hark, those loud tri - um-phant chords! Je - sus takes the high - est sta - tion; O what joy the sight af - fords! Crown him! Crown him! Crown him! Crown him! King of kings, and Lord of lords; King of kings, and Lord of lords. A-men.

ASCENSION AND REIGN

187 Lo! He Comes, with Clouds Descending

Charles Wesley, 1707-1788

ST. THOMAS (Wade) 8.7.8.7.8.7.
John Francis Wade? 1711-1786

1 Lo! he comes, with clouds de-scend-ing, Once for our sal-
2 Ev-ery eye shall now be-hold him, Robed in dread-ful
3 Yea, a-men! let all a-dore thee, High on thine e-

va-tion slain; Thou-sand thou-sand saints at-tend-ing
maj-es-ty; Those who set at naught and sold him,
ter-nal throne; Sav-ior, take the power and glo-ry;

Swell the tri-umph of his train: Al-le-lu-ia,
Pierced and nailed him to the tree, Deep-ly wail-ing,
Claim the king-dom for thine own: Al-le-lu-ia,

al-le-lu-ia! Christ the Lord re-turns to reign.
deep-ly wail-ing. Shall the true Mes-si-ah see.
al-le-lu-ia! Thou shalt reign, and thou a-lone. A-men.

ASCENSION AND REIGN

Rejoice, the Lord Is King

Charles Wesley, 1707-1788

DARWALL 148   6.6.6.6.8.8.
John Darwall, 1731-1789

1 Re - joice, the Lord is King! Your Lord and King a - dore!
2 The Lord the Sav - ior reigns, The God of truth and love:
3 His king - dom can - not fail; He rules o'er earth and heaven;
4 Re - joice in glo - rious hope! Our Lord the Judge shall come,

Man - kind, give thanks and sing, And tri - umph ev - er - more.
When he had purged our stains, He took his seat a - bove.
The keys of death and hell To Christ the Lord are given.
And take his ser - vants up To their e - ter - nal home.

Lift up your heart! lift up your voice!

Re - joice! a - gain I say, re - joice! A - men.

ASCENSION AND REIGN

O Holy Spirit, Comforter

T. Ernest Holling, 1867-

PONDEN COTE 8.6.8.6.6.6.6.6.
Charles H. Heaton, 1928-

1 O Ho - ly Spir - it, Com-fort - er, Blest Ad - vo-cate and Friend,
2 O Ho - ly Spir - it, Com-fort - er, Thou prom-ised guide di - vine,
3 O Ho - ly Spir - it, Com-fort - er, Thou search-ing, cleans-ing fire,

Be near us in the stress of life, Thy heaven-ly aid to lend.
On all the journ-ey of our life, Com-mand thy light to shine.
Come purge a - way the dross of sin, Make pure the heart's de - sire;

For thou the Spir - it art Of life and light and love,
So shall we nev - er stray From ways our Mas - ter trod,
Then kin - dle in us zeal, And crown with tongues of flame,

THE HOLY SPIRIT

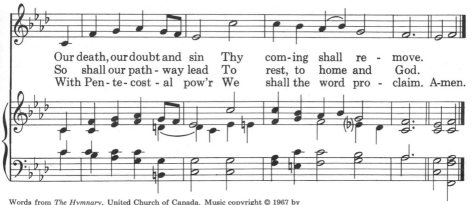

Our death, our doubt and sin Thy com-ing shall re - move.
So shall our path - way lead To rest, to home and God.
With Pen - te - cost - al pow'r We shall the word pro - claim. A-men.

O Holy Spirit, Come to Me   190

J. M. Blough, 1876 –

ISLEWORTH 8.6.8.6.
Samuel Howard, 1710-1782, alt.

1 O Ho - ly Spir - it, come to me And
2 O Ho - ly Spir - it, dwell in me And
3 O Ho - ly Spir - it, show to me The
4 O Ho - ly Spir - it, quick - en me And

take me for thine own; Come with thy power and
cleanse my heart from sin; Re - deem from ev - ery
truth that sets men free; Teach me to love thy
set my soul a - flame; Urge me to mag - ni -

with thy grace, And make my heart thy home.
guilt and stain, O make me pure with - in.
work di - vine, And all its glor - ies see.
fy the Lord, And thus pro - claim his name. A- men.

THE HOLY SPIRIT

191

Holy Spirit, Truth Divine

Samuel Longfellow, 1819-1892

First Tune

SONG 13 7.7.7.7.
Adapt. Orlando Gibbons, 1583-1625

1 Ho - ly Spir - it, Truth di - vine, Dawn up - on this soul of mine;
2 Ho - ly Spir - it, Love di - vine, Glow with - in this heart of mine;
3 Ho - ly Spir - it, Power di - vine, Fill and nerve this will of mine;
4 Ho - ly Spir - it, Right di - vine, King with - in my con - science reign;

Word of God, and in - ward light, Wake my spir - it, clear my sight.
Kin - dle ev - ery high de - sire; Per - ish self in thy pure fire.
By thee may I strong - ly live, Brave - ly bear, and no - bly strive.
Be my law, and I shall be Firm - ly bound, for - ev - er free. A - men.

192

Holy Spirit, Truth Divine

Samuel Longfellow, 1819-1892

Second Tune

MERCY 7.7.7.7.
Louis M. Gottschalk, 1829-1869

1 Ho - ly Spir - it, Truth di - vine, Dawn up - on this soul of mine;
2 Ho - ly Spir - it, Love di - vine, Glow with - in this heart of mine;
3 Ho - ly Spir - it, Power di - vine, Fill and nerve this will of mine;
4 Ho - ly Spir - it, Right di - vine, King with - in my con - science reign;

Word of God, and in - ward light, Wake my spir - it, clear my sight.
Kin - dle ev - ery high de - sire; Per - ish self in thy pure fire.
By thee may I strong - ly live, Brave - ly bear, and no - bly strive.
Be my law, and I shall be Firm - ly bound, for - ev - er free. A - men.

THE HOLY SPIRIT

Come, Holy Spirit, God and Lord! 193

Komm, heiliger Geist, Herre Gott
Martin Luther, 1483-1546
Tr. Catherine Winkworth, 1827-1878, alt.
Vs. 3 alt. W. Sherman Skinner, 1906-

DAS NEUGEBORNE KINDELEIN L.M.
Melody by Melchior Vulpius, *c.* 1560-1616
Harm. J. S. Bach, 1685-1750

1 Come, Ho - ly Spir - it, God and Lord!
2 Thou strong De - fense, thou ho - ly Light,
3 That we may love no stran - ger's creed,
4 From ev - ery er - ror keep us free;

Be all thy gra - ces now out - poured
Teach us to know our God a - right,
Nor fol - low oth - er teach - er's lead,
Let none but Christ our Mas - ter be

On the be - liev - er's mind and soul,
And call him Fa - ther from the heart.
But Je - sus for our Mas - ter own,
That we in liv - ing faith a - bide,

To strength - en, save, and make us whole.
The Word of life and truth im - part,
And put our trust in him a - lone.
In him with all our might con - fide.

THE HOLY SPIRIT

194

Gracious Spirit, Dwell with Me

Thomas T. Lynch, 1818-1871

REDHEAD NO. 76 7.7.7.7.7.7.
Richard Redhead, 1820-1901

1 Gra - cious Spir - it, dwell with me, I my - self would
2 Might - y Spir - it, dwell with me, I my - self would
3 Ho - ly Spir - it, dwell with me, I my - self would

gra - cious be; And with words that help and heal
might - y be; Might - y so as to pre - vail
ho - ly be; Sep - a - rate from sin, I would

Would thy life in mine re - veal, And with ac - tions
Where un - aid - ed man must fail; Ev - er by a
Choose and cher - ish all things good, And what - ev - er

bold and meek Would for Christ my Sav - ior speak.
might - y hope, Press - ing on and bear - ing up.
I can be Give to him who gave me thee! A - men.

THE HOLY SPIRIT

Come, Holy Spirit, Heavenly Dove 195

Isaac Watts, 1674-1748

ST. AGNES C.M.
John B. Dykes, 1823-1876

1 Come, Ho - ly Spir - it, heaven-ly Dove, With all thy quick-ening powers;
2 In vain we tune our for - mal songs, In vain we strive to rise;
3 Come, Ho - ly Spir - it, heaven-ly Dove, With all thy quick-ening powers;

Kin - dle a flame of sa - cred love In these cold hearts of ours.
Ho - san-nas lan-guish on our tongues, And our de - vo - tion dies.
Come, shed a-broad a Sav-ior's love, And that shall kin - dle ours. A - men.

Spirit Divine, Attend Our Prayers 196

Andrew Reed, 1787-1862

NUN DANKET ALL' (GRÄFENBERG) C.M.
Johann Crüger, 1598-1662

1 Spir - it di - vine, at - tend our prayers And make this house thy home;
2 Come as the fire, and purge our hearts Like sac - ri - fi - cial flame;
3 Come as the dove, and spread thy wings, The wings of peace - ful love,
4 Spir - it di - vine, at - tend our prayers And make this world thy home;

De-scend with all thy gra-cious powers, O come, great Spir - it, come!
Let our whole soul an of-fering be To our Re - deem - er's name.
And let thy Church on earth be - come Blest as the Church a - bove.
De-scend with all thy gra-cious powers, O come, great Spir - it, come! A - men.

Harmonization from *Gesangbuchs* No. 231 *von* Paul Gerhardt; used by permission of the Verlagskontor des Evangelischen Gesangbuchs in Stuttgart.

THE HOLY SPIRIT

Come, O Creator Spirit, Come

Veni Creator Spiritus, 9th century
Tr. Robert Bridges, 1844-1930

VENI CREATOR L.M.
Sarum plainsong, Mode VIII
Harm. Winfred Douglas, 1867-1944

1 Come, O Cre - a - tor Spir - it, come, And make with-in our
2 O Com - fort - er, that name is thine, Of God most high the
3 Our sens - es with thy light in - flame, Our hearts to heaven-ly
4 May we by thee the Fa - ther learn, And know the Son, and

hearts thy home; To us thy grace ce - les - tial give,
gift di - vine; The well of life, the fire of love,
love re - claim; Our bod - ies' poor in - fir - mi - ty
thee dis - cern, Who art of both; and so a - dore

Who of thy breath - ing move and live.
Our souls' a - noint - ing from a - bove.
With strength per - pet - ual for - ti - fy.
In per - fect faith for - ev - er-more. A - men.

THE HOLY SPIRIT

Words from *The Yattendon Hymnal* by permission of Oxford University Press.

Lord God, the Holy Ghost

198

James Montgomery, 1771-1854

PLATTEN S.M.
Lee Hastings Bristol, Jr., 1923-

1 Lord God, the Ho - ly Ghost: In this ac - cept - ed hour,
2 Like might-y, rush - ing wind Up - on the waves be - neath,
3 The young, the old in - spire With wis - dom from a - bove:
4 Spir - it of truth, be thou In life and death our guide!

As on the Day of Pent - e - cost, De-scend in all thy power.
Move with one im-pulse ev - ery mind, One soul, one feel - ing breathe.
And give us hearts and tongues of fire, To pray and praise and love.
O, spir - it of a - dop-tion, now May we be sanc - ti - fied! A-men.

Music copyright © 1967 by The Bethany Press.

Holy Spirit, Hear Us

199

William Henry Parker, 1845-1929

GLENFINLAS 6.5.6.5.
Kenneth G. Finlay, 1882-

1 Ho - ly Spir - it, hear us; Help us while we sing;
2 Ho - ly Spir - it, prompt us When we kneel to pray;
3 Ho - ly Spir - it, shine thou On the book we read;
4 Ho - ly Spir - it, help us Dai - ly by thy might,

Breathe in - to the mu - sic Of the praise we bring.
Near - er come and teach us What we ought to say.
Gild its ho - ly pag - es With the light we need.
What is wrong to con - quer, And to choose the right. A - men.

Words used by permission of National Christian Education Council; music by permission of Kenneth G. Finlay.

THE HOLY SPIRIT

Breathe on Me, Breath of God

Edwin Hatch, 1835-1889, alt.

TRENTHAM S.M.
Robert Jackson, 1840-1914

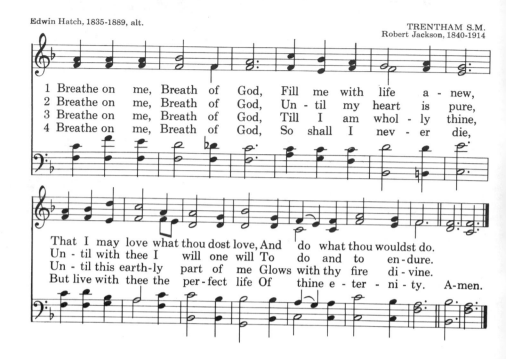

1 Breathe on me, Breath of God, Fill me with life a - new,
2 Breathe on me, Breath of God, Un - til my heart is pure,
3 Breathe on me, Breath of God, Till I am whol - ly thine,
4 Breathe on me, Breath of God, So shall I nev - er die,

That I may love what thou dost love, And do what thou wouldst do.
Un - til with thee I will one will To do and to en - dure.
Un - til this earth-ly part of me Glows with thy fire di - vine.
But live with thee the per - fect life Of thine e - ter - ni - ty. A-men.

Spirit of God, Descend Upon My Heart

Attr. to George Croly, 1780-1860

MORECAMBE 10.10.10.10.
Frederick C. Atkinson, 1841-1897

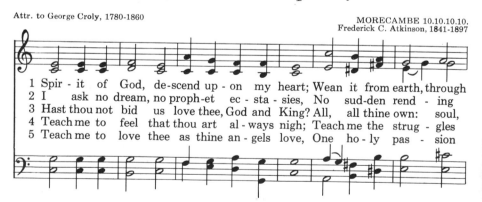

1 Spir - it of God, de-scend up - on my heart; Wean it from earth, through
2 I ask no dream, no proph-et ec - sta - sies, No sud-den rend - ing
3 Hast thou not bid us love thee, God and King? All, all thine own: soul,
4 Teach me to feel that thou art al - ways nigh; Teach me the strug - gles
5 Teach me to love thee as thine an - gels love, One ho - ly pas - sion

THE HOLY SPIRIT

all   its   puls - es move; Stoop to my weak - ness, might-y as thou art,
of   the   veil   of clay, No an - gel vis - it - ant, no o-pening skies,
heart, and strength, and mind; I see thy cross—there teach my heart to cling;
of   the soul to bear: To check the ris - ing doubt, the reb - el sigh;
fill - ing all   my frame; The bap-tism of the heaven-de-scend-ed Dove.

And   make   me   love thee   as   I   ought to   love.
But   take   the dim - ness   of   my   soul   a - way.
O   let   me   seek thee, and   O   let   me   find!
Teach me   the pa - tience of   un - an - swered prayer.
My   heart an   al - tar,   and thy love   the flame. A - men.

Spirit, Strength of All the Weak   202

Thomas Benson Pollock, 1836-1896

TON-MÂN 7.7.7.6.
David Evans, 1874-1948

1 Spir - it, strength of all   the weak, Giv - ing cour - age to   the meek,
2 Spir - it, aid - ing all   who yearn More of truth di - vine to learn.
3 Spir - it, fount of faith and joy, Giv - ing peace with - out al - loy,
4 Source of love and light di - vine, With that hal - lowing grace of thine,

Teach-ing   fal-tering tongues to speak; Hear us, Ho - ly Spir - it.
And   with deep-er love to burn; Hear us, Ho - ly Spir - it.
Hope that noth-ing can de-stroy; Hear us, Ho - ly Spir - it.
More and more up - on us shine; Hear us, Ho - ly Spir - it.   A-men.

THE HOLY SPIRIT

God Almighty, God Eternal

Mary Jackson Cathey, 1926-

GENEVA 8.7.8.7.D.
George Henry Day, 1883-

1 God al-might-y, God e-ter-nal, To thy throne we bring our prayer,
2 God un-chang-ing, God for-ev-er, In these times of sky and space,
3 God the Sov-ereign, our Cre-a-tor, Thou to whom all things be-long,

Ask-ing help and seek-ing guid-ance For thy peo-ple ev-ery-where.
When has come a new di-men-sion To our wide-spread hu-man race,
Thou who speak-est through the a-ges To the u-ni-ver-sal throng,

In this age of chang-ing boun-dries, Wide-ning spa-ces, spread-ing spheres,
Lend to us thine un-der-stand-ing, Lov-ing spir-it, fer-vent zeal,
Speak a-gain to all thy chil-dren, Voice thy truth to us we pray,

GOSPEL CALL AND RESPONSE

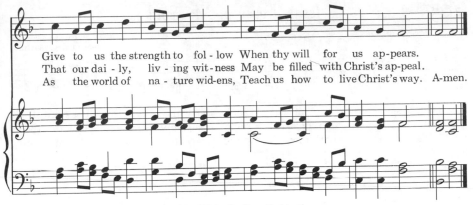

Give to us the strength to fol-low When thy will for us ap-pears.
That our dai-ly, liv-ing wit-ness May be filled with Christ's ap-peal.
As the world of na-ture wid-ens, Teach us how to live Christ's way. A-men.

Jesus Calls Us O'er the Tumult 204

Cecil F. Alexander, 1818-1895

REGENSBURG 8.7.8.7.
Mel. Johann Crüger, 1598-1662

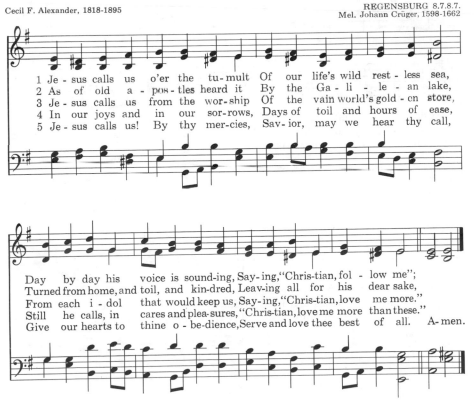

1 Je - sus calls us o'er the tu-mult Of our life's wild rest - less sea,
2 As of old a - pos - tles heard it By the Ga - li - le - an lake,
3 Je - sus calls us from the wor-ship Of the vain world's gold - en store,
4 In our joys and in our sor-rows, Days of toil and hours of ease,
5 Je - sus calls us! By thy mer-cies, Sav-ior, may we hear thy call,

Day by day his voice is sound-ing, Say-ing,"Chris-tian, fol - low me";
Turned from home, and toil, and kin-dred, Leav-ing all for his dear sake,
From each i - dol that would keep us, Say-ing,"Chris-tian, love me more."
Still he calls, in cares and plea-sures,"Chris-tian, love me more than these."
Give our hearts to thine o - be-dience, Serve and love thee best of all. A-men.

GOSPEL CALL AND RESPONSE

Jesus, Lover of My Soul

Charles Wesley, 1707-1788

ABERYSTWYTH 7.7.7.7.D.
Joseph Parry, 1841-1903

1 Je-sus, lov-er of my soul, Let me to thy bos-om fly,
2 Oth-er ref-uge have I none; Hangs my help-less soul on thee;
3 Plen-teous grace with thee is found, Grace to cov-er all my sin;

While the near-er wa-ters roll, While the tem-pest still is high;
Leave, ah! leave me not a-lone, Still sup-port and com-fort me.
Let the heal-ing streams a-bound, Make and keep me pure with-in.

Hide me, O my Sav-ior, hide, Till the storm of life is past;
All my trust on thee is stayed, All my help from thee I bring;
Thou of life the foun-tain art, Free-ly let me take of thee;

Safe in-to the ha-ven guide, O re-ceive my soul at last!
Cov-er my de-fense-less head With the shad-ow of thy wing.
Spring thou up with-in my heart, Rise to all e-ter-ni-ty. A-men.

GOSPEL CALL AND RESPONSE

More About Jesus Would I Know

Eliza E. Hewitt, 1851-1920

MORE ABOUT JESUS 8.8.8.8. with Refrain
John R. Sweney, 1837-1899

1 More a-bout Je-sus would I know, More of his grace to oth-ers show;
2 More a-bout Je-sus let me learn, More of his ho-ly will dis-cern,
3 More a-bout Je-sus; in his Word Hold-ing com-mun-ion with my Lord;

More of his sav-ing full-ness see, More of his love who died for me.
Spir-it of God, my teach-er be, Show-ing the things of Christ to me.
Hear-ing his voice in ev-ery line, Mak-ing each faith-ful say-ing mine.

More, more a-bout Je - sus, More, more a-bout Je - sus,

More of his sav-ing full-ness see, More of his love who died for me. A-men.

GOSPEL CALL AND RESPONSE

207   O Christ, We Climb the Hill with Thee

Kenneth Morse, 1913-

WINCHESTER NEW L.M.
Adapted from
Musicalisch Hand-Buch, Hamburg, 1690

1 O Christ, we climb the hill with thee, thou Mas - ter of the up - ward way. We scale the heights that we may see thy vis - ion of the com - ing day.

2 Show us thy king - dom, thou our King, point out the paths of peace and right; Though feet are wea - ry, hearts will sing, we climb in - to thy glo - rious light.

3 Give us the cour - age of thy cross to dare to live and die for thee; To walk through fire, to suf - fer loss in faith that keeps us strong and free.

4 New worlds of beau - ty greet our eyes as far hor - i - zons now we see; O Mas - ter of the hills that rise, to un-known heights we climb with thee. A - men.

Words used by permission of The Brethren Press.

208   In the Cross of Christ I Glory

John Bowring, 1792-1872

RATHBUN 8.7.8.7.
Ithamar Conkey, 1815-1867

1 In the cross of Christ I glo - ry, Tow-ering o'er the wrecks of time;

2 When the woes of life o'er-take me, Hopes de - ceive, and fears an - noy,

3 When the sun of bliss is beam-ing Light and love up - on my way,

4 Bane and bless-ing, pain and plea-sure, By the cross are sanc - ti - fied;

GOSPEL CALL AND RESPONSE

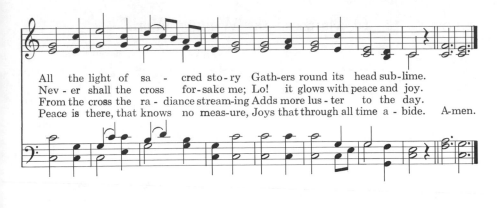

All the light of sa - cred sto-ry Gath-ers round its head sub-lime.
Nev - er shall the cross for-sake me; Lo! it glows with peace and joy.
From the cross the ra - diance stream-ing Adds more lus - ter to the day.
Peace is there, that knows no meas-ure, Joys that through all time a - bide. A-men.

Art Thou Weary, Heavy Laden? 209

John Mason Neale, 1818-1866
Based on Stephen the Sabaite, 725-794

STEPHANOS 8.5.8.3.
Henry W. Baker, 1821-1877

1 Art thou wear - y, heav - y lad - en, Art thou sore dis - tressed?
2 Hath he marks to lead me to him If he be my Guide?
3 If I find him, if I fol - low, What his guer - don here?
4 Find - ing, fol - lowing, keep - ing, strug-gling, Is he sure to bless?

"Come to me," saith One, "and, com-ing, Be at rest."
"In his feet and hands are wound-prints, And his side!"
"Man - y a sor - row, man - y a la - bor, Man - y a tear!"
"Saints, a - pos - tles, proph - ets, mar - tyrs, An - swer, Yes!" A-men.

GOSPEL CALL AND RESPONSE

O Master of the Waking World

Frank Mason North, 1850-1935

MELITA 8.8.8.8.8.8.
John B. Dykes, 1823-1876

1 O Mas - ter of the wak - ing world, Who hast the na - tions
2 We hear the throb of surg - ing life, The clank of chains, the
3 Thy wit - ness in the souls of men, Thy Spir - it's cease - less,

in thy heart The heart that bled and broke to send God's
curse of greed, The moan of pain, the fu - tile cries Of
brood - ing power, In lands where shad - ows hide the light, A -

love to earth's re - mot - est part: Show us a - new in
sup - er - sti - tion's cru - el creed; The peo - ples hun - ger
wait a new cre - a - tive hour: O might - y God, set

Cal - va - ry The won - drous power that makes men free.
for thee, Lord, The isles are wait - ing for thy word.
us a - flame To show the glo - ry of thy Name. A - men.

GOSPEL CALL AND RESPONSE

Father, Long Before Creation

211

Chinese: anon. c. 1952
Francis P. Jones, 1890-

WINTER: 8.7.8.7.4.4.7.
Paul E. Koch, 1929-

1 Fa - ther, long be - fore cre - a - tion Thou hadst cho - sen
2 Though the world may change its fash - ion, Yet our God is
3 God's com - pas - sion is my sto - ry, Is my boast - ing
4 Lov - ing Fa - ther, now be - fore thee We will ev - er

us in love; And that love, so deep so mov - ing,
e'er the same; His com - pas - sion and his cov - enant
all the day; Mer - cy free and nev - er fail - ing
praise thy love; And our song will sound un - ceas - ing

Draws us close to Christ a - bove, Still it keeps us,
Through all a - ges will re - main. God's own chil - dren,
Moves my will, di - rects my way. God so loved us,
Till we reach our home a - bove, Giv - ing glo - ry,

Still it keeps us Firm - ly fixed in Christ a - lone.
God's own chil - dren, Must for - ev - er praise his name.
God so loved us, That his on - ly Son he gave.
Giv - ing glo - ry, To our God and to the Lamb. A - men.

GOSPEL CALL AND RESPONSE

212

Blessed Jesus, at Thy Word

Liebster Jesu, wir sind hier
Tobias Clausnitzer, 1619-1684
Tr. Catherine Winkworth, 1827-1878

LIEBSTER JESU 7.8.7.8.8.8.
Johann Rudolph Ahle, 1625-1673
Harm. J. S. Bach, 1685-1750

1 Bless-ed Je-sus, at thy word We are gath-ered all to hear
2 All our knowl-edge, sense, and sight Lie in deep-est dark-ness shroud-
3 Glo-rious Lord, thy-self im-part! Light of light, from God pro-ceed-

thee; Let our hearts and souls be stirred Now to seek and
ed, Till thy Spir-it breaks our night With the beams of
ing, O-pen thou our ears and heart, Help us by thy

love and fear thee; By thy teach-ings sweet and ho-ly,
truth un-cloud-ed; Thou a-lone to God canst win us,
Spir-it's plead-ing; Hear the cry thy peo-ple rais-es,

Drawn from earth to love thee sole-ly.
Thou must work all good with-in us.
Hear, and bless our prayers and prais-es. A-men.

GOSPEL CALL AND RESPONSE

A simpler version of this tune is No. 329

O Jesus, I Have Promised

John E. Bode, 1816-1874

ANGEL'S STORY 7.6.7.6.D.
Arthur H. Mann, 1850-1929

1 O Je - sus, I have prom - ised To serve thee to the end;
2 O let me feel thee near me! The world is ev - er near;
3 O let me hear thee speak - ing In ac - cents clear and still,

Be thou for - ev - er near me, My mas - ter and my friend;
I see the sights that daz - zle, The tempt - ing sounds I hear;
A - bove the storms of pas - sion, The mur - murs of self - will;

I shall not fear the bat - tle If thou art by my side,
My foes are ev - er near me, A - round me and with - in;
O speak to re - as - sure me, To has - ten or con - trol;

Nor wan - der from the path - way If thou wilt be my guide.
But, Je - sus, draw thou near - er, And shield my soul from sin.
O speak, and make me lis - ten, Thou guard - ian of my soul. A - men.

GOSPEL CALL AND RESPONSE

214 Go, Make of All Disciples

Matthew 28:19-20
Leon M. Adkins, 1896-

LANCASHIRE 7.6.7.6.D.
Henry Smart, 1813-1879

1 "Go, make of all dis - ci - ples." We hear the call, O Lord,
2 "Go, make of all dis - ci - ples." Bap - tiz - ing in the name
3 "Go, make of all dis - ci - ples." We at thy feet would stay

That comes from thee, our Fa - ther, In thy e - ter - nal Word.
Of Fa - ther, Son, and Spir - it From age to age the same,
Un - til each life's vo - ca - tion Ac - cents thy ho - ly way.

In - spire our ways of learn - ing Through ear-nest, fer-vent prayer,
We call each new dis - ci - ple To fol - low thee, O Lord,
We cul - ti - vate the na - ture God plants in ev - ery heart,

And let our dai - ly liv - ing Re - veal thee ev - ery - where.
Re - deem-ing soul and bod - y By wa - ter and the Word.
Re - veal-ing in our wit - ness The mas-ter teach-er's art. A - men.

GOSPEL CALL AND RESPONSE

Make Me a Captive, Lord

George Matheson, 1842-1906

LLANLLYFNI S.M.D.
John Jones, 1797-1857
Adapt. David Jenkins, 1849-1915

215

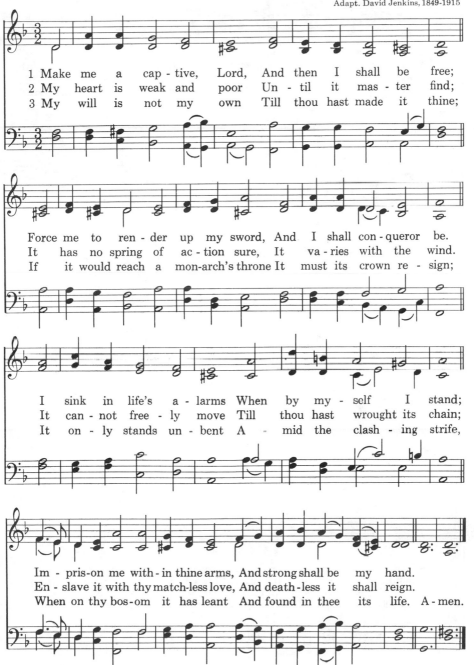

1 Make me a cap-tive, Lord, And then I shall be free;
2 My heart is weak and poor Un-til it mas-ter find;
3 My will is not my own Till thou hast made it thine;

Force me to ren-der up my sword, And I shall con-queror be.
It has no spring of ac-tion sure, It va-ries with the wind.
If it would reach a mon-arch's throne It must its crown re-sign;

I sink in life's a-larms When by my-self I stand;
It can-not free-ly move Till thou hast wrought its chain;
It on-ly stands un-bent A-mid the clash-ing strife,

Im-pris-on me with-in thine arms, And strong shall be my hand.
En-slave it with thy match-less love, And death-less it shall reign.
When on thy bos-om it has leant And found in thee its life. A-men.

GOSPEL CALL AND RESPONSE

216   *Just as I Am, Without One Plea*

Charlotte Elliott, 1789-1871

WOODWORTH L. M.
William B. Bradbury, 1816-1868

1 Just as I am, with-out one plea, But
2 Just as I am, though tossed a-bout With
3 Just as I am, thou wilt re-ceive, Wilt
4 Just as I am, thy love un-known, Hast

that thy blood was shed for me, And that thou bid'st me
man-y a con-flict, man-y a doubt; Fight-ings and fears with-
wel-come, par-don, cleanse, re-lieve; Be-cause thy prom-ise
bro-ken ev-'ry bar-rier down; Now, to be thine, yea,

come to thee, O Lamb of God, I come, I come!
in, with-out, O Lamb of God, I come, I come!
I be-lieve, O Lamb of God, I come, I come!
thine a-lone, O Lamb of God, I come, I come! A-men.

217   *Just as I Am, Thine Own to Be*

Marianne Farningham, 1834-1909

SAFFRON WALDEN 8.8.8.6.
A. H. Brown, 1830-1926

1 Just as I am, thine own to be, Friend of the young, who lov-est me,
2 I would live ev-er in the light, I would work ev-er for the right,
3 Just as I am, young, strong, and free, To be the best that I can be,
4 In the glad morn-ing of my day, My life to give, my vows to pay,

GOSPEL CALL AND RESPONSE

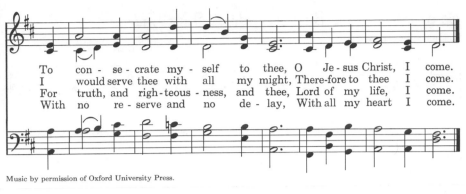

To con-se-crate my-self to thee, O Je-sus Christ, I come.
I would serve thee with all my might, There-fore to thee I come.
For truth, and righ-teous-ness, and thee, Lord of my life, I come.
With no re-serve and no de-lay, With all my heart I come.

O Master, Let Me Walk with Thee 218

Washington Gladden, 1836-1918

MARYTON L. M.
H. Percy Smith, 1825-1898

1 O Mas - ter, let me walk with thee In low - ly
2 Help me the slow of heart to move By some clear,
3 Teach me thy pa - tience; still with thee In clos - er,
4 In hope that sends a shin - ing ray Far down the

paths of serv - ice free; Tell me thy se - cret, help me
win - ning word of love; Teach me the way - ward feet to
dear - er com - pa - ny, In work that keeps faith sweet and
fu - ture's broad-ening way, In peace that on - ly thou canst

bear The strain of toil, the fret of care.
stay, And guide them in the home - ward way.
strong, In trust that tri - umphs o - ver wrong.
give, With thee, O Mas - ter, let me live. A - men.

GOSPEL CALL AND RESPONSE

219   # I Bind My Heart This Tide

Lauchlan MacLean Watt, 1867-1957

FEALTY 6.7.7.7.6.7.7.7.
Grace Wilbur Conant, 1880-1948

1 I bind my heart this tide To the Gal - i - le - an's side,
2 I bind my heart in thrall To the God, the Lord of All,

To the wounds of Cal - va - ry, To the Christ who died for me.
To the God, the poor man's Friend, And the Christ whom he did send.

I bind my soul this day To the broth-er far a - way,
I bind my-self to peace, To make strife and en - vy cease,

And the broth-er near at hand, In this town, and in this land.
God, knit thou sure the cord Of my thral-dom to my Lord. A-men.

GOSPEL CALL AND RESPONSE

Words used by permission of Andrew MacLean Watt and David Watt.
Music used by permission of Fleming H. Revell Co.

Savior, Like a Shepherd Lead Us

Attr. to Dorothy A. Thrupp, 1779-1847

BRADBURY 8.7.8.7.D.
William B. Bradbury, 1816-1868

1 Sav-ior, like a shep-herd lead us, Much we need thy ten-der care;
2 We are thine; do thou be-friend us; Be the guard-ian of our way;
3 Ear-ly let us seek thy fa-vor; Ear-ly let us do thy will;

In thy pleas-ant pas-tures feed us, For our use thy folds pre-pare.
Keep thy flock; from sin de-fend us; Seek us when we go a-stray.
Bless-ed Lord and on-ly Sav-ior, With thy love our bos-oms fill.

Bless-ed Je-sus, Bless-ed Je-sus, Thou hast bought us, thine we are;
Bless-ed Je-sus, Bless-ed Je-sus, Hear thy chil-dren when they pray;
Bless-ed Je-sus, Bless-ed Je-sus, Thou hast loved us, love us still;

Bless-ed Je-sus, Bless-ed Je-sus, Thou hast bought us, thine we are.
Bless-ed Je-sus, Bless-ed Je-sus, Hear thy chil-dren when they pray.
Bless-ed Je-sus, Bless-ed Je-sus, Thou hast loved us, love us still. A-men.

GOSPEL CALL AND RESPONSE

221 O Jesus, Thou Art Standing

William W. How, 1823-1897

ST. HILDA 7.6.7.6.D.
Justin H. Knecht, 1752-1817, and
Edward Husband, 1843-1908

1 O Je - sus, thou art stand - ing Out - side the fast-closed door,
2 O Je - sus, thou art knock - ing, And lo! that hand is scarred,
3 O Je - sus, thou art plead - ing In ac - cents meek and low,

In low - ly pa - tience wait - ing To pass the thresh - old o'er.
And thorns thy brow en - cir - cle, And tears thy face have marred.
"I died for you, my chil - dren, And will ye treat me so?"

Shame on us, Chris - tian broth - ers, His name and sign who bear;
O love that pass - eth knowl - edge, So pa - tient - ly to wait!
O Lord, with shame and sor - row We o - pen now the door;

O shame, thrice shame up - on us, To keep him stand - ing there!
O sin that hath no e - qual, So fast to bar the gate!
Dear Sav - ior, en - ter, en - ter, And leave us nev - er - more! A-men.

GOSPEL CALL AND RESPONSE

Lord Christ, When First Thou Cam'st 222

W. Russell Bowie, 1882-1969

MIT FREUDEN ZART 8.7.8.7.8.8.7.
Bohemian Brethren's *Kirchengesänge*, 1566

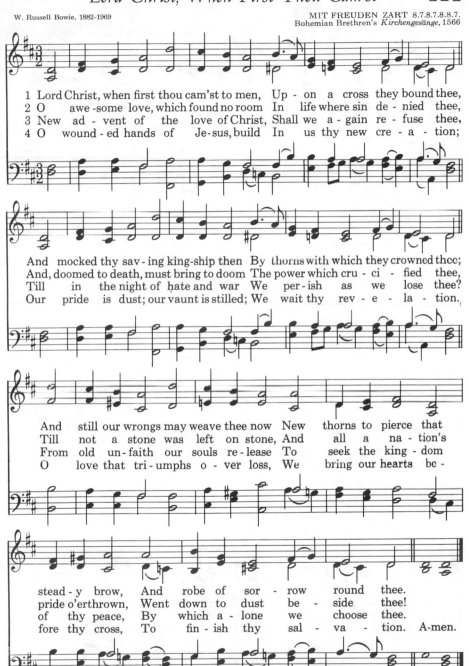

1 Lord Christ, when first thou cam'st to men, Up - on a cross they bound thee,
2 O awe -some love, which found no room In life where sin de - nied thee,
3 New ad - vent of the love of Christ, Shall we a - gain re - fuse thee,
4 O wound - ed hands of Je-sus, build In us thy new cre - a - tion;

And mocked thy sav - ing king-ship then By thorns with which they crowned thee;
And, doomed to death, must bring to doom The power which cru - ci - fied thee,
Till in the night of hate and war We per - ish as we lose thee?
Our pride is dust; our vaunt is stilled; We wait thy rev - e - la - tion.

And still our wrongs may weave thee now New thorns to pierce that
Till not a stone was left on stone, And all a na - tion's
From old un - faith our souls re - lease To seek the king - dom
O love that tri - umphs o - ver loss, We bring our hearts be -

stead - y brow, And robe of sor - row round thee.
pride o'erthrown, Went down to dust be - side thee!
of thy peace, By which a - lone we choose thee.
fore thy cross, To fin - ish thy sal - va - tion. A-men.

GOSPEL CALL AND RESPONSE

I Heard the Voice of Jesus Say

Horatius Bonar, 1808-1889

KINGSFOLD C.M.D.
Traditional English Melody
Arr. and harm. R. Vaughan Williams, 1872-1958

1 I heard the voice of Je-sus say, "Come un-to me and rest;
2 I heard the voice of Je-sus say, "Be-hold, I free-ly give
3 I heard the voice of Je-sus say, "I am this dark world's Light;

Lay down, thou wea-ry one, lay down Thy head up-on my breast."
The liv-ing wa-ter; thirst-y one, Stoop down and drink, and live."
Look un-to me, thy morn shall rise, And all thy day be bright."

I came to Je-sus as I was, Wea-ry and worn and sad,
I came to Je-sus, and I drank Of that life-giv-ing stream;
I looked to Je-sus, and I found In him my Star, my Sun;

I found in him a rest-ing place, And he has made me glad.
My thirst was quenched, my soul re-vived, And now I live in him.
And in that Light of life I'll walk, Till trav-el-ing days are done. A-men.

GOSPEL CALL AND RESPONSE   Music from *The English Hymnal* by permission of Oxford University Press.

What a Friend We Have in Jesus 224

Joseph Scriven, 1819-1886

ERIE 8.7.8.7.D
Charles C. Converse, 1832-1918

1 What a friend we have in Je - sus, All our sins and griefs to bear!
2 Have we tri - als and temp - ta - tions? Is there trou-ble an - y - where?
3 Are we weak and heav - y lad - en, Cum-bered with a load of care?

What a priv - i - lege to car - ry Ev - ery-thing to God in prayer!
We should nev - er be dis - cour - aged; Take it to the Lord in prayer!
Pre - cious Sav - ior, still our ref - uge, Take it to the Lord in prayer!

Oh, what peace we of - ten for - feit, Oh, what need-less pain we bear,
Can we find a friend so faith - ful, Who will all our sor - rows share?
Do thy friends de-spise, for - sake thee? Take it to the Lord in prayer!

All be-cause we do not car - ry Ev - ery-thing to God in prayer.
Je - sus knows our ev - ery weak-ness; Take it to the Lord in prayer!
In his arms he'll take and shield thee, Thou wilt find a sol - ace there. A-men.

PRAYER

Father, in Thy Mysterious Presence

Samuel Johnson, 1822-1882

DONNE SECOURS 11.10.11.10.
Genevan Psalter, 1551

1 Fa - ther, in thy mys - te - rious pres - ence kneel - ing,
2 Lord, we have wan - dered forth through doubt and sor - row,
3 Now, Fa - ther, now, in thy dear pres - ence kneel - ing,

Fain would our souls feel all thy kin - dling
And thou hast made each step an on - ward
Our spir - its yearn to feel thy kin - dling

love, For we are weak, and need some deep re - veal - ing
one, And we will ev - er trust each un - known mor - row;
love; Now make us strong, we need thy deep re - veal - ing

PRAYER

Of   trust and strength and   calm - ness from   a - bove.
Thou wilt sus - tain   us   till its work is   done.
Of   trust and strength and   calm - ness from   a - bove. A - men.

Father, Hear

226

L. M. Willis, 1824-1908

FATHER, HEAR 8.7.8.7.
Jacob Singer, 1883-1964
Adapted from folk-melody of *Eliyahu Hanavi*

1 Fa - ther, hear the prayer we of - fer! Not for ease that prayer shall be,
2 Not for - ev - er   by still wa - ters Would we i - dly   qui - et stay,
3 Be our strength in hours of weak - ness, In our wander-ings be our guide;

But for strength that we may ev - er   Live our lives cour - a - geous - ly.
But would smite the   liv-ing foun-tains From the rocks a - long our way.
Through en - deav - or, fail - ure, dan - ger, Fa - ther, be   thou at our side. A - men.

PRAYER

Have Thine Own Way, Lord!

Adelaide A. Pollard, 1860-1934

ADELAIDE 5.4.5.4.D.
George C. Stebbins, 1846-1945

1 Have thine own way, Lord! Have thine own way! Thou art the
2 Have thine own way, Lord! Have thine own way! Search me and
3 Have thine own way, Lord! Have thine own way! Wound-ed and
4 Have thine own way, Lord! Have thine own way! Hold o'er my

Pot - ter; I am the clay. Mould me and make me Aft - er thy
try me, Mas-ter, to - day! Whit - er than snow, Lord, Wash me just
wea - ry, Help me, I pray! Pow - er, all pow - er Sure - ly is
be - ing Ab - so - lute sway! Fill with thy Spir - it Till all shall

will, While I am wait - ing, Yield - ed and still.
now, As in thy pres - ence Hum - bly I bow.
thine! Touch me and heal me, Sav - ior di - vine!
see Christ on - ly, al - ways, Liv - ing in me! A - men.

Lord Jesus Christ, Be Present Now

J. Niedling's *Lutherisch Handbüchlein*, 1638
Tr. Catherine Winkworth, 1827-1878, alt.

HERR JESU CHRIST L.M.
Pensum Sacrum, 1648
Harm. from *Cantionale Sacrum*, 1651

1 Lord Je - sus Christ, be pres-ent now, Our hearts in true de - vo-tion bow,
2 Un - seal our lips to sing thy praise, Our souls to thee in wor-ship raise,

PRAYER

Thy Spir-it send with grace di-vine, And let thy truth with-in us shine.
Make strong our faith, in-crease our light That we may know thy name a-right. A-men.

Father Almighty, Bless Us with Thy Blessing 229

Berwick Hymnal, 1886

FLEMMING 11.11.11.5.
Friedrich F. Flemming, 1778-1813

1 Fa - ther al - might - y, bless us with thy bless - ing; An - swer in
2 Shep-herd of souls, who bring-est all who seek thee To pas-tures
3 Fa - ther of mer - cy, from thy watch and keep - ing No place can

love thy chil-dren's sup - pli - ca - tion; Hear thou our prayer, the
green be - side the peace-ful wa - ters, Ten - der - est guide, in
part, nor hour of time re - move us; Give us thy good, and

spo - ken and un - spo - ken; Hear us, our Fa - ther.
ways of cheer-ful du - ty Lead us, good Shep - herd.
save us from our e - vil, In - fi - nite Spir - it. A-men.

PRAYER

230

Take Time to Be Holy

W. D. Longstaff, 1822-1894

HOLINESS 6.5.6.5.D.
George C. Stebbins, 1846-1945

1 Take time to be ho - ly, Speak oft with thy Lord;
2 Take time to be ho - ly, The world rush - es on;
3 Take time to be ho - ly, Let him be thy Guide,
4 Take time to be ho - ly, Be calm in thy soul;

A - bide in him al - ways, And feed on his word.
Spend much time in se - cret With Je - sus a - lone.
And run not be - fore him, What - ev - er be - tide;
Each thought and each mo - tive Be - neath his con - trol;

Make friends of God's chil - dren; Help those who are weak;
By look - ing to Je - sus, Like him thou shalt be;
In joy or in sor - row, Still fol - low thy Lord.
Thus led by his Spir - it To foun-tains of love,

For - get-ting in noth - ing His bless-ing to seek.
Thy friends in thy con - duct His like-ness shall see.
And, look-ing to Je - sus, Still trust in his word.
Thou soon shalt be fit - ted For serv-ice a - bove. A - men.

PRAYER

Behold Us, Lord, a Little Space 231

John Ellerton, 1826-1893

WINCHESTER OLD C.M.
Thomas Este's *Whole Book of Psalms*, 1592

1 Be - hold us, Lord, a lit - tle space From dai - ly tasks set free,
2 A - round us rolls the cease-less tide Of busi - ness, toil, and care,
3 Yet these are not the on - ly walls Where-in thou mayst be sought;
4 Thine are the loom, the forge, the mart, The wealth of land and sea,
5 Work shall be prayer, if all be wrought As thou wouldst have it done;

And met with-in thy ho - ly place To rest a - while with thee.
And scarce - ly can we turn a - side For one brief hour of prayer.
On home-liest work thy bless-ing falls, In truth and pa-tience wrought.
The worlds of sci - ence and of art, Re - vealed and ruled by thee.
And prayer, by thee in-spired and taught, It - self with work be one. A-men.

'Mid All the Traffic of the Ways 232

John Oxenham, 1852-1941

ST. AGNES C.M.
John B. Dykes, 1823-1876

1 'Mid all the traf - fic of the ways Tur-moil with - out, with - in
2 A lit - tle shrine of qui - et - ness, All sac - red to thy - self,
3 A lit - tle place of mys - tic grace, Of self and sin swept bare,

Make in my heart a qui - et place, And come and dwell there - in.
Where thou shalt all my soul pos-sess, And I may find my - self.
Where I may look up - on thy face, And talk with thee in prayer. A-men.

PRAYER

233

Talk with Us, Lord

Charles Wesley, 1707-1788

NUN DANKET ALL' (Gräfenberg) C.M.
Johann Crüger, 1598-1662

1 Talk with us, Lord, thy - self re - veal, While here o'er earth we rove;
2 With thee con - vers - ing, we for - get All time and toil and care;
3 Here, then, my God, vouch-safe to stay, And bid my heart re - joice;
4 Let this my ev - ery hour em - ploy, Till I thy glo - ry see;

Speak to our hearts, and let us feel The kin - dling of thy love.
La - bor is rest, and pain is sweet, If thou, my God, art here.
My bound-ing heart shall own thy sway, And ech - o to thy voice.
En - ter in - to my Mas-ter's joy, And find my heaven in thee.

Harmonization from *Gesangbuchs* No. 231 *von* Paul Gerhardt; used by permission of the Verlagskontor des Evangelischen Gesangbuchs in Stuttgart.

234

Have Faith in God

Bryn A. Rees, 1911-

SOUTHWELL S.M.
Adapted from Damon's *Psalmes*, 1579

1 Have faith in God, my heart; Trust and be un - a - fraid;
2 Have faith in God, my mind, Though oft thy light burns low;
3 Have faith in God, my soul; His cross for - ev - er stands,
4 Lord Je - sus, make me whole; Grant me no rest - ing place,

God will ful - fill in ev - ery part Each prom-ise he has made.
God's mer - cy holds a wis - er plan Than thou canst ful - ly know.
And nei - ther life nor death can pluck His chil-dren from his hands.
Un - til I rest, heart, mind, and soul, The cap - tive of thy grace. A-men.

FAITH, HOPE, LOVE

Father of Heaven

235

Edward Cooper, 1770-1833

ANGLORUM APOSTOLUS L.M.
A. Gregory Murray, O.S.B., 1905-

1 Fa - ther of heaven, whose love pro - found
2 Al - might - y Son, In - car - nate Word,
3 E - ter - nal Spir - it! By whose breath
4 Thrice Ho - ly! Fa - ther, Spir - it, Son,

A ran - som for our souls hath found,
Our Proph - et, Priest, Re - deem - er, Lord!
The soul is raised from sin and death,
Mys - ter - ious God - head, Three in One!

Be - fore thy throne we sin - ners bend;
Be - fore thy throne we sin - ners bend:
Be - fore thy throne we sin - ners bend;
Be - fore thy throne we sin - ners bend:

To us thy par - doning love ex - tend.
To us thy sav - ing grace ex - tend.
To us thy quick - ening power ex - tend.
Grace, par - don, life, to us ex - tend. A - men.

FAITH, HOPE, LOVE

Hope of the World

Georgia Harkness, 1891-

DONNE SECOURS 11.10.11.10.
Genevan Psalter, 1551

1 Hope of the world, thou Christ of great com - pas - sion,
2 Hope of the world, God's gift from high - est heav - en,
3 Hope of the world, who by thy cross didst save us
4 Hope of the world, O Christ, o'er death vic - to - rious,

Speak to our fear - ful hearts by con - flict
Bring - ing to hun - gry souls the bread of
From death and dark des - pair, from sin and
Who by this sign didst con - quer grief and

rent; Save us thy peo - ple, from con - sum - ing pas - sion,
life, Still let thy spir - it un - to us be giv - en,
guilt; We ren - der back the love thy mer - cy gave us;
pain, We would be faith - ful to thy gos - pel glo - rious:

Who by our own false hopes and aims are spent.
To heal earth's wounds and end her bit - ter strife.
Take thou our lives, and use them as thou wilt.
Thou art our Lord! Thou dost for - ev - er reign!

FAITH, HOPE, LOVE

O Lord, We Do Adore Thee

237

Edgerton Grant, 1931-1969

PEARSALL 7.6.7.6.D.
Robert L. Pearsall, 1795-1856

1 O Lord, we do a-dore thee, Thy beau-ty and thy grace;
2 O Lord, our lives are fail-ing When lived a-part from thee;

We bend the knee be-fore thee, And long to see thy face;
Our ef-forts un-a-vail-ing Till faith shall set us free.

But still we strive for plea-sure, The joy that's all too brief,
Be-hold our deep de-sire; Thy grace we would re-ceive;

And miss thy price-less trea-sure: Lord, help our un-be-lief!
Do thou our hearts in-spire To cry, "Lord, we be-lieve!" A-men.

FAITH, HOPE, LOVE

238   *Jesus, My Lord, My God, My All*

Henry Collins, 1827-1919

ST. CHRYSOSTOM 8.8.8.8.8.8.8.
Joseph Barnby, 1838-1896

1 Je - sus, my Lord, my God, my all, Hear me, blest Sa - vior,
2 Je - sus, too late I thee have sought; How can I love thee
3 Je - sus, what didst thou find in me That thou hast dealt so

when I call; Hear me, and from thy dwell - ing place Pour
as I ought, And how ex - tol thy match - less fame, The
lov - ing - ly? How great the joy that thou hast brought! O

down the rich - es of thy grace. Je - sus, my Lord, I
glo - rious beau - ty of thy Name? Je - sus, my Lord, I
far ex - ceed - ing hope or thought! Je - sus, my Lord, I

thee a - dore; O make me love thee more and more!
thee a - dore; O make me love thee more and more!
thee a - dore; O make me love thee more and more! A - men.

FAITH, HOPE, LOVE

I Look to Thee in Every Need

Samuel Longfellow, 1819-1892, alt.

O JESU 8.6.8.6.8.8.
Melody from *Hirschberg Gesangbuch*, 1741

1 I look to thee in ev - ery need,
2 Dis - cour - aged in the work of life,
3 Thy calm - ness bends se - rene a - bove,
4 En - fold - ed deep in thy dear love,

And nev - er look in vain; I feel thy strong and ten - der love,
Dis - heart-ened by its load, Shamed by its fail - ures or its fears,
My rest - less-ness to still; A - round me flows thy quick - ening life,
Held in thy law, I stand; Thy hand in all things I be - hold,

And all is well a - gain: The thought of thee is might-ier far
I sink be - side the road; But let me on - ly think of thee
To nerve my fal-tering will: Thy pres-ence fills my sol - i - tude;
And all things in thy hand; Thou lead - est me by un-sought ways,

Than sin and pain and sor - row are.
And then new heart springs up in me.
Thy prov - i - dence turns all to good.
And turn'st my mourn - ing in - to praise. A - men.

FAITH, HOPE, LOVE

240   *I Need Thee Every Hour*

Annie S. Hawks, 1835-1918
Robert Lowry, 1826-1899, Refrain

NEED 6.4.6.4. with Refrain
Robert Lowry, 1826-1899

1 I need thee ev - ery hour, Most gra - cious Lord;
2 I need thee ev - ery hour; Stay thou near by;
3 I need thee ev - ery hour In joy or pain;
4 I need thee ev - ery hour; Teach me thy will,

No ten - der voice like thine Can peace af - ford.
Temp - ta - tions lose their power When thou art nigh.
Come quick - ly, and a - bide Or life is vain.
And thy rich prom - is - es In me ful - fill.

I need thee, oh, I need thee; Ev - ery hour I need thee;

O bless me now, my Sav - ior, I come to thee. A - men.

FAITH, HOPE, LOVE

And Can It Be

Charles Wesley. 1707-1788

SAGINA 8.8.8.8.8.8.
Thomas Campbell, 1825-1876

1 And can it be that I should gain An in-terest in the
2 'Tis mys-tery all! The im-mor-tal dies: Who can ex-plore his
3 He left his Fa-ther's throne a-bove So free, so in-fi-

Sav-ior's blood? He died for me, who caused his pain? For
strange de-sign? In vain the first-born ser-aph tries To
nite his grace Emp-tied him-self of all but love And

me, who him to death pur-sued? A-maz-ing love! how
sound the depths of love di-vine. 'Tis mer-cy all! let
bled for A-dam's help-less race. 'Tis mer-cy all! im-

can it be That thou, my God, shouldst die for me!
earth a-dore, Let an-gel minds in-quire no more.
mense and free; For, O my God, it found out me! A-men.

FAITH, HOPE, LOVE

Jesus, Still Lead On

Jesu, geh' voran
Nicolaus L. von Zinzendorf, 1700-1760
Tr. Jane L. Borthwick, 1813-1897

ROCHELLE 5.5.8.8.5.5.
Adam Drese, 1620-1701

1 Je - sus, still lead on, Till our rest be won; And al -
2 If the way be drear, If the foe be near, Let not
3 Je - sus, still lead on Till our rest be won; Heaven-ly

though the way be cheer-less, We will fol - low, calm and fear - less:
faith - less fears o'er-take us, Let not faith and hope for - sake us;
lead - er, still di - rect us, Still sup -port, con - sole, pro - tect us,

Guide us by thy hand To the bless - ed land.
For, through man - y a foe, To our home we go.
Till we safe - ly stand In the bless - ed land. A - men.

243 We Walk by Faith, and Not by Sight

Henry Alford, 1810-1871

AZMON C.M.
Carl G. Gläser, 1784-1829
Mason's *Modern Psalmody*, 1839

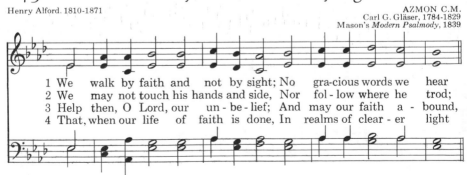

1 We walk by faith and not by sight; No gra-cious words we hear
2 We may not touch his hands and side, Nor fol - low where he trod;
3 Help then, O Lord, our un - be - lief; And may our faith a - bound,
4 That, when our life of faith is done, In realms of clear - er light

FAITH, HOPE, LOVE

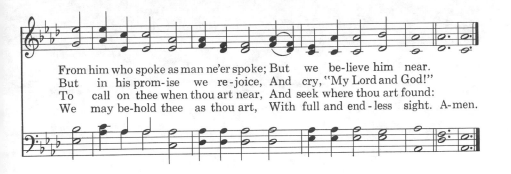

From him who spoke as man ne'er spoke; But we be-lieve him near.
But in his prom-ise we re-joice, And cry, "My Lord and God!"
To call on thee when thou art near, And seek where thou art found:
We may be-hold thee as thou art, With full and end-less sight. A-men.

My Faith Looks Up to Thee 244

Ray Palmer, 1808-1887, alt.

OLIVET 6.6.4.6.6.6.4.
Lowell Mason, 1792-1872

1 My faith looks up to thee, Thou Lamb of Cal - va - ry,
2 May thy rich grace im-part Strength to my faint - ing heart,
3 While life's dark maze I tread, And griefs a - round me spread,

Sav - ior di - vine! Now hear me while I pray; Take all my
My zeal in - spire; As thou hast died for me, Oh, may my
Be thou my guide; Bid dark-ness turn to day; Wipe sor-row's

guilt a - way; Oh, let me from this day Be whol - ly thine.
love to thee Pure, warm, and change-less be, A liv - ing fire.
tears a - way; Nor let me ev - er stray From thee a - side. A-men.

FAITH, HOPE, LOVE

245 God of Grace and God of Glory

Harry Emerson Fosdick, 1878-1969

CWM RHONDDA 8.7.8.7.8.7.7.
John Hughes, 1873-1932

1 God of grace and God of glo - ry, On thy peo - ple
2 Lo! the hosts of e - vil round us Scorn thy Christ, as -
3 Cure thy chil - dren's war - ring mad - ness; Bend our pride to
4 Set our feet on loft - y pla - ces; Gird our lives that
5 Save us from weak res - ig - na - tion To the e - vils

pour thy power; Crown thine an - cient church's sto - ry; Bring her bud to
sail his ways! From the fears that long have bound us, Free our hearts to
thy con - trol; Shame our wan - ton, self - ish glad - ness, Rich in things and
they may be Arm-ored with all Christ-like gra - ces In the fight to
we de - plore; Let the search for thy sal - va - tion Be our glo - ry

glo - rious flower. Grant us wis - dom, Grant us cour - age,
faith and praise. Grant us wis - dom, Grant us cour - age,
poor in soul. Grant us wis - dom, Grant us cour - age,
set men free. Grant us wis - dom, Grant us cour - age,
ev - er - more. Grant us wis - dom, Grant us cour - age,

For the fac - ing of this hour, For the fac - ing of this hour,
For the liv - ing of these days, For the liv - ing of these days,
Lest we miss thy king-dom's goal, Lest we miss thy king-dom's goal.
That we fail not man nor thee, That we fail not man nor thee.
Serv-ing thee whom we a - dore, Serv-ing thee whom we a - dore. A-men.

Alternate tune No. 144

CONFLICT AND CHALLENGE

Lead On, O King Eternal

246

Ernest W. Shurtleff, 1862-1917

LANCASHIRE 7.6.7.6.D.
Henry Smart, 1813-1879

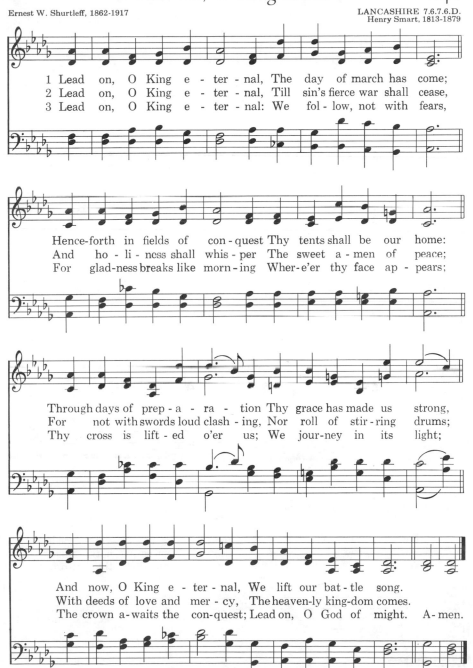

1 Lead on, O King e - ter - nal, The day of march has come;
2 Lead on, O King e - ter - nal, Till sin's fierce war shall cease,
3 Lead on, O King e - ter - nal: We fol - low, not with fears,

Hence-forth in fields of con - quest Thy tents shall be our home:
And ho - li - ness shall whis - per The sweet a - men of peace;
For glad-ness breaks like morn - ing Wher-e'er thy face ap - pears;

Through days of prep - a - ra - tion Thy grace has made us strong,
For not with swords loud clash - ing, Nor roll of stir - ring drums;
Thy cross is lift - ed o'er us; We jour-ney in its light;

And now, O King e - ter - nal, We lift our bat - tle song.
With deeds of love and mer - cy, The heaven-ly king-dom comes.
The crown a-waits the con-quest; Lead on, O God of might. A - men.

CONFLICT AND CHALLENGE

247 Once to Every Man and Nation

James Russell Lowell, 1819-1891
Adapt. W. Garrett Horder, 1814-1922

EBENEZER 8.7.8.7.D.
Thomas John Williams, 1869-1944

1 Once to ev-ery man and na-tion Comes the mo-ment
2 By the light of burn-ing mar-tyrs, Je - sus' bleed-ing
3 Though the cause of e - vil pros-per, Yet 'tis truth a-

to de-cide, In the strife of truth with false-hood,
feet I track, Toil-ing up new Cal - varies ev - er
lone is strong, Truth for - ev - er on the scaf - fold,

For the good or e - vil side;
With the cross that turns not back;
Wrong for - ev - er on the throne.

CONFLICT AND CHALLENGE

Some great cause, God's new mes - si - ah, Of - fering each the
New oc - ca - sions teach new du - ties, Time makes an - cient
Yet that scaf - fold sways the fu - ture, And, be - hind the

bloom or blight, And the choice goes by for - ev - er
good un - couth; They must up - ward still and on - ward,
dim un - known, Stand - eth God with - in the shad - ow

'Twixt that dark - ness and that light.
Who would keep a - breast of truth.
Keep - ing watch a - bove his own. A - men.

CONFLICT AND CHALLENGE

248 Christian, Dost Thou See Them

Attr. to St. Andrew of Crete, c. 660-c. 732
Tr. John M. Neale, 1818-1866, alt.

KING'S WESTON 6.5.6.5.D.
R. Vaughan Williams, 1872-1958

1 Chris-tian, dost thou see them On the ho - ly ground,
2 Chris-tian, dost thou feel them, How they work with - in,
3 Chris-tian, dost thou hear them, How they speak thee fair,
4 "Well I know thy trou - ble, O my serv - ant true;

How the powers of dark - ness Com-pass thee a - round?
Striv-ing, tempt-ing, lur - ing, Goad-ing in - to sin?
"Al-ways fast and vig - il, Al - ways watch and prayer"?
Thou art ver - y wea - ry; I was wea - ry, too.

Chris-tian, up and smite them, Count-ing gain but loss,
Chris-tian, nev - er trem - ble, Nev - er be down - cast;
Chris-tian, an - swer bold - ly, "While I breathe I pray!"
But that toil shall make thee Some day all mine own,

CONFLICT AND CHALLENGE

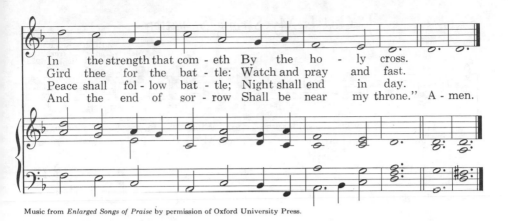

In   the strength that com - eth   By   the   ho - ly   cross.
Gird   thee   for   the   bat - tle: Watch and pray   and   fast.
Peace shall   fol - low bat - tle;   Night shall end   in   day.
And   the   end   of   sor - row   Shall be near   my throne." A - men.

Music from *Enlarged Songs of Praise* by permission of Oxford University Press.

That Cause Can Neither Be Lost nor Stayed 249

Kristian Ostergaard, 1855-1931
Tr. Jens Christian Aaberg, 1877-

OSTERGAARD 9.9.10.10.
Danish folk tune
Arr. Ellwood S. Wolf, 1903-

1 That cause can nei - ther be lost nor stayed Which takes the
2 Each no - ble serv - ice that men have wrought Was first con -
3 There - by it - self like a tree it shows; That high it
4 Be then no more by a storm dis - mayed, For by it

course of what God has made, And is not trust - ing in
ceived as a fruit - ful thought; Each wor - thy cause with a
reach - es as deep it grows; And, when the storms are its
the full-grown seeds are laid; And though the tree by its

walls and tow - ers But slow - ly grow - ing from seeds to flow - ers.
fu - ture glo - rious By qui - et grow - ing be - comes vic - to - rious.
branch - es shak - ing, It deep - er root in the soil is tak - ing.
might it shat - ters, What then, if thou-sands of seeds it scat - ters!

Words from *A World of Song*. Used by permission of Grand View College. Music arrangement copyright © 1966 by The Judson Press. *CONFLICT AND CHALLENGE*

God Is My Strong Salvation

James Montgomery, 1771-1854

WEDLOCK 7.6.7.6.D.
Melody *The Sacred Harp*, 1844
Harm. C. H. Heaton, 1928-

Unison

1 God is my strong sal - va - tion: What foe have I to fear?
2 Place on the Lord re - li - ance; My soul, with cour-age wait;

In dark-ness and temp - ta - tion, My light, my help is near:
His truth be thine af - fi - ance, When faint and des - o - late.

Though hosts en-camp a - round me, Firm in the fight I stand;
His might thy heart shall strength-en, His love thy joy in - crease;

What ter - ror can con-found me, With God at my right hand?
Mer - cy thy days shall length - en; The Lord will give thee peace. A-men.

CONFLICT AND CHALLENGE

William Williams, 1717-1791
Tr. Peter Williams, 1727-1796, and others

CWM RHONDDA 8.7.8.7.8.7.7.
John Hughes, 1873-1932

1 Guide me, O thou great Je - ho - vah, Pil - grim through this
2 O - pen now the crys - tal foun - tain, Whence the heal - ing
3 When I tread the verge of Jor - dan, Bid my anx - ious

bar - ren land; I am weak, but thou art might-y; Hold me with thy
stream doth flow; Let the fire and cloud-y pil - lar Lead me all my
fears sub - side; Death of death, and hell's de-struc-tion, Land me safe on

power - ful hand; Bread of heav - en, bread of heav - en,
jour - ney through; Strong De - liv - er - er, strong De - liv - er - er,
Ca - naan's side; Songs of prais - es, songs of prais - es,

Feed me till I want no more, Feed me till I want no more.
Be thou still my strength and shield, Be thou still my strength and shield.
I will ev - er give to thee, I will ev - er give to thee. A-men.

CONFLICT AND CHALLENGE

He Who Would Valiant Be

John Bunyan, 1628-1688, alt.
Adapt. Percy Dearmer, 1867-1936

ST. DUNSTAN'S 6.5.6.5.6.6.6.5.
C. Winfred Douglas, 1867-1944

1 He who would val - iant be 'Gainst all dis - as - ter,
2 Who so be - set him round With dis - mal sto - ries,
3 Since, Lord, thou dost de - fend Us with thy Spir - it,

Let him in con - stan - cy Fol - low the Mas - ter.
Do but them - selves con - found; His strength the more is.
We know we at the end Shall life in - her - it.

There's no dis - cour - age - ment Shall make him once re - lent
No foes shall stay his might, Though he with gi - ants fight;
Then fan - cies, flee a - way! I'll fear not what men say;

His first a - vowed in - tent To be a pil - grim.
He will make good his right To be a pil - grim.
I'll la - bor night and day To be a pil - grim. A - men.

CONFLICT AND CHALLENGE

Faith of Our Fathers! Living Still

Frederick W. Faber, 1814-1863, alt.

ST. CATHERINE 8.8.8.8.8.8.
Henri F. Hemy, 1818-1888
Adapt. James G. Walton, 1821-1905

253

1 Faith of our fa - thers! liv - ing still In spite of dun - geon, fire, and sword, O how our hearts beat high with joy When-e'er we hear that glo - rious word! Faith of our fa - thers, ho - ly faith! We will be true to thee till death.

2 Faith of our fa - thers! we will strive To win all na - tions un - to thee, And through the truth that comes from God Man - kind shall then be tru - ly free. Faith of our fa - thers, ho - ly faith! We will be true to thee till death.

3 Faith of our fa - thers! we will love Both friend and foe in all our strife, And preach thee, too, as love knows how By kind - ly words and vir - tuous life: Faith of our fa - thers, ho - ly faith! We will be true to thee till death. A - men.

CONFLICT AND CHALLENGE

254 Soldiers of Christ, Arise

Charles Wesley, 1707-1788

SILVER STREET S.M.
Isaac Smith, 1725-1800

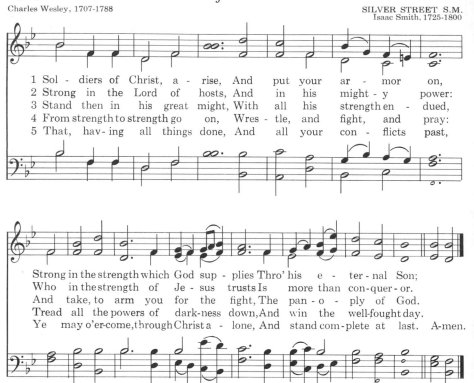

1 Sol - diers of Christ, a - rise, And put your ar - mor on,
2 Strong in the Lord of hosts, And in his might - y power:
3 Stand then in his great might, With all his strength en - dued,
4 From strength to strength go on, Wres - tle, and fight, and pray:
5 That, hav - ing all things done, And all your con - flicts past,

Strong in the strength which God sup - plies Thro' his e - ter - nal Son;
Who in the strength of Je - sus trusts Is more than con-quer- or.
And take, to arm you for the fight, The pan - o - ply of God.
Tread all the powers of dark-ness down, And win the well-fought day.
Ye may o'er-come, through Christ a - lone, And stand com-plete at last. A-men.

255 Lord Jesus, Think on Me

Synesius of Cyrene, c. 375-430
Tr. Allen W. Chatfield, 1808-1896, alt.

SOUTHWELL S.M.
Adapted from Damon's *Psalmes*, 1579

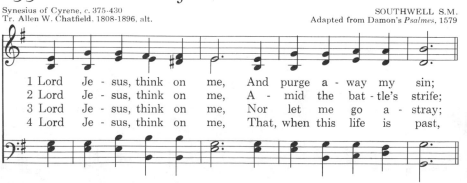

1 Lord Je - sus, think on me, And purge a - way my sin;
2 Lord Je - sus, think on me, A - mid the bat - tle's strife;
3 Lord Je - sus, think on me, Nor let me go a - stray;
4 Lord Je - sus, think on me, That, when this life is past,

CONFLICT AND CHALLENGE

257 **Now in the Days of Youth**

Walter J. Mathams, 1853-1932

DIADEMATA S.M.D.
George J. Elvey, 1816-1893

1 Now in the days of youth, When life flows fresh and free,
2 Teach us wher-e'er we live To act as in thy sight,
3 Teach us to love the true, The beau - ti - ful and pure,

Thou Lord of all our hearts and lives, We give our-selves to thee.
And do what thou wouldst have us do With ra - di - ant de - light;
And let us not for one short hour An e - vil thought en - dure;

Our fer - vent gift re - ceive, And fit us to ful - fill,
Not choos - ing what is great, Nor spurn - ing what is small,
But give us grace to stand De - cid - ed, brave, and strong,

Through all our days, in all our ways, Our heaven-ly Fa-ther's will.
But take as from thy hands our tasks, And glo - ri - fy them all.
The lov - ers of all ho - ly things, The foes of all things wrong. A-men.

CONFLICT AND CHALLENGE

Words from *New Worship and Song*. The Pilgrim Press.

Lord, as to Thy Dear Cross We Flee 258

John H. Gurney, 1802-1862

ST. COLUMBA 8.7.8.7.
Ancient Irish Melody

1 Lord, as to thy dear cross we flee, And plead to be for - giv - en,
2 Help us, through good re - port and ill, Our dai - ly cross to bear,
3 Should friends mis-judge, or foes de - fame, Or breth-ren faith-less prove,
4 Kept peace - ful in the midst of strife For - giv - ing and for - giv - en,

So let thy life our pat - tern be, And form our souls for heav - en.
Like thee, to do our Fa-ther's will, Our breth-ren's grief to share.
Then, like thine own, be all our aim To con - quer them by love.
O may we lead the pil-grim's life, And fol - low thee to heav - en. A - men.

Give to the Winds Thy Fears 259

Paul Gerhardt, 1607-1676
Tr. John Wesley, 1703-1791, alt.

ST. BRIDE S.M.
Samuel Howard, 1710-1782
Harm. David Evans, 1874-1948

1 Give to the winds thy fears; Hope and be un - dis - mayed;
2 Through waves, and clouds, and storms, He gen - tly clears thy way;
3 Leave to his sov - ereign sway To choose and to com - mand;
4 Far, far a - bove thy thought His coun - sel shall ap - pear,

God hears thy sighs and counts thy tears; God shall lift up thy head.
Wait thou his time; so shall this night Soon end in joy - ous day.
So shalt thou, won-dering, own his way How wise, how strong his hand!
When ful - ly he the work hath wrought That caused thy need-less fear. A-men.

STEWARDSHIP

260 *Savior, Thy Dying Love*

S. Dryden Phelps, 1816-1895, alt.

SOMETHING FOR JESUS 6.4.6.4.6.6.6.4.
Robert Lowry, 1826-1899

1 Sav - ior, thy dy - ing love Thou gav - est me, Nor should I
2 Give me a faith - ful heart, Guid - ed by thee, That each de -
3 All that I am and have, Thy gifts so free, Ev - er in

aught with-hold, Dear Lord, from thee; In love my soul would bow, My heart ful-
part - ing day Henceforth may see Some work of love be - gun, Some deed of
joy or grief, My Lord, for thee; And when thy face I see, My ran-somed

fill its vow, Some of-fering bring thee now, Some-thing for thee.
kind-ness done, Some wan-derer sought and won, Some-thing for thee.
soul shall be, Through all e - ter - ni - ty, Of - fered to thee. A-men.

261 *We Give Thee But Thine Own*

William Walsham How, 1823-1897

SCHUMANN S.M.
Mason and Webb's *Cantica Laudis*
Boston, 1850

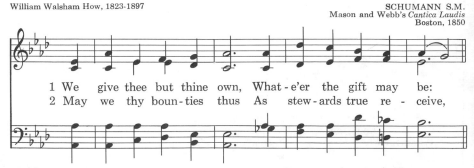

1 We give thee but thine own, What - e'er the gift may be:
2 May we thy boun - ties thus As stew - ards true re - ceive,

STEWARDSHIP

Alternate tune No. 400

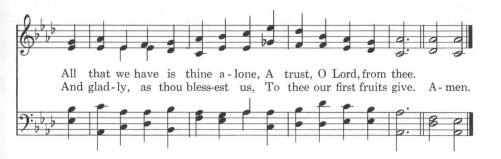

All that we have is thine a-lone, A trust, O Lord, from thee.
And glad-ly, as thou bless-est us, To thee our first fruits give. A-men.

All Things Are Thine; No Gift Have We   262

John G. Whittier, 1807-1892

GERMANY L.M.
Gardiner's *Sacred Melodies*, 1815

1 All things are thine; no gift have we, Lord of all
2 Thy will was in the build-er's thought; Thy hand un-
3 In weak-ness and in want we call On thee for
4 O Fa-ther, deign these walls to bless; Fill with thy

gifts, to of-fer thee, And hence with grate-ful hearts to-
seen a-midst us wrought; Through mor-tal mo-tive, scheme and
whom the heavens are small; Thy glo-ry is thy chil-dren's
love their emp-ti-ness; And let their door a gate-way

day Thine own be-fore thy feet we lay.
plan, Thy wise e-ter-nal pur-pose ran.
good, Thy joy thy ten-der Fa-ther-hood.
be To lead us from our-selves to thee. A-men.

STEWARDSHIP

263 The Wise May Bring Their Learning

Anonymous
From *The Book of Praise for Children*, 1881

FOREST GREEN C.M.D.
English traditional melody
Arr. R. Vaughan Williams, 1872-1958

1 The wise may bring their learn - ing, The rich may bring their wealth,
2 We'll bring him hearts that love him; We'll bring him thank-ful praise,

And some may bring their great - ness, And some bring strength and health;
And young souls meek-ly striv - ing To walk in ho - ly ways:

We, too, would bring our treas - ures To of - fer to the King;
And these shall be the treas - ures We of - fer to the King,

We have no wealth or learn - ing: What shall we chil-dren bring?
And these are gifts that ev - en The poor - est child may bring. A-men.

O Brother Man, Fold to Thy Heart 264

John Greenleaf Whittier, 1807-1892

WELWYN 11.10.11.10.
Alfred Scott-Gatty, 1847-1918

1 O broth - er man, fold to thy heart thy broth - er;
2 Fol - low with rev - erent steps the great ex - am - ple
3 Then shall all shack - les fall; the storm - y clan - gor

Where pit - y dwells, the peace of God is there;
Of him whose ho - ly work was do - ing good;
Of wild war mu - sic o'er the earth shall cease;

To wor - ship right - ly is to love each oth - er,
So shall the wide earth seem our Fa - ther's tem - ple,
Love shall tread out the bale - ful fire of an - ger,

Each smile a hymn, each kind - ly deed a prayer.
Each lov - ing life a psalm of grat - i - tude.
And in its ash - es plant the tree of peace. A - men.

BROTHERHOOD

265 Father Eternal, Ruler of Creation

Laurence Housman, 1865-1959

LANGHAM 11.10.11.10.10.
Geoffrey Shaw, 1879-1943

1 Fa - ther e - ter - nal, Rul - er of cre - a - tion, Spir - it of life, which moved ere form was made, Through the thick dark - ness cov - ering ev - ery na - tion, Light to man's blind-ness, O be thou our

2 Ra - ces and peo - ples, lo, we stand di - vid - ed, And shar - ing not our griefs, no joy can share; By wars and tu - mults love is mocked, de - rid - ed, His con-quering cross no king - dom wills to

3 En - vious of heart, blind-eyed, with tongues con-found-ed, Na - tion by na - tion still goes un - for - given; In wrath and fear, by jeal - ous-ies sur - round - ed, Build-ing proud towers which shall not reach to

4 How shall we love thee, ho - ly, hid - den Be - ing, If we love not the world which thou hast made? O give us broth - er - love for bet - ter see - ing Thy Word made flesh, and in a man - ger

BROTHERHOOD

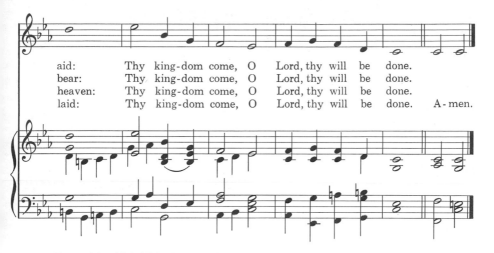

aid: Thy king-dom come, O Lord, thy will be done.
bear: Thy king-dom come, O Lord, thy will be done.
heaven: Thy king-dom come, O Lord, thy will be done.
laid: Thy king-dom come, O Lord, thy will be done. A-men.

O Day of God, Draw Nigh — 266

R. B. Y. Scott, 1899-, alt.

ST. MICHAEL S.M.
Adapted from *Genevan Psalter*, 1551

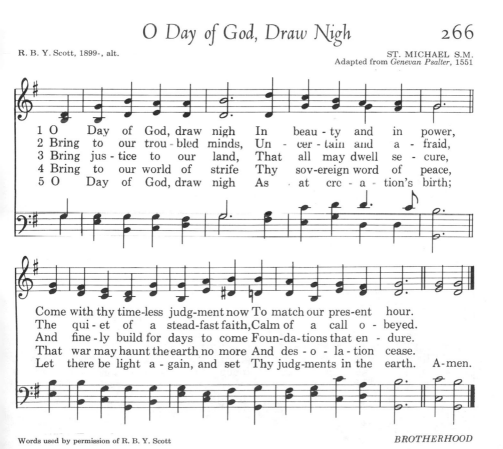

1 O Day of God, draw nigh In beau-ty and in power,
2 Bring to our trou-bled minds, Un-cer-tain and a-fraid,
3 Bring jus-tice to our land, That all may dwell se-cure,
4 Bring to our world of strife Thy sov-ereign word of peace,
5 O Day of God, draw nigh As at cre-a-tion's birth;

Come with thy time-less judg-ment now To match our pres-ent hour.
The qui-et of a stead-fast faith, Calm of a call o-beyed.
And fine-ly build for days to come Foun-da-tions that en-dure.
That war may haunt the earth no more And des-o-la-tion cease.
Let there be light a-gain, and set Thy judg-ments in the earth. A-men.

BROTHERHOOD

267 The Savior's Wondrous Love

Tai Jun Park, 1900-
Tr. William Scott and
Yung Oon Kim, 1950

KOREA S.M.
Tai Jun Park, 1900-

1 The Sav-ior's won-drous love, Hath made all na-tions one.
2 In this vast world of men, A world so filled with pain,
3 In this sad world of war Can peace be ev-er found?
4 The Mas-ter's new com-mand Was love each oth-er well.

U - nit-ed let us praise this deed The Fa-ther's love hath done.
No oth-er theme can be our prayer Than this:thy king-dom come.
Un - less the love of Christ pre-vail True peace will not a-bound.
O broth-ers, let us all u-nite To do his ho-ly will. A-men.

From *Cantate Domino*. Copyright © by the World Student Christian Federation.
Used by permission.

268 Where Cross the Crowded Ways of Life

Frank Mason North, 1850-1935

GERMANY L.M.
Gardiner's *Sacred Melodies*, 1815

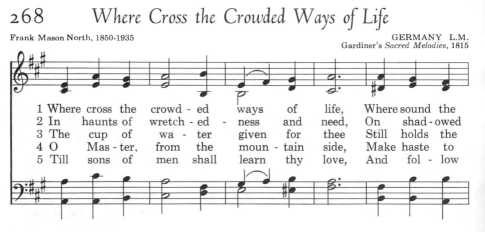

1 Where cross the crowd - ed ways of life, Where sound the
2 In haunts of wretch - ed - ness and need, On shad-owed
3 The cup of wa - ter given for thee Still holds the
4 O Mas - ter, from the moun - tain side, Make haste to
5 Till sons of men shall learn thy love, And fol - low

BROTHERHOOD

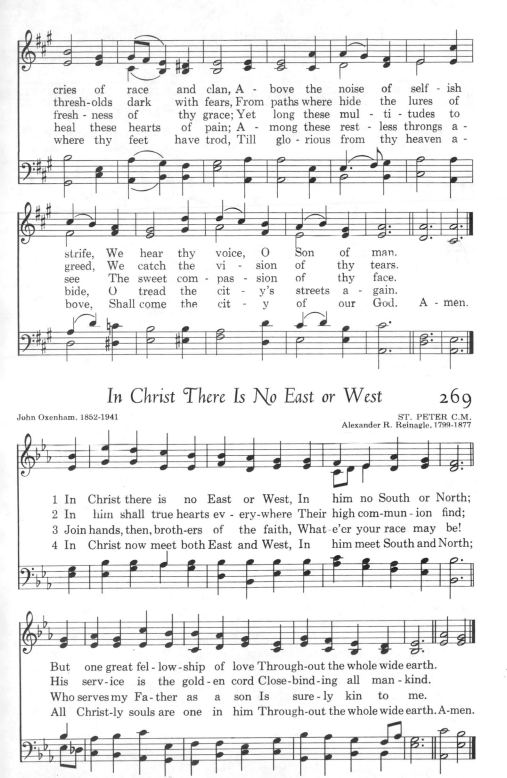

cries of race and clan, A - bove the noise of self - ish
thresh-olds dark with fears, From paths where hide the lures of
fresh - ness of thy grace; Yet long these mul - ti - tudes to
heal these hearts of pain; A - mong these rest - less throngs a -
where thy feet have trod, Till glo - rious from thy heaven a -

strife, We hear thy voice, O Son of man.
greed, We catch the vi - sion of thy tears.
see The sweet com - pas - sion of thy face.
bide, O tread the cit - y's streets a - gain.
bove, Shall come the cit - y of our God. A - men.

In Christ There Is No East or West 269

John Oxenham, 1852-1941

ST. PETER C.M.
Alexander R. Reinagle, 1799-1877

1 In Christ there is no East or West, In him no South or North;
2 In him shall true hearts ev - ery-where Their high com-mun - ion find;
3 Join hands, then, broth-ers of the faith, What e'er your race may be!
4 In Christ now meet both East and West, In him meet South and North;

But one great fel - low-ship of love Through-out the whole wide earth.
His serv - ice is the gold - en cord Close-bind-ing all man - kind.
Who serves my Fa - ther as a son Is sure - ly kin to me.
All Christ-ly souls are one in him Through-out the whole wide earth. A-men.

BROTHERHOOD

From Thee All Skill and Science Flow

Charles Kingsley, 1819-1875

ST. MARIA C.M.D.
William Gawler, c. 1750-1809

1 From thee all skill and sci - ence flow, All pit - y, care, and love.
2 And has - ten, Lord, that per - fect day When pain and death shall cease,

All calm and cour-age, faith and hope: O pour them from a - bove.
And thy just rule shall fill the earth With health and light and peace.

And part them, Lord, to each and all, As each and all shall need,
When ev - er blue the sky shall gleam, And ev - er green the sod,

To rise, like in - cense, each to thee, In no - ble thought and deed.
And man's rude work de-face no more the par - a - dise of God. A-men.

BROTHERHOOD

The Voice of God Is Calling

271

John Haynes Holmes, 1879-1964

MEIRIONYDD 7.6.7.6.D.
William Lloyd, 1786-1852

1 The voice of God is call-ing Its sum-mons un-to men;
2 I hear my peo-ple cry-ing In cot and mine and slum;
3 We heed, O Lord, thy sum-mons, And an-swer: Here are we!
4 From ease and plen-ty save us; From pride of place ab-solve;

As once he spake in Zi-on, So now he speaks a-gain:
No field or mart is si-lent, No cit-y street is dumb.
Send us up-on thine er-rand; Let us thy serv-ants be.
Purge us of low de-sire; Lift us to high re-solve;

Whom shall I send to suc-cor My peo-ple in their need?
I see my peo-ple fall-ing In dark-ness and de-spair.
Our strength is dust and ash-es, Our years a pass-ing hour,
Take us, and make us ho-ly; Teach us thy will and way.

Whom shall I send to loos-en The bonds of shame and greed?
Whom shall I send to shat-ter The fet-ters which they bear?
But thou canst use our weak-ness To mag-ni-fy thy power.
Speak, and, be-hold! we an-swer; Command, and we o-bey! A-men.

Words used by permission of Roger W. Holmes.

BROTHERHOOD

272   *Where Restless Crowds Are Thronging*

Thomas Curtis Clark, 1877-1953

MEIRIONYDD 7.6.7.6.D.
William Lloyd, 1786-1852

1 Where rest-less crowds are throng-ing A - long the cit - y ways,
2 In scenes of want and sor - row And haunts of fla - grant wrong,
3 O Christ, be - hold thy peo - ple They press on ev - ery hand!

Where pride and greed and tur - moil Con - sume the fe - vered days,
In homes where kind-ness fal - ters, And strife and fear are strong,
Bring light to all the cit - ies Of our be - lov - ed land.

Where vain am - bi - tions ban - ish All thoughts of praise and prayer,
In bus - y street of bar - ter, In lone - ly thor - ough - fare,
May all our bit - ter striv - ing Give way to vi - sions fair

The peo - ple's spir - its wav - er: But thou, O Christ, art there.
The peo - ple's spir - its lan-guish: But thou, O Christ, art there.
Of right-eous-ness and jus - tice: For thou, O Christ, art there. A-men.

BROTHERHOOD

Blest Be the Tie that Binds

273

John Fawcett, 1740-1817

DENNIS S.M.
Johann G. Nägeli, 1768-1836
Arr. Lowell Mason, 1792-1872

1 Blest be the tie that binds Our hearts in Chris-tian love:
2 Be - fore our Fa - ther's throne We pour our ar - dent prayers;
3 We share each oth - er's woes, Each oth - er's bur - dens bear,
4 When we are called to part, It gives us in - ward pain;

The fel - low - ship of kin - dred minds Is like to that a - bove.
Our fears, our hopes, our aims are one, Our com - forts and our cares.
And of - ten for each oth - er flows The sym - pa - thiz - ing tear.
But we shall still be joined in heart, And hope to meet a - gain. A-men.

O Lord, May Church and Home

274

Carlton C. Buck, 1907-

LAND OF REST C.M.
Traditional American Melody
Harm. Annabel Morris Buchanan, 1888-

1 O Lord, may church and home com - bine To teach thy per - fect way,
2 Let us un - wor - thy aims de - part, Im - bue us with thy grace;
3 Shine, Light Di - vine; re - veal thy face Where dark-ness else might be.
4 May stead-fast faith and earn - est prayer Keep sa - cred vows se - cure;

With gen - tle - ness and love like thine, That none shall ev - er stray.
With - in the home let ev - ery heart Be - come thy dwell - ing place.
Grant, Love Di - vine, in ev - ery place Glad fel - low - ship with thee.
Build thou a hal-lowed dwell-ing where True joy and peace en - dure. A-men.

HOME AND FAMILY

Our Father, by Whose Name

F. Bland Tucker, 1895-

RHOSYMEDRE 6.6.6.6.8.8.8.8.
John D. Edwards, 1806-1885

1 Our Father, by whose name, All fa-ther-hood is known,
2 O Christ, thy-self a child With-in an earth-ly home,
3 O Spir-it, who dost bind Our hearts in u-ni-ty,

Who dost in love pro-claim Each fam-i-ly thine own,
With heart still un-de-filed, Thou didst to man-hood come;
Who teach-est us to find The love from self set free,

Bless thou all par-ents, guard-ing well, With con-stant love as
Our chil-dren bless, in ev-ery place, That they may all be-
In all our hearts such love in-crease, That ev-ery home, by

sen-ti-nel, The homes in which thy peo-ple dwell.
hold thy face, And know-ing thee may grow in grace.
this re-lease, May be the dwell-ing place of peace. A-men.

HOME AND FAMILY

Blest Is the Home When God Is There 276

Henry Ware, 1794-1843

ABBEY C.M.
Scottish Psalter, 1615

1 Blest is the home when God is there, And love fills ev - ery breast, When one their wish and one their prayer, And one their heaven - ly rest.

2 Blest is the home where Je - sus' name Is known to ev - ery ear, Where chil - dren ear - ly speak his fame, And par - ents hold him dear.

3 Blest is the home where prayer is heard, And praise to God doth rise, Where par - ents love the sac - red Word, And all its wis - dom prize.

4 Lord, let us in our homes a - gree This bless - ed peace to gain; U - nite our hearts in love to thee, And love to all will reign. A - men.

HOME AND FAMILY

277   O God, Who to a Loyal Home

Harry Emerson Fosdick, 1878-1969

KINGSFOLD C.M.D.
Traditional English Melody
Arr. and harm. R. Vaughan Williams, 1872-1958

1 O God who to a loy-al home Didst trust thy Son di-vine,
2 De-liv-er us from sins which harm Our homes, and mar their peace,
3 Thou art our Fa-ther, and from thee All faith-ful fam-i-lies spring;
4 We pray that child-hood's la-tent powers May grow to bless man-kind;

Where faith-ful love and pa-tient work Made dai-ly life be-nign;
May self-less and de-vo-ted love Make strife and dis-cord cease,
To homes where love and hon-or dwell Thou dost thy bless-ing bring.
That we may guide a-right young lives, For un-guessed good de-signed,

With con-trite shame thy grace we claim, And lift to thee our prayer;
With an-xious zeal, for man-kind's weal And world-wide peace we pray,
O God of love, send from a-bove Thy suc-cor, swift and strong,
O Fa-ther God, whose Son has trod Such low-ly paths as we,

Re-deem our oft un-wor-thy homes Till all is Christ-like there.
But all in vain, if way-ward homes Cause child-hood's steps to stray.
That from such homes stout souls may come To tri-umph o-ver wrong.
Help us to build on earth true homes, Till we come home to thee. A-men.

HOME AND FAMILY

O Happy Home, Where Thou Art Loved 278

O selig Haus
Karl Johann Philipp Spitta, 1801-1859
Tr. Sarah Borthwick Findlater, 1823-1907

WELWYN 11.10.11.10.
Alfred Scott-Gatty, 1847-1918

1 O happy home, where thou art loved the dear - est,
2 O happy home, where each one serves thee, low - ly,
3 O happy home, where thou art not for - got - ten
4 Un - til at last, when earth's day's work is end - ed,

Thou lov - ing friend, and Sav - ior of our race,
What - ev - er his ap - point - ed work may be,
When joy is o - ver - flow - ing, full and free,
All meet thee in the bless - ed home a - bove,

And where a - mong the guests there nev - er com - eth
Till ev - ery com - mon task seems great and ho - ly
O hap - py home, where ev - ery wound-ed spir - it
From whence thou cam - est, where thou hast as - cend - ed,

One who can hold such high and hon - ored place!
When it is done, O Lord, as un - to thee.
Is brought, Phy - si - cian, Com - for - ter, to thee.
Thy ev - er - last - ing home of peace and love! A - men.

Music used by permission of the Abbott of Downside.

HOME AND FAMILY

For All the Saints

William Walsham How, 1823-1897

SINE NOMINE 10.10.10.4.
R. Vaughan Williams, 1872-1958

1 For all the saints, who from their la - bors rest, Who
2 Thou wast their rock, their for - tress, and their might:
3 O may thy sol - diers, faith - ful, true, and bold,
6 From earth's wide bounds, from o - cean's far - thest coast, Through

thee by faith be - fore the world con - fessed, Thy
Thou, Lord, their Cap - tain in the well-fought fight;
Fight as the saints who no - bly fought of old, And
gates of pearl streams in the count - less host,

Name, O Je - sus, be for - ev - er blest.
Thou, in the dark - ness drear, the one true light.
win, with them, the vic - tor's crown of gold.
Sing - ing to Fa - ther, Son, and Ho - ly Ghost,

VICTORY OVER DEATH

Music from *The English Hymnal* by permission of Oxford University Press.

Al - le-lu - ia, al - le-lu - ia! A-men.

4 O blest com-mun - ion, fel-low-ship di - vine! We fee-bly strug-gle,
5 And when the strife is fierce, the war-fare long, Steals on the ear the

they in glo-ry shine; Yet all are one in thee, for all are thine.
dis-tant tri-umph song, And hearts are brave a - gain, and arms are strong.

D.C. for stanza 6

Al - le-lu - ia, al - le-lu - ia!

VICTORY OVER DEATH

280 What Joy to Think of That Vast Host

Norwegian
W. A. Wexels, 1796-1866
Tr. R. Birch Hoyle, 1875-1939

LOBT GOTT IHR CHRISTEN C.M.
Melody by Nikolaus Herman, c. 1485-1561

1 What joy to think of that vast host, Of
2 Glad thought, that all who served the Lord, The
3 What bliss, their loves and joys to tell! What
4 Great God, in mer - cy save us all; Raise

ev - ery tribe and tongue, Who come from ev - ery
a - pos - tol - ic band, The myr - iads trust - ing
won - drous strains they sing! Ex - ul - tant an - thems
us to dwell with thee. With the re - deemed, when

clime and coast, Who raise in heaven their
in their word Shall all to - geth - er
rise and swell Till heaven's high arch - es
thou shalt call, Grant that our place may

song, Their glad tri - um - phal song.
stand, Re - deemed at God's right hand.
ring As they a - dore their King.
be, Through all e - ter - ni - ty. A - men.

VICTORY OVER DEATH

Softly Now the Light of Day

281

George W. Doane, 1799-1859

SEYMOUR 7.7.7.7.
Arr. from Carl M. von Weber, 1786-1826

1 Soft - ly now the light of day Fades up - on my sight a - way;
2 Thou, whose all - per - vad - ing eye Naught es - capes, with - out, with - in,
3 Soon for me the light of day Shall for - ev - er pass a - way;
4 Thou who, sin - less, yet hast known All of man's in - firm - i - ty,

Free from care, from la - bor free, Lord, I would com-mune with thee.
Par - don each in - firm - i - ty, O - pen fault, and se - cret sin.
Then, from sin and sor - row free, Take me, Lord, to dwell with thee.
Then, from thine e - ter - nal throne, Je - sus, look with pity - ing eye. A - men.

Jesus, the Very Thought of Thee

282

Jesu dulcis memoria
Latin: 12th century
Tr. Edward Caswall, 1814-1878, alt.

ST. AGNES C.M.
John B. Dykes, 1823-1876

1 Je - sus, the ver - y thought of thee, With sweet-ness fills my breast;
2 No voice can sing, no heart can frame, Nor can the mem - ory find
3 O hope of ev - ery con - trite heart, O joy of all the meek,
4 Je - sus, our on - ly joy be thou, As thou our prize wilt be;

But sweet-er far thy face to see, And in thy pres-ence rest.
A sweet-er sound than thy blest name, O Sav - ior of man-kind.
To those who fall, how kind thou art! How good to those who seek!
Je - sus, be thou our glo - ry now, And through e-ter - ni - ty. A - men.

PRAISE TO CHRIST

283   *O Splendor of God's Glory Bright*

Splendor paternae gloriae
St. Ambrose, 338?-397
Tr. Compilers of *Hymns Ancient & Modern*, 1904

SOLEMNIS HAEC FESTIVITAS L.M.
Paris Gradual, 1689

1 O splen - dor of God's glo - ry bright,
2 Come, ver - y Sun of truth and love,
3 Teach us to work with all our might;
4 All praise to God the Fa - ther be,

Who bring - est forth the light from Light;
Come in thy ra - diance from a - bove,
Put Sa - tan's fierce as - saults to flight;
All praise, e - ter - nal Son, to thee,

O Light of light, the foun - tain spring;
And shed the Ho - ly Spir - it's ray
Turn all to good that seems most ill;
Whom with the Spir - it we a - dore,

O Day, our days il - lu - min - ing;
On all we think or do to - day.
Help us our call - ing to ful - fill.
For ev - er and for ev - er - more. A - men.

PRAISE TO CHRIST

Music from *Hymnal for Colleges and Schools;* used by permission of Yale University Press.

All Hail the Power of Jesus' Name

Edward Perronet, 1726-1792
Alt. John Rippon, 1751-1836

CORONATION C.M.
Oliver Holden, 1765-1844

284

1 All hail the power of Je-sus' name! Let an-gels pros-trate
2 Ye seed of Is-rael's cho-sen race, Ye ran-somed of the
3 Sin-ners, whose love can ne'er for-get The worm-wood and the
4 Let ev-ery kin-dred, ev-ery tribe, On this ter-res-trial
5 O that with yon-der sac-red throng We at his feet may

fall; Bring forth the roy-al di-a-dem, And
fall, Hail him who saves you by his grace, And
gall, Go spread your tro-phies at his feet, And
ball, To him all maj-es-ty as-cribe, And
fall! We'll join the ev-er-last-ing song, And

crown him Lord of all; Bring forth the roy-al
crown him Lord of all; Hail him who saves you
crown him Lord of all; Go spread your tro-phies
crown him Lord of all; To him all maj-es-
crown him Lord of all; We'll join the ev-er-

di-a-dem, And crown him Lord of all.
by his grace, And crown him Lord of all.
at his feet And crown him Lord of all.
ty as-cribe, And crown him Lord of all.
last-ing song, And crown him Lord of all. A-men.

PRAISE TO CHRIST

285 Christ, Whose Glory Fills the Skies

Charles Wesley, 1707-1788

LUX PRIMA 7.7.7.7.7.7.
Charles F. Gounod, 1818-1893

1 Christ, whose glo - ry fills the skies; Christ, the true, the
2 Dark and cheer - less is the morn Un - ac - com - pa -
3 Vis - it, then, this soul of mine; Pierce the gloom of

on - ly Light, Sun of Right - eous - ness, a - rise,
nied by thee; Joy - less is the day's re - turn
sin and grief; Fill me, Ra - dian - cy di - vine;

Tri - umph o'er the shades of night; Day - spring from on
Till thy mer - cy's beams I see; Till they in - ward
Scat - ter all my un - be - lief; More and more thy -

high, be near; Day - star, in my heart ap - pear.
light im - part, Glad my eyes and warm my heart.
self dis - play, Shin - ing to the per - fect day. A - men.

PRAISE TO CHRIST

Fairest Lord Jesus

Anonymous in *Münster Gesangbuch*, 1677

ST. ELIZABETH 5.6.8.5.5.8.
Silesian Melody

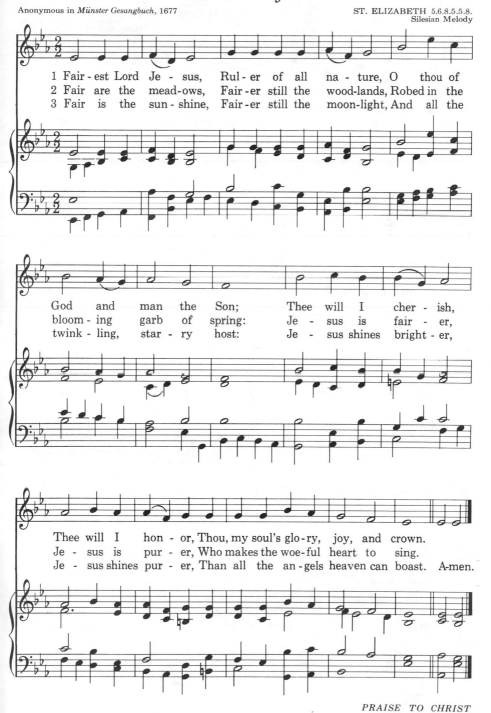

1 Fair - est Lord Je - sus, Rul - er of all na - ture, O thou of
2 Fair are the mead-ows, Fair - er still the wood-lands, Robed in the
3 Fair is the sun - shine, Fair - er still the moon-light, And all the

God and man the Son; Thee will I cher - ish,
bloom - ing garb of spring: Je - sus is fair - er,
twink - ling, star - ry host: Je - sus shines bright - er,

Thee will I hon - or, Thou, my soul's glo - ry, joy, and crown.
Je - sus is pur - er, Who makes the woe-ful heart to sing.
Je - sus shines pur - er, Than all the an - gels heaven can boast. A-men.

PRAISE TO CHRIST

287 *How Brightly Beams the Morning Star*

Philipp Nicolai, 1556-1608
Tr. Hymnal Version, 1955

WIE SCHÖN LEUCHTET DER MORGENSTERN 8.8.7.8.8.7.4.8.4.8.
Philipp Nicolai?, 1556-1608
Harm. by J. S. Bach, 1685-1750

1 How bright-ly beams the morn-ing star! What sud-den ra-diance from a-far Doth cheer us with its shin-ing? Bright- ness of God, that breaks our night And fills the dark-ened souls with light, Who long for truth were pin-ing!

2 Through thee a-lone can we be blest; Then deep be on our hearts im-prest The love that thou hast borne us; So make us read-y to ful-fill With ar-dent zeal thy ho-ly will, Though men may vex or scorn us;

3 All praise to him who came to save, Who con-quered death and scorned the grave; Each day new praise re-sound-eth To him, the Life who once was slain, The friend whom none shall trust in vain, Whose grace for aye a-bound-eth;

PRAISE TO CHRIST

New - ly, tru - ly, God's Word feeds us, Right-ly leads us, Life be -
Hold us, fold us, lest we fail thee, Lo, we hail thee, Long to
Sing then, ring then, tell the stor - y Of his glo - ry, Till his

stow - ing. Praise, O praise such love o'er - flow - ing!
know thee! All we are and have we owe thee.
prais - es Flood with light earth's dark-est maz - es! A-men.

Words from *The Lutheran Service Book and Hymnal* by permission of the Commission on the Liturgy and Hymnal.

Jesus Shall Reign Where'er the Sun 288

Isaac Watts, 1674-1748

DUKE STREET L.M.
John Hatton, 1793

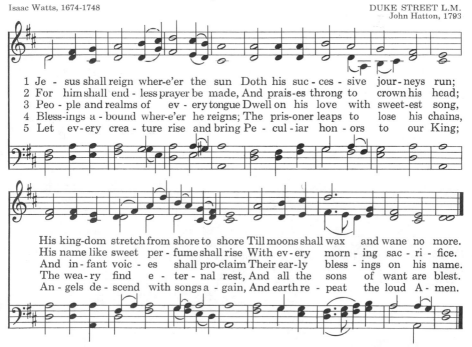

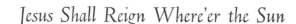

1 Je - sus shall reign wher-e'er the sun Doth his suc - ces - sive jour-neys run;
2 For him shall end - less prayer be made, And prais-es throng to crown his head;
3 Peo - ple and realms of ev - ery tongue Dwell on his love with sweet-est song,
4 Bless-ings a - bound wher-e'er he reigns; The pris-oner leaps to lose his chains,
5 Let ev-ery crea - ture rise and bring Pe - cul - iar hon - ors to our King;

His king-dom stretch from shore to shore Till moons shall wax and wane no more.
His name like sweet per - fume shall rise With ev - ery morn - ing sac - ri - fice.
And in - fant voic - es shall pro-claim Their ear - ly bless - ings on his name.
The wea - ry find e - ter - nal rest, And all the sons of want are blest.
An - gels de - scend with songs a - gain, And earth re - peat the loud A - men.

PRAISE TO CHRIST

Jesus, Priceless Treasure

Jesu, meine Freude
Johann Franck, 1618-1677
Tr. Catherine Winkworth, 1827-1878 alt.

JESU, MEINE FREUDE 6.6.5.6.6.5.7.8.6.
German Traditional Melody
Adapt. and harm. Johann Crüger, 1598-1662

1 Je - sus, price - less treas - ure, Source of pur - est pleas - ure,
2 In thine arm I rest me; Foes who would mo - lest me
3 Hence, all thoughts of sad - ness! For the Lord of glad - ness,

Tru - est friend to me; Long my heart hath pant - ed, Till it well - nigh
Can - not reach me here. Though the earth be shak - ing, Ev - ery heart be
Je - sus, en - ters in; Those who love the Fa - ther, Though the storms may

faint - ed, Thirst - ing af - ter thee. Thine I am, O spot - less Lamb
quak - ing, God dis - pels our fear; Sin and hell in con - flict fell
gath - er, Still have peace with - in; Yea, what - e'er we here must bear,

I will suf - fer nought to hide thee, Ask for nought be - side thee.
With their heav - iest storms as - sail us; Je - sus will not fail us.
Still in thee lies pur - est pleas - ure, Je - sus, price - less treas - ure! A - men.

PRAISE TO CHRIST

The Church's One Foundation

290

Samuel John Stone, 1839-1900

AURELIA 7.6.7.6.D.
Samuel Sebastian Wesley, 1810-1876

1 The Church 's one foun - da - tion Is Je - sus Christ her Lord;
2 E - lect from ev - ery na - tion, Yet one o'er all the earth,
3 'Mid toil and trib - u - la - tion, And tu - mult of her war,
4 Yet she on earth hath un - ion With God, the Three in One,

She is his new cre - a - tion By wa - ter and the word;
Her char - ter of sal - va - tion, One Lord, one faith, one birth,
She waits the con - sum - ma - tion Of peace for ev - er - more;
And mys - tic sweet com - mun - ion With those whose rest is won.

From heaven he came and sought her To be his ho - ly bride;
One ho - ly name she bless - es, Par - takes one ho - ly food,
Till with the vi - sion glo - rious, Her long - ing eyes are blest,
O hap - py ones and ho - ly! Lord, give us grace that we

With his own blood he bought her, And for her life he died.
And to one hope she press - es, With ev - ery grace en - dued.
And the great Church vic - to - rious Shall be the Church at rest.
Like them, the meek and low - ly, On high may dwell with thee. A - men.

PRAISE TO CHRIST

291 At the Name of Jesus

Caroline Maria Noel, 1817-1877

KING'S WESTON 6.5.6.5.D.
Ralph Vaughan Williams, 1872-1958

1 At the name of Je - sus Ev - ery knee shall bow,
2 At his voice cre - a - tion Sprang at once to sight
3 Hum-bled for a sea - son, To re - ceive a name
4 In your hearts en - throne him; There let him sub - due

Ev - ery tongue con - fess him King of glo - ry now;
All the an - gel fac - es, All the hosts of light,
From the lips of sin - ners, Un - to whom he came.
All that is not ho - ly, All that is not true.

'Tis the Fa - ther's pleas - ure We should call him Lord,
Thrones and dom - i - na - tions, Stars up - on their way,
Faith - ful - ly he bore it, Spot - less to the last,
Crown him as your cap - tain In temp-ta - tion's hour;

PRAISE TO CHRIST

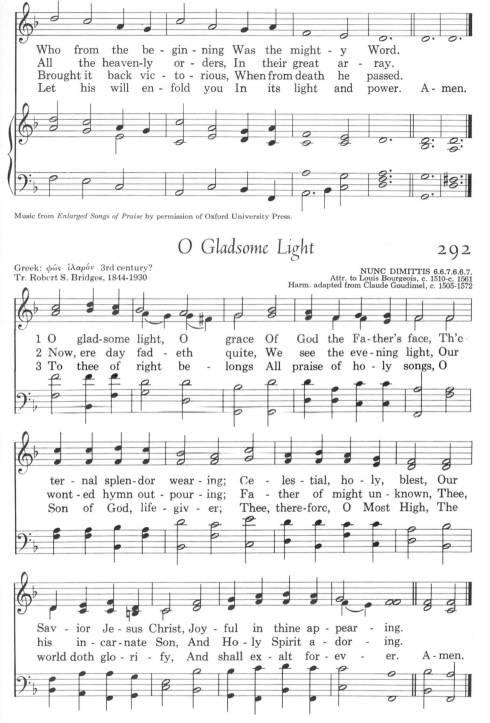

Music from *Enlarged Songs of Praise* by permission of Oxford University Press.

O Gladsome Light

292

Greek: φῶς ἱλαρόν 3rd century?
Tr. Robert S. Bridges, 1844-1930

NUNC DIMITTIS 6.6.7.6.6.7.
Attr. to Louis Bourgeois, c. 1510-c. 1561
Harm. adapted from Claude Goudimel, c. 1505-1572

Who from the be - gin - ning Was the might - y Word.
All the heaven-ly or - ders, In their great ar - ray.
Brought it back vic - to - rious, When from death he passed.
Let his will en - fold you In its light and power. A - men.

1 O glad-some light, O grace Of God the Fa-ther's face, Th'e-
2 Now, ere day fad - eth quite, We see the eve - ning light, Our
3 To thee of right be - longs All praise of ho - ly songs, O

ter - nal splen-dor wear - ing; Ce - les - tial, ho - ly, blest, Our
wont - ed hymn out - pour - ing; Fa - ther of might un - known, Thee,
Son of God, life - giv - er; Thee, there-fore, O Most High, The

Sav - ior Je - sus Christ, Joy - ful in thine ap - pear - ing.
his in - car - nate Son, And Ho - ly Spirit a - dor - ing.
world doth glo - ri - fy, And shall ex - alt for - ev - er. A - men.

Words from *The Yattendon Hymnal* by permission of Oxford University Press.

PRAISE TO CHRIST

293

Master of Eager Youth

St. Clement of Alexandria, c. 170-220
Para. F. Bland Tucker, 1895-

ST. DUNSTAN'S 6.5.6.5.6.6.6.5.
Winfred Douglas, 1867-1944

1 Mas - ter of ea - ger youth, Con - trol - ling, guid - ing,
2 Thou art our might - y Lord, Our strength in sad - ness,
3 Good Shep - herd of thy sheep, Thine own de - fend - ing,
4 Glo - rious their life who sing, With glad thanks - giv - ing,

Lift - ing our hearts to truth, New power pro - vid - ing;
The Fa - ther's con - quering Word, True source of glad - ness;
In love thy chil - dren keep To life un - end - ing;
True hymns to Christ the King In all their liv - ing:

Shep - herd of in - no - cence, Thou art our Con - fi - dence;
Thy name we glo - ri - fy, O Je - sus, throned on high,
Thou art thy - self the Way: Lead us then day by day
Ye who con - fess his Name, Come then with hearts a - flame;

To thee, our sure De - fence, We bring our prais - es.
Who gav'st thy - self to die For man's sal - va - tion.
In thine own steps, we pray, O Lord most ho - ly.
Let word and life ac - claim Our Lord and Sav - ior. A - men.

PRAISE TO CHRIST

Words and music by permission of The Church Pension Fund.

Alleluia! Sing to Jesus

William Chatterton Dix, 1837-1898

HYFRYDOL 8.7.8.7.D.
Melody by Rowland H. Prichard, 1811-1887

1 Al - le - lu - ia! sing to Je - sus, His the scep - tre, his the throne;
2 Al - le - lu - ia! not as or - phans We are left in sor - row now;
3 Al - le - lu - ia! Bread of Heav - en, Thou on earth our food and stay;

Al - le - lu - ia! his the tri - umph, His the vic - to - ry a - lone.
Al - le - lu - ia! he is near us, Faith be - lieves, nor ques - tions how;
Al - le - lu - ia! here the sin - ful Flee to thee from day to day;

Hark! the songs of peace-ful Si - on Thun-der like a might-y flood,
Though the cloud from sight re - ceived him When the for - ty days were o'er,
In - ter - ces - sor, friend of sin - ners, Earth's Re - deem - er, plead for me,

"Je - sus out of ev - ery na - tion Hath re - deemed us by his blood."
Shall our hearts for-get his prom-ise, "I am with you ev - er-more"?
Where the songs of all the sin - less Sweep a - cross the crys-tal sea. A-men.

PRAISE TO CHRIST

Come, Christians, Join to Sing

Christian Henry Bateman, 1813-1889

MADRID 6.6.6.6.D.
Source unknown
Harm. David Evans, 1874-1948

1 Come, Chris-tians, join to sing, Al - le - lu - ia! A - men!
2 Come, lift your hearts on high; Al - le - lu - ia! A - men!
3 Praise yet our Christ a - gain; Al - le - lu - ia! A - men!

Loud praise to Christ our King; Al - le - lu - ia! A - men!
Let prais - es fill the sky; Al - le - lu - ia! A - men!
Life shall not end the strain; Al - le - lu - ia! A - men!

Let all, with heart and voice, Be - fore his throne re - joice;
He is our Guide and Friend; To us he'll con - de - scend;
On heav - en's bliss - ful shore His good - ness we'll a - dore,

Praise is his gra-cious choice: Al - le - lu - ia! A - men!
His love shall nev - er end: Al - le - lu - ia! A - men!
Sing - ing for - ev - er-more, Al - le - lu - ia! A - men!

PRAISE TO CHRIST

Tune copyright reprinted by permission of the Executors of the Late Professor David Evans.

When Morning Gilds the Skies

Beim frühen Morgenlicht
German: anon., 1828
Tr. Edward Caswall, 1814-1878, alt.

LAUDES DOMINI 6.6.6.6.6.6.
Joseph Barnby, 1838-1896

1 When morn - ing gilds the skies, My heart a - wak - ing
2 Be this, while life is mine, My can - ti - cle di -
3 Ye na - tions of man - kind, In this your con - cord
4 Sing, suns and stars of space, Sing, ye that see his

cries, May Je - sus Christ be praised! A -
vine, May Je - sus Christ be praised! Be
find: May Je - sus Christ be praised! Let
face, Sing, Je - sus Christ be praised! God's

like at work and prayer To Je - sus I re -
this the e - ter - nal song, Through all the a - ges
all the earth a - round Ring joy - ous with the
whole cre - a - tion o'er, For aye and ev - er -

pair; May Je - sus Christ be praised!
long, May Je - sus Christ be praised!
sound: May Je - sus Christ be praised!
more Shall Je - sus Christ be praised! A - men.

PRAISE TO CHRIST

Love Divine, All Loves Excelling

Charles Wesley, 1707-1788, alt.

BEECHER 8.7.8.7.D.
John Zundel, 1815-1882

1 Love di - vine, all loves ex - cel - ling, Joy of heaven, to earth come down;
2 Breathe, O breathe thy lov - ing Spir - it In - to ev - ery trou - bled breast;
3 Come, al - might - y to de - liv - er, Let us all thy life re - ceive;
4 Fin - ish, then, thy new cre - a - tion; Pure and spot - less let us be,

Fix in us thy hum - ble dwell - ing, All thy faith - ful mer - cies crown;
Let us all in thee in - her - it, Let us find thy prom - ised rest;
Sud - den - ly re - turn and nev - er, Nev - er - more thy tem - ples leave.
Let us see thy great sal - va - tion Per - fect - ly re - stored in thee;

Je - sus, thou art all com - pas - sion, Pure, un - bound - ed love thou art;
Take a - way our love of sin - ning; Al - pha and O - me - ga be;
Thee we would be al - ways bless - ing, Serve thee as thy hosts a - bove,
Changed from glo - ry in - to glo - ry, Till in heaven we take our place,

Vis - it us with thy sal - va - tion, En - ter ev - ery trem - bling heart.
End of faith, as its be - gin - ning, Set our hearts at lib - er - ty.
Pray, and praise thee with - out ceas - ing, Glo - ry in thy per - fect love.
Till we cast our crowns be - fore thee, Lost in won - der, love, and praise. A - men.

PRAISE TO CHRIST

Alternate tune No. 294

Jesus, Our Lord and King

Anonymous

POTSDAM S.M.
Church Psalter and Hymn Book, 1854

298

1 Je - sus, our Lord and King, To thee our prais - es rise;
2 Now jus - ti - fied by grace And made a - live to God,
3 As dead in - deed to sin, From its do - min - ion free,
4 Bap - tized in - to thy death, With thee a - gain we rise,

To thee our bod-ies we pres-ent, A liv- ing sac - ri - fice.
Formed for thy-self, to show thy praise, We sound thy love a - broad.
Hence-forth, as not our own, but thine, We fol- low on - ly thee.
To new-ness of a life of faith, To new and end - less joys. A-men.

Master, We Thy Footsteps Follow

299

F. A. Jackson, 1867-1942

STEPHANOS 8.5.8.3.
H. W. Baker, 1821-1877

1 Mas - ter, we thy foot-steps fol - low, We thy word o - bey,
2 Now in - to thy death bap - tiz - ed, We our-selves would be
3 Ris - ing with thee, make us like thee, In thy love and care,
4 Let the love that knows no fail - ing Cast out all our fears,
5 Till we hear the trum-pets sound-ing On the oth - er side,

Hear us, thy dear name con - fess-ing, While we pray.
Dead to all the sin that made Thy Cal - va - ry.
In thy zeal, and in thy la - bor, And thy prayer.
Let thy pure and faith - ful spir - it Fill our years.
And for - ev - er, in thy heav - en We a - bide. A-men.

BAPTISM

300   *Come, Holy Spirit, Dove Divine*

A. Judson, 1788-1850

WILTON L.M.
S. Stanley, 1767-1822

1 Come, Ho - ly Spir - it, Dove di - vine,
2 We love thy name, we love thy laws,
3 And as we rise, with thee to live,

On these bap - tis - mal wa - ters shine,
And joy - ful - ly em - brace thy cause;
O let the Ho - ly Spir - it give

And teach our hearts in high - est strain,
We love thy cross, the shame, the pain,
The seal - ing unc - tion from a - bove,

To praise the Lamb for sin - ners slain.
O Lamb of God, for sin - ners slain.
The breath of life, the fire of love. A - men.

BAPTISM

Dear Master, in Thy Way

John Thomas, 1859-1944

301

ST. AUGUSTINE S.M.
Choralgesänge, 1769

1 Dear Mas - ter, in thy way   Our will - ing feet shall tread;
2 The clos - ing wa - ters hid   Our form - er world, and we,
3 And as we rise a - gain,   Be this con - fes - sion given,
4 So would we die to live,   And live no more to die;

What joy thy man-date to o - bey, Our great and glo-rious Head:
Seek-ing through death our Sav-ior's side, Re - joice to die with thee.
That we have risen with Christ to reign The Lord of earth and heaven.
Our ris - en lives, O Christ, re-ceive, And seal them in the sky. A-men.

A Parting Hymn We Sing

Aaron R. Wolfe, 1821-1902

302

FRANCONIA S.M.
Melody by J. B. König, 1691-1758
Arr. by William H. Havergal, 1793-1870

1 A part - ing hymn we sing   A - round thy ta - ble, Lord;
2 Here have we seen thy face,   And felt thy pres - ence here;
3 In self - for - get - ting love   Be our com - mun - ion shown,

A - gain our grate-ful trib-ute bring, Our sol-emn vows re - cord.
So may the sav - or of thy grace In word and life ap - pear.
Un - til we join the church a-bove, And know as we are known. A-men.

THE LORD'S SUPPER

303

Bread of the World, in Mercy Broken

First Tune

Reginald Heber, 1783-1826

RENDEZ À DIEU 9.8.9.8.D.
Genevan Psalter, 1543

Bread of the world, in mer - cy bro - ken, Wine of the soul, in mer - cy shed, By whom the words of life were spo - ken, And in whose death our sins are dead; Look on the heart by sor - row bro - ken, Look on the tears by sin - ners shed, And

THE LORD'S SUPPER

be thy feast to us the tok - en That by thy grace our souls are fed. A-men.

Bread of the World, in Mercy Broken

Second Tune

304

Reginald Heber, 1783 1826

EUCHARISTIC HYMN 9.8.9.8.
John S. B. Hodges, 1830-1915

1 Bread of the world, in mer - cy bro - ken, Wine of the
2 Look on the heart by sor - row bro - ken, Look on the

soul, in mer - cy shed, By whom the words of life were spo - ken,
tears by sin - ners shed, And be thy feast to us the to - ken

And in whose death our sins are dead,
That by thy grace our souls are fed. A - men.

THE LORD'S SUPPER

305 Come, Risen Lord, and Deign to Be Our Guest

First Tune

George W. Briggs, 1875-1959

HOLBORN 10.10.10.10.
Eric H. Thiman, 1900-

1 Come, ris - en Lord, and deign to be our guest;
2 We meet, as in that up - per room they met;
3 One bod - y we, one bod - y who par - take,
4 One with each oth - er, Lord, for one in thee,

Nay, let us be thy guests; the feast is thine.
Thou at the ta - ble, bless - ing, yet dost stand;
One Church u - ni - ted in com - mun - ion blest;
Who art one Sav - ior and one liv - ing Head;

Thy - self at thine own board make man - i - fest
"This is my bod - y:" so thou giv - est yet;
One name we bear, one bread of life we break,
Then o - pen thou our eyes, that we may see;

In this our sac - ra - ment of bread and wine.
Faith still re - ceives the cup as from thy hand.
With all thy saints on earth and saints at rest.
Be known to us in break-ing of the bread. A - men.

THE LORD'S SUPPER

Words from *Enlarged Songs of Praise* by permission of Oxford University Press;
music copyright Independent Press Ltd. Used by permission.

Come, Risen Lord, and Deign to Be Our Guest 306

Second Tune

George W. Briggs, 1875-1959

BIRMINGHAM 10.10.10.10.
From F. Cunningham's *A Selection of Psalm Tunes*, 1834

1 Come, ris - en Lord, and deign to be our guest;
2 We meet, as in that up - per room they met;
3 One bod - y we, one bod - y who par - take,
4 One with each oth - er, Lord, for one in thee,

Nay, let us be thy guests; the feast is thine;
Thou at the ta - ble, bless - ing, yet dost stand;
One Church u - ni - ted in com - mu - nion blest;
Who art one Sav - ior and one liv - ing Head;

Thy - self at thine own board make man - i - fest,
"This is my bod - y:" so thou giv - est yet;
One name we bear, one bread of life we break,
Then o - pen thou our eyes, that we may see;

In thine own sa - cra - ment of bread and wine
Faith still re - ceives the cup as from thy hand.
With all thy saints on earth and saints at rest.
Be known to us in break - ing of the bread. A - men.

Words from *Enlarged Songs of Praise* by permission of Oxford University Press.

THE LORD'S SUPPER

307

Here at Thy Table, Lord

May P. Hoyt

BREAD OF LIFE 6.4.6.4.D.
William F. Sherwin, 1826-1888

1 Here at thy ta - ble, Lord, This sa - cred hour, O let us
2 Sit at the feast, dear Lord, Break thou the bread; Fill thou the
3 So shall our life of faith Be full, be sweet; And we shall
4 Come then, O ho - ly Christ, Feed us, we pray; Touch with thy

feel thee near, In lov - ing power; Call - ing our thoughts a - way
cup that brings Life to the dead; That we may find in thee,
find our strength For each day meet; Fed by thy liv - ing bread,
pierc - ed hand Each com - mon day; Mak - ing this earth - ly life

From self and sin. As to thy ban-quet hall We en - ter in.
Par - don and peace; And from all bond-age win A full re - lease.
All hun - ger past, We shall be sat - is - fied, And saved at last.
Full of thy grace, Till in the home of heaven We find our place. A-men.

308

Jesus, to Thy Table Led

Robert Hall Baynes, 1831-1895, alt.

TYHOLLAND 7.7.7.
German Carol Melody
Adapt. D. F. R. Wilson, 1871-1957

1 Je - sus, to thy ta - ble led, Now let ev - ery
2 When we taste the mys - tic wine, Of thine out-poured
3 From the bonds of sin re - lease; Cold and wav-ering

THE LORD'S SUPPER

heart be fed With the true and liv - ing bread.
blood the sign, Fill our hearts with love di - vine.
faith in - crease; Grant us, Lamb of God, thy peace. A - men.

For the Bread, Which Thou Hast Broken 309

Louis F. Benson, 1855-1930

KINGDOM 8.7.8.7.
V. Earle Copes, 1921-

1 For the bread, which thou hast bro - ken, For the
2 By this pledge that thou dost love us, By thy
3 With our saint - ed ones in glo - ry Seat - ed
4 In thy ser - vice, Lord, de - fend us; In our

wine, which thou hast poured, For the words, which thou hast
gift of peace re - stored, By thy call to heaven a -
at our Fa - ther's board, May the Church that wait - eth
hearts keep watch and ward; In the world where thou dost

spo - ken, Now we give thee thanks, O Lord.
bove us, Hal - low all our lives, O Lord.
for thee Keep love's tie un - bro - ken, Lord.
send us Let thy king - dom come, O Lord. A - men.

THE LORD'S SUPPER

310 Deck Thyself, My Soul, with Gladness

Schmücke dich, O liebe Seele
Johann Franck, 1618-1677
Tr. Catherine Winkworth, 1827-1878

SCHMÜCKE DICH 8.8.8.8.D.
Johann Crüger, 1598-1662

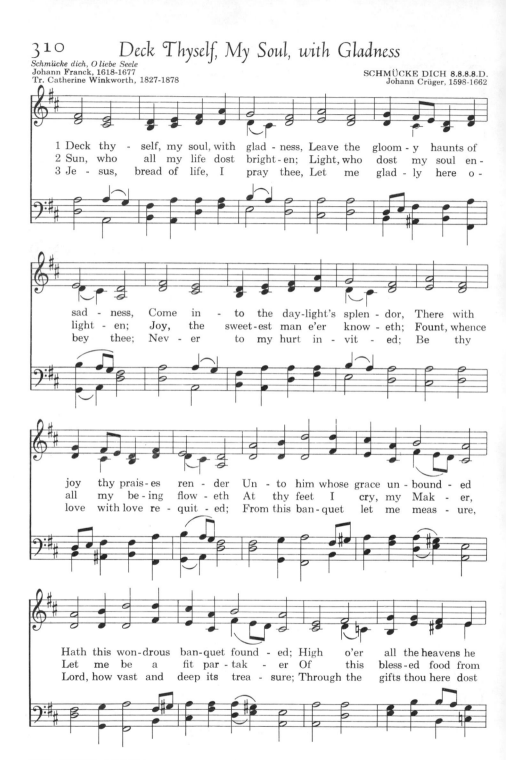

1 Deck thy - self, my soul, with glad - ness, Leave the gloom - y haunts of
2 Sun, who all my life dost bright - en; Light, who dost my soul en -
3 Je - sus, bread of life, I pray thee, Let me glad - ly here o -

sad - ness, Come in - to the day-light's splen - dor, There with
light - en; Joy, the sweet-est man e'er know - eth; Fount, whence
bey thee; Nev - er to my hurt in - vit - ed; Be thy

joy thy prais - es ren - der Un - to him whose grace un - bound - ed
all my be - ing flow - eth At thy feet I cry, my Mak - er,
love with love re - quit - ed; From this ban - quet let me meas - ure,

Hath this won-drous ban-quet found - ed; High o'er all the heavens he
Let me be a fit par - tak - er Of this bless - ed food from
Lord, how vast and deep its trea - sure; Through the gifts thou here dost

THE LORD'S SUPPER

reign - eth, Yet to dwell with thee he deign - eth.
heav - en, For our good, the glo - ry, giv - en.
give me, As thy guest in heaven re - ceive me. A - men.

Be Known to Us in Breaking Bread 311

James Montgomery, 1771-1854

DUNFERMLINE C.M.
Scottish Psalter, 1615

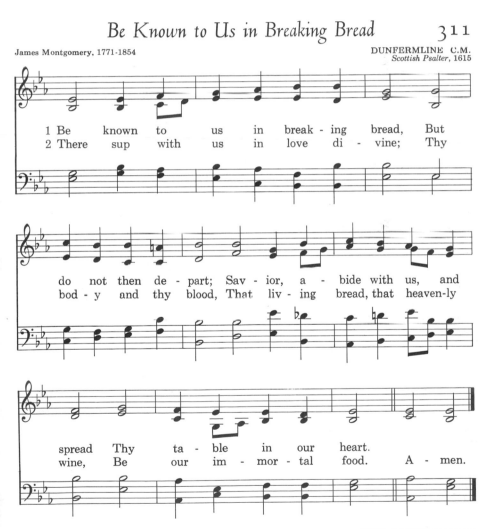

1 Be known to us in break - ing bread, But
2 There sup with us in love di - vine; Thy

do not then de - part; Sav - ior, a - bide with us, and
bod - y and thy blood, That liv - ing bread, that heaven - ly

spread Thy ta - ble in our heart.
wine, Be our im - mor - tal food. A - men.

THE LORD'S SUPPER

312 O Lord and Savior, as We Kneel Before Thee

George MacLaren Brydon, 1875-

DONNE SECOURS 11.10.11.10.
Genevan Psalter, 1551

1 O Lord and Sav - ior, as we kneel be - fore thee,
2 With eag - er hearts, as one, we bow to - geth - er,
3 In shin - ing glo - ry thou dost go be - fore us,
4 Help us to seek thy lost and scat - tered chil - dren,

Tak - ing from thee by faith the bread of
We who have sworn to hear and heed thy
Lead - ing us forth to tell a - broad thy
Find - ing them out where - ev - er they may

life, Drink - ing the wine poured out for our sal - va - tion,
call, Pray - ing that thou, whom we u - nite in serv - ing,
love, Bid - ding us fol - low thee our el - der broth - er,
roam, Woo - ing their hearts by deeds of lov - ing kind - ness

THE LORD'S SUPPER

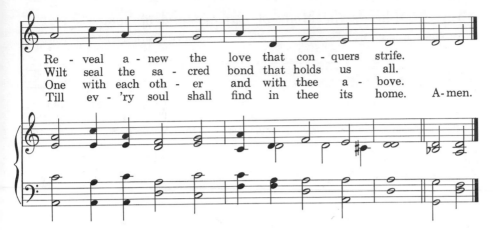

Re-	veal	a -	new	the	love	that	con -	quers	strife.
Wilt	seal	the	sa -	cred	bond	that	holds	us	all.
One	with	each	oth -	er	and	with	thee	a -	bove.
Till	ev -	'ry	soul	shall	find	in	thee	its	home.	A-men.

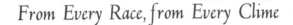

From Every Race, from Every Clime 313

Thomas B. McDormand, 1904-

BLACKBOURNE C.M.
Harrison's *Sacred Harmony,* 1784

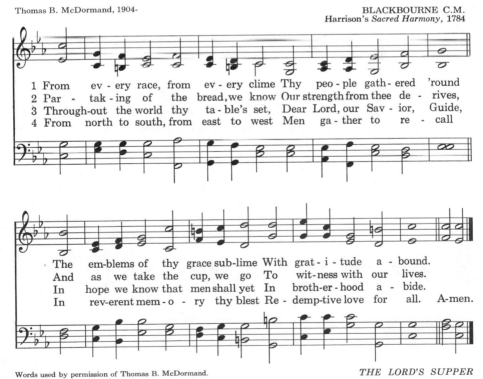

1 From	ev - ery race, from	ev - ery clime	Thy	peo - ple gath - ered	'round
2 Par -	tak - ing of	the bread, we know	Our	strength from thee de -	rives,
3 Through-out	the world thy	ta - ble's set,	Dear Lord, our Sav -	ior,	Guide,
4 From	north to south, from	east to west	Men	ga - ther to	re - call

The	em-blems of	thy grace sub-lime	With grat - i - tude	a - bound.
And	as we take the	cup, we go	To	wit-ness with	our lives.
In	hope we know that men shall yet	In	broth-er - hood	a - bide.
In	rev-erent mem - o - ry thy blest	Re - demp-tive love	for all.	A-men.

THE LORD'S SUPPER

314 This Is the Hour of Banquet and of Song

Horatius Bonar, 1808-1889, alt.

CANTICUM REFECTIONIS 10.10.10.10.
David McKinley Williams, 1887-

1 This is the hour of ban-quet and of song; This is the heaven-ly
2 Too soon we rise; we go our sev-eral ways; The feast, though not the
3 Feast af - ter feast thus comes and pass-es by, Yet, pass - ing, points to

ta - ble spread for me; Here let me feast, and, feast-ing, still pro -
love, is past and gone, The bread and wine con-sumed: yet all our
the glad feast a - bove, Giv - ing us fore-taste of the fes - tal

long The brief, bright hour of fel - low - ship with thee.
days Thou still art here with us our shield and sun.
joy, The Lord's e - ter - nal feast of bliss and love.

THE LORD'S SUPPER

Let Us Break Bread Together

Negro Spiritual

LET US BREAK BREAD 7.3.7.3. with Refrain
Negro Melody

Unison

1 Let us break bread to - geth - er on our knees;
2 Let us drink wine to - geth - er on our knees;
3 Let us praise God to - geth - er on our knees;

Let us break bread to - geth - er on our knees.
Let us drink wine to - geth - er on our knees.
Let us praise God to - geth - er on our knees.

When I fall on my knees, with my face to the ris - ing sun,

O Lord, have mer - cy on me.

THE LORD'S SUPPER

316

Draw Us in the Spirit's Tether

Percy Dearmer, 1867-1936

UNION SEMINARY 8.7.8.7.4.4.7.
Harold Friedell, 1905-1958
Adapt. Jet Turner, 1928-

1 Draw us in the Spir-it's te-ther, For when hum-bly in thy name, Two or three are met to-geth-er, Thou art in the midst of them; Al-le-lu - ya! Al-le-lu - ya! Touch we now thy gar - ment's hem.

2 As the breth-ren used to gath-er In the name of Christ to sup, Then with thanks to God the Fa - ther Break the bread and bless the cup, Al-le-lu - ya, Al-le-lu - ya, So knit thou our friend - ship up.

3 All our meals and all our liv-ing Make as sac - ra-ments of thee, That by car - ing, help-ing, giv - ing, We may true dis - ci - ples be. Al-le-lu - ya, Al-le-lu - ya, We will serve thee faith - ful - ly. A-men.

THE LORD'S SUPPER

Beneath the Forms of Outward Rite

First Tune

317

James A. Blaisdell, 1867-1957

BELMONT C.M.
William Gardiner's *Sacred Melodies* 1815

1 Be-neath the forms of out-ward rite Thy sup-per, Lord, is spread
2 The bread is al-ways con-se-crate Which men di-vide with men;
3 The bless-ed cup is on-ly passed True mem-o-ry of thee,
4 O Mas-ter, through these sym-bols shared, Thine own dear self im-part,

In ev-ery qui-et up-per room Where faint-ing souls are fed.
And ev-ery act of broth-er-hood Re-peats thy feast a-gain.
When life a-new pours out its wine With rich suf-fi-cien-cy.
That in our dai-ly life may flame The pas-sion of thy heart. A-men.

Beneath the Forms of Outward Rite

Second Tune

318

James A. Blaisdell, 1867-1957

PERRY C.M.
Leo Sowerby, 1895-1968

1 Be-neath the forms of out-ward rite Thy sup-per, Lord, is spread
2 The bread is al-ways con-se-crate Which men di-vide with men;
3 The bless-ed cup is on-ly passed True mem-o-ry of thee,
4 O Mas-ter, through these sym-bols shared, Thine own dear self im-part,

In ev-ery qui-et up-per room Where faint-ing souls are fed.
And ev-ery act of broth-er-hood Re-peats thy feast a-gain.
When life a-new pours out its wine With rich suf-fi-cien-cy.
That in our dai-ly life may flame The pas-sion of thy heart. A-men.

Music copyright © 1964 by Abingdon Press. Used by permission.

THE LORD'S SUPPER

319

Humbly I Adore Thee

Thomas Aquinas, 1227-1274
Tr. J. R. Woodford, 1820-1885 (vss. 2, 3)

ADORO TE DEVOTE 11.11.11.11.
Solesmes version of the plainsong
melody; adapted

1 Hum - bly I a - dore thee, Ver - i - ty un - seen.
2 O blest me - mo - rial of our dy - ing Lord!
3 O Christ, whom now be - neath a veil we see,

Who thy glo - ry hid - est 'neath these shad - ows mean;
Thou liv - ing Bread, who life dost here af - ford,
May what we thirst for soon our por - tion be,

Lo, to thee sur - ren - dered, my whole heart is bowed,
O may our souls for - ev - er live by thee,
There in the glo - ry of thy dwell - ing place

THE LORD'S SUPPER

Tranced as it be - holds thee, shrined with - in the cloud.
And thou to us for - ev - er pre - cious be.
To gaze on thee un - veiled, and see thy face.

Jesus, Thou Joy of Loving Hearts 320

Anonymous, Latin, 12th century
Tr. and arr. by Ray Palmer, 1808-1887

HESPERUS L.M.
Henry Baker, 1835-1910

1 Je - sus, thou joy of lov - ing hearts, Thou fount of
2 Thy truth un - changed hath ev - er stood; Thou sav - est
3 Our rest - less spir - its yearn for thee, Wher - e'er our
4 O Je - sus, ev - er with us stay; Make all our

life, thou light of men, From the blest bliss that earth im - parts
those that on thee call; To them that seek thee, thou art good;
change - ful lot is cast: Glad when thy gra - cious smile we see;
mo - ments calm and bright; Chase the dark night of sin a - way;

We turn un - filled to thee a - gain.
To them that find thee, all in all.
Blest when our faith can hold thee fast.
Shed o'er the world thy ho - ly light. A - men.

THE LORD'S SUPPER

Jesus Christ, Our Blessed Savior

Jesus Christus nostra salus
?Jan Hus, 1369?-1415
German version, Martin Luther, 1483-1546.
Tr. from *Hymnal for Colleges and Schools*, 1956

JESUS CHRISTUS, UNSER HEILAND 8.8.9.8.
Enchiridion, Erfurt, 1524
Harm. from *Songs of Syon*, 1904

1 Je - sus Christ, our bless - ed Sav - ior,
2 As his pledge of love un - dy - ing
3 Praise the Fa - ther, who from heav - en
4 If thy heart this truth pro - fess - es,

Shows his Fa - ther's love for - ev - er;
He, this pre - cious food sup - ply - ing,
Un - to us such food hath giv - en,
And thy mouth thy sin con - fess - es,

By his bit - ter grief and cru - el pain
Gives his sa - cred bod - y with the bread,
And, to mend the wrong that we have done,
As his wel - come guest thou here shalt be,

He purg - es us from ev - ery stain.
And with the wine the blood he shed.
Gave un - to death his on - ly Son.
And Christ him - self shall ban - quet thee. A - men.

THE LORD'S SUPPER

Music used by permission of Schott & Co. Ltd.

Father, We Thank Thee Who Hast Planted   322

Greek, from the Didache, *c.* 110
Tr. F. Bland Tucker, 1895-

WEISSE 9.8.9.8.
Source unknown
Harm. J. S. Bach, 1685-1750

1 Fa - ther, we thank thee who has plant - ed Thy ho - ly
2 Thou, Lord, didst make all for thy plea - sure, Didst give man
3 Watch o'er thy Church, O Lord, in mer - cy, Save it from
4 As grain, once scat - tered on the hill - sides, Was in the

name with - in our hearts. Know-ledge and faith and
food for all his days, Giv - ing in Christ the
e - vil, guard it still, Per - fect it in thy
bro - ken bread made one, So from all lands thy

life im - mor - tal Je - sus thy Son to us im - parts.
bread e - ter - nal; Thine is the power, be thine the praise.
love, u - nite it Cleansed and con-formed un-to thy will.
Church be ga - thered In - to thy king - dom by thy Son. A-men.

THE LORD'S SUPPER

323 Here, O My Lord, I See Thee Face to Face

Horatius Bonar, 1808-1889

HOLBORN 10.10.10.10.
Eric H. Thiman, 1900-

1 Here, O my Lord, I see thee face to face;
Here would I touch and han - dle things un - seen;
Here grasp with firm - er hand e - ter - nal grace,
And all my wea - ri - ness up - on thee lean.

2 Here would I feed up - on the bread of God;
Here drink with thee the roy - al wine of heaven;
Here would I lay a - side each earth - ly load,
Here taste a - fresh the calm of sin for - given.

3 I have no help but thine; nor do I need
An - oth - er arm save thine to lean up - on;
It is e - nough, my Lord, e - nough in - deed;
My strength is in thy might, thy might a - lone. A - men.

THE LORD'S SUPPER

According to Thy Gracious Word

324

James Montgomery, 1771-1854

DUNDEE C.M.
Scottish Psalter, 1615

1 Ac - cord - ing to thy gra-cious word, In meek hu - mil - i - ty,
2 Thy bod - y, bro - ken for my sake, My bread from heaven shall be;
3 Re - mem-ber thee, and all thy pains, And all thy love to me;
4 And when these fail-ing lips grow dumb And mind and mem-ory flee

This will I do, my dy - ing Lord, I will re - mem-ber thee.
Thy test - a - ment - al cup I take, And thus re - mem-ber thee.
Yea, while a breath, a pulse re-mains, Will I re - mem-ber thee.
When thou shalt in thy king-dom come, Je - sus, re - mem-ber me. A-men.

The Heavens Declare Thy Glory, Lord

325

Based on Psalm 19
Isaac Watts, 1674 1748

UXBRIDGE L.M.
Lowell Mason, 1792-1872

1 The heavens de-clare thy glo - ry, Lord; In ev - ery star thy wis-dom shines;
2 The roll-ing sun, the chang-ing light, And nights and days, thy power con-fess;
3 Sun, moon, and stars con-vey thy praise Round the whole earth and nev-er stand,
4 Nor shall thy spread-ing gos-pel rest Till through the world thy truth has run,

But when our eyes be-hold thy Word, We read thy name in fair-er lines.
But the blest vol-ume thou hast writ Re-veals thy jus-tice and thy grace.
So when thy truth be-gan its race, It touched and glanced on ev-ery land.
Till Christ has all the na-tions blest That see the light or feel the sun. A-men.

SCRIPTURES

Lord, Thy Word Abideth

H. W. Baker, 1821-1877

CHESTERTON 6.6.6.6.D.
Geoffrey Beaumont, 1903-

1 Lord, thy word a - bid - eth, And our foot-steps guid - eth;
2 When the storms are o'er us, And dark clouds be - fore us,
3 Word of mer - cy, giv - ing Suc - cor to the liv - ing;

Who its truth be - liev - eth Light and joy re - ceiv - eth.
Then its light di - rect - eth, And our way pro - tect - eth.
Word of life, sup - ply - ing Com - fort to the dy - ing!

When our foes are near us, Then thy word doth cheer us, Word of con - so -
Who can tell the plea-sure, Who re - count the trea-sure, By thy word im -
O that we, dis-cern-ing Its most ho - ly learn-ing, Lord, may love and

SCRIPTURES

vs. 1,2.   v. 3.

la - tion, Mes-sage of sal - va - tion.
part - ed To the sim - ple heart - ed?
fear thee, Ev - er-more be   near thee!

vs. 1,2.   v. 3.

Music taken from *Three Hymn Tunes from 20th-Century Folk Mass* by permission of the publishers, W. Paxton & Co. Ltd., London, W.1., England.

Break Thou the Bread of Life

327

Mary A. Lathbury, 1841-1913

BREAD OF LIFE 6.4.6.4.D.
William F. Sherwin, 1826-1888

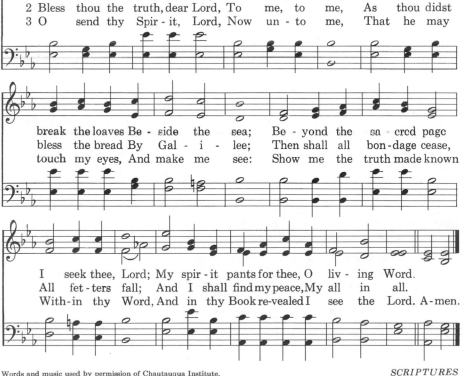

1 Break thou the bread of life, Dear Lord, to me, As thou didst
2 Bless thou the truth, dear Lord, To me, to me, As thou didst
3 O send thy Spir - it, Lord, Now un - to me, That he may

break the loaves Be - side the sea; Be - yond the sa - cred page
bless the bread By Gal - i - lee; Then shall all bon - dage cease,
touch my eyes, And make me see: Show me the truth made known

I seek thee, Lord; My spir - it pants for thee, O liv - ing Word.
All fet - ters fall; And I shall find my peace, My all in all.
With-in thy Word, And in thy Book re-vealed I see the Lord. A - men.

SCRIPTURES

O Word of God Incarnate

William W. How, 1823-1897

MUNICH 7.6.7.6.D.
Neu-vermehrtes Gesangbuch, Meiningen, 1693
Harm. Felix Mendelssohn, 1809-1847

1 O Word of God in - car - nate, O Wis - dom from on high,
2 The Church from her dear Mas - ter Re - ceived the gift di - vine,
3 It float-eth like a ban - ner Be - fore God's host un - furled;
4 O make thy Church, dear Sav - ior, A lamp of bur-nished gold,

O Truth un-changed, un - chang - ing, O Light of our dark sky,
And still that light she lift - eth O'er all the earth to shine.
It shin-eth like a bea - con A - bove the dark - ling world;
To bear a - mong the na - tions Thy true light as of old!

We praise thee for the ra - diance That from the hal - lowed page,
It is the gold - en cas - ket Where gems of truth are stored;
It is the chart and com - pass That o'er life's surg - ing sea,
O teach thy wan-dering pil - grims By this their path to trace,

A lan-tern to our foot-steps, Shines on from age to age.
It is the heaven-drawn pic-ture Of Christ, the liv - ing Word.
'Mid mists, and rocks, and quick-sands Still guides, O Christ, to thee.
Till, clouds and dark - ness end - ed, They see thee face to face! A-men.

SCRIPTURES

Book of Books, Our People's Strength

329

Percy Dearmer, 1867-1936

LIEBSTER JESU 7.8.7.8.8.8.
Melody by Johann R. Ahle, 1625-1673

1 Book of books, our peo-ple's strength, States-man's, teach-er's, he - ro's
2 Thank we those who toiled in thought, Man - y di - verse scrolls com-
3 Praise we God, who hath in - spired Those whose wis-dom still di -

treas - ure, Bring - ing free - dom; spread - ing truth,
plet - ing, Po - ets, proph - ets, schol - ars, saints,
rects us; Praise him for the Word made flesh,

Shed - ding light that none can meas - ure; Wis - dom comes to
Each his word from God re - peat - ing, Till they came, who
For the Spir - it which pro - tects us. Light of know-ledge,

those who know thee, All the best we have we owe thee.
told the sto - ry Of the Word, and showed his glo - ry.
ev - er burn-ing, Shed on us thy death-less learn - ing. A-men.

Alternate version No. 212
Words from *Enlarged Songs of Praise* by permission of Oxford University Press.

SCRIPTURES

O Zion, Haste, Thy Mission High Fulfilling

Mary A. Thomson, 1834-1923

TIDINGS 11.10.11.10. with Refrain
James Walch, 1837-1901

1 O Zi - on, haste, thy mis - sion high ful - fill - ing,
2 Pro - claim to ev - ery peo - ple, tongue, and na - tion
3 Give of thy sons to bear the mes - sage glo - rious;

To tell to all the world that God is light, That he who
That God, in whom they live and move, is love, Tell how he
Give of thy wealth to speed them on their way; Pour out thy

made all na - tions is not will - ing One soul should per - ish,
stooped to save his lost cre - a - tion, And died on earth that
soul for them in prayer vic - to - rious, O Zi - on haste to

lost in shades of night.
man might live a - bove. Pub - lish glad ti - dings, Ti - dings of peace,
bring the bright-er day.

MINISTRY AND MISSION

Ti - dings of Je - sus, Re - demp-tion and re - lease. A-men.

Let There Be Light, Lord God of Hosts
331

William M. Vories, 1880-1964, alt.

ELTON L.M.
Lowell Mason, 1792-1872

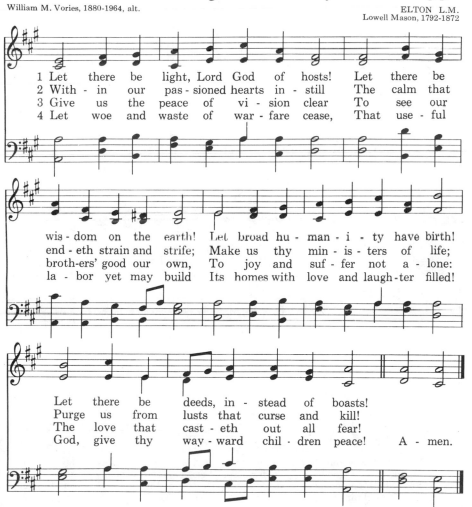

1 Let there be light, Lord God of hosts! Let there be
2 With - in our pas - sioned hearts in - still The calm that
3 Give us the peace of vi - sion clear To see our
4 Let woe and waste of war - fare cease, That use - ful

wis - dom on the earth! Let broad hu - man - i - ty have birth!
end - eth strain and strife; Make us thy min - is - ters of life;
broth-ers' good our own, To joy and suf - fer not a - lone:
la - bor yet may build Its homes with love and laugh-ter filled!

Let there be deeds, in - stead of boasts!
Purge us from lusts that curse and kill!
The love that cast - eth out all fear!
God, give thy way - ward chil - dren peace! A - men.

MINISTRY AND MISSION

Draw Thou My Soul, O Christ

Lucy Larcom, 1826-1893

ST. EDMUND 6.4.6.4.6.6.6.4.
Arthur S. Sullivan, 1842-1900

1 Draw thou my soul, O Christ, Clos - er to thine; Breathe in - to
2 Lead forth my soul, O Christ, One with thine own, Joy - ful to
3 Not for my-self a - lone May my prayer be; Lift thou thy

ev - ery wish Thy will di - vine; Raised my low self a - bove, Won by thy
fol-low thee Through paths unknown; In thee my strength renew; Give me thy
world, O Christ, Clos - er to thee; Cleanse it from guilt and wrong; Teach it sal-

death-less love, Ev - er, O Christ, through mine Let thy life shine.
work to do; Through me thy truth be shown, Thy love made known.
va - tion's song, Till earth, as heaven, ful - fill God's ho - ly will. A-men.

Not Always on the Mount

Frederick Lucian Hosmer, 1840-1929

DANIEL L.M.
Irish Traditional Melody

1 Not al-ways on the mount may we Rapt in the heaven-ly vi - sion be:
2 "Lord, it is good a - bid-ing here," We cry, the heaven-ly pres-ence near:
3 Yet hath one such ex - alt - ed hour Up - on the soul re - deem-ing power,
4 The mount for vi - sion: but be - low The paths of dai - ly dut - y go,

MINISTRY AND MISSION

The shores of thought and feel-ing know The Spir-it's ti - dal ebb and flow.
The vi-sion van-ish-es, our eyes Are lift-ed in-to va-cant skies.
And in its strength, through af-ter days, We trav-el our ap-point-ed ways,
And no-bler life there-in shall own The pat-tern on the moun-tain shown. A-men.

Words from *Hymns of the Spirit*, copyright 1937 by the Beacon Press. Used by permission. Music from *Songs of Praise for Boys and Girls*, by permission of Oxford University Press.

God of the Prophets! Bless the Prophets' Sons 334

Denis Wortman, 1835-1922

TOULON 10.10.10.10.
Genevan Psalter, 1551

1 God of the proph-ets! Bless the proph-ets' sons; E - li-jah's
2 A - noint them proph-ets! Make their ears at - tent To thy di-
3 A - noint them priests! Strong in - ter-ces - sors they For par-don,
4 Make them a - pos - tles! Her-alds of the cross, Forth may they

man - tle o'er E - li - sha cast; Each age its sol - emn task may
vin - est speech; their hearts a - wake To hu - man need; their lips make
and for char - i - ty and peace! O that with them might pass the
go to tell all realms thy grace, In - spired of thee, may they count

claim but once; Make each one no-bler, strong-er than the last.
el - o - quent To as-sure the right, and ev - ery e - vil break.
world, a - stray, In - to the dear Christ's life of sac - ri - fice.
all but loss, And stand at last with joy be - fore thy face. A-men.

MINISTRY AND MISSION

335 Renew Thy Church, Her Ministries Restore

Kenneth L. Cober, 1902-

ALL IS WELL 10.6.10.6.8.8.8.8.6.
Old English Melody

1 Re - new thy church, her min - is - tries re-store: Both to serve and a - dore.
2 Teach us thy word, re - veal its truth di - vine, On our path let it shine;
3 Teach us to pray, for thou art ev - er near, Thy still voice let us hear.
4 Teach us to love, with strength of heart and mind, Ev - ery-one, all man-kind,

Make her a - gain as salt through-out the land, And as light from a stand.
Tell of thy works, thy might-y acts of grace, From each page show thy face.
Our souls are rest - less 'til they rest in thee, This our glad des - ti - ny.
Break down old walls of pre - ju - dice and hate, Leave us not to our fate.

'Mid som-ber shad-ows of the night, Where greed and ha - tred spread their blight,
As thou hast loved us, sent thy Son, And our sal - va - tion now is won,
Be - fore thy pres-ence keep us still That we may find for us thy will
As thou hast loved and given thy life, To end hos - til - i - ty and strife,

O send us forth with power en-dued, Help us, Lord, be re-newed.
O let our hearts with love be stirred, Help us, Lord, know thy word.
And seek thy guid - ance ev - ery day, Teach us, Lord, how to pray.
O share thy grace from heaven a - bove, Teach us, Lord, how to love. A-men.

MINISTRY AND MISSION

Mid Blackness of the City's Night

Sarah E. Taylor, 1883-1954

336

ST. PETERSBURG 8.8.8.8.8.8.
Arr. from Dmitri S. Bortniansky, 1751-1825

1 Mid black - ness of the cit - y's night Be - yond its cheer - ing
2 We see thee in the star - ry height, A God of mys - ter -
3 For - give thy serv-ants, Lord, we pray, Who name thy name from
4 As our Re-deem-er, sent of thee, Through bus - y towns of

warmth and light, The sons of want and mis - er - y Send
y and might; But from the crowd - ed cit - y street, Its
day to day, Yet hide thee from the soul in need By
Gal - i - lee Re-vealed thy good - ness and thy love, In -

forth their an - guished prayers to thee; With wea - ry eyes they
tur - moil, con - flict and de - feat, The chil - dren of thine
care - less word and self - ish deed; While love of gold and
spire thy serv - ants, Lord to prove To ev - ery son of

seek thy face, O God of mer - cy and of grace.
err - ing race En - treat thy mer - cy and thy grace.
pride of race Hin - der thy mer - cy and thy grace.
ev - ery race Thy way of u - ni - ver - sal grace. A-men.

Words from *Five City Hymns* copyright 1954 by The Hymn Society of America.
Used by permission.

MINISTRY AND MISSION

337 Give Me the Eyes to See This Child

Miriam Dewey Ross, 1927-

SALVATION 8.6.8.8.6.
Ananias Davisson's *Kentucky Harmony*, c. 1815, adapted

1 Give me the eyes to see this child As thou dost see him, whole; See through his mask of need and doubt, Of fear with-in and noise with-out, Till I can reach his soul.

2 Give me the ears that I may hear More than his words a-lone, And find, with-in, his deep de-sires For truth and love, as he as-pires To be in-deed thine own.

3 Give me the hands to do my task With sym-pa-thy and skill; To reach and touch and hold him fast Till he is bound by thee at last De-light-ing in thy will.

4 Give me the grace to know my need, My con-stant need of thee; So chil-dren both, this child and I To thee may ea-ger-ly draw nigh, And blessed to-geth-er be. A-men.

MINISTRY AND MISSION

Words from *Fifteen Christian Education Hymns* copyright 1959 by The Hymn Society of America. Used by permission. Music from *Hymnal for Colleges and Schools;* used by permission of Yale University Press.

Come, Labor On

338

Jane L. Borthwick, 1813-1897, alt.

ORA LABORA 4.10.10.10.4.
T. Tertius Noble, 1867-1953

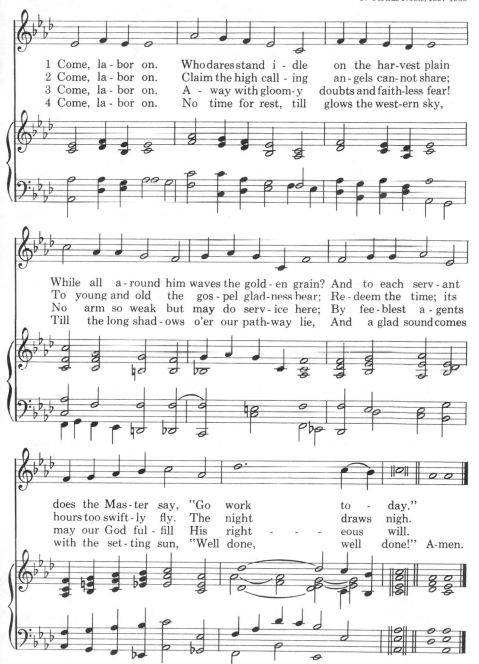

1 Come, la - bor on. Who dares stand i - dle on the har - vest plain
2 Come, la - bor on. Claim the high call - ing an - gels can - not share;
3 Come, la - bor on. A - way with gloom - y doubts and faith-less fear!
4 Come, la - bor on. No time for rest, till glows the west - ern sky,

While all a - round him waves the gold - en grain? And to each serv - ant
To young and old the gos - pel glad - ness bear; Re - deem the time; its
No arm so weak but may do serv - ice here; By fee - blest a - gents
Till the long shad - ows o'er our path-way lie, And a glad sound comes

does the Mas - ter say, "Go work to - day."
hours too swift - ly fly. The night draws nigh.
may our God ful - fill His right - - - eous will.
with the set - ting sun, "Well done, well done!" A - men.

MINISTRY AND MISSION

339 Turn Back, O Man, Forswear Thy Foolish Ways

Clifford Bax, 1886-1962

OLD 124th 10.10.10.10.10.
Genevan Psalter, 1551

1 Turn back, O man, for-swear thy fool-ish ways. Old now is
2 Earth might be fair and all men glad and wise. Age aft-er
3 Earth shall be fair, and all her peo-ple one; Nor till that

earth, and none may count her days; Yet thou, her child, whose
age their trag-ic em-pires rise, Built while they dream, and
hour shall God's whole will be done. Now, e-ven now, once

head is crowned with flame, Still wilt not hear thine in-ner God pro-
in that dream-ing weep; Would man but wake from out his haunt-ed
more from earth to sky, Peals forth in joy man's old un-daunt-ed

claim: "Turn back, O man, for-swear thy fool-ish ways!"
sleep, Earth might be fair and all men glad and wise.
cry: "Earth shall be fair, and all her folk be one!" A-men.

MINISTRY AND MISSION

Words used by permission of A. D. Peters & Co.

Word of Life, Most Pure, Most Strong

340

J. F. Bahnmaier, 1774-1841
Tr. Catherine Winkworth, 1827-1878, alt.

PLEYEL'S HYMN 7.7.7.7.
Ignace Pleyel, 1757-1831

1 Word of Life, most pure, most strong, Lo, for thee the na-tions long;
2 Lo, the ripe-ning fields we see, Might-y shall the har-vest be;
3 Lord of har-vest, let there be Joy and strength to work for thee,

Spread, till from its drear-y night All the world a-wakes to light.
But the reap-ers still are few, Great the work they have to do.
Till the na-tions far and near See thy light, thy law re-vere. A-men.

Teach Me, My God and King

341

George Herbert, 1593-1632
Adapt. John Wesley, 1703-1791

MORNINGTON S.M.
Garrett Wellesley, 1735-1781

1 Teach me, my God and King, In all things thee to see;
2 To scorn the sens-es sway, While still to thee I tend,
3 All may of thee par-take; Noth-ing so small can be,
4 If done be-neath thy laws, E'en ser-vile la-bors shine;

And what I do in an-y-thing, To do it as for thee.
In all I do, be thou the way, In all, be thou the end.
But draws, when act-ed for thy sake, Great-ness and worth from thee.
Hal-lowed is toil if this the cause; The mean-est work di-vine. A-men.

MINISTRY AND MISSION

342 ## We Are Living, We Are Dwelling

Arthur C. Coxe, 1818-1896, alt.

EBENEZER 8.7.8.7.D.
Thomas John Williams, 1869-1944

1 We are liv-ing, we are dwell-ing In a grand and
2 Will ye play then? will ye dal-ly Far be-hind the
3 Sworn to yield, to wav-er, nev-er, Con-se-crat-ed,.

aw-ful time, In an age on a-ges tell-ing;
bat-tle line? Up! it is Je-ho-vah's ral-ly;
born a-gain, Sworn to be Christ's sol-diers ev-er,

To be liv-ing is sub-lime.
God's own arm hath need of thine.
O for Christ at least be men!

MINISTRY AND MISSION

Hark! the wak-ing up of na-tions, Hosts ad - vanc-ing
Worlds are charg-ing, heaven be - hold-ing; Thou hast but an
O let all the soul with - in you For the truth's sake

to the fray, Hark! what sound-eth is cre - a - tion's
hour to fight; Now, the blaz-oned cross un - fold - ing,
go a - broad! Strike! let ev - ery nerve and sin - ew

Groan - ing for the lat - ter day.
On, right on - ward for the right!
Tell on a - ges, tell for God. A - men.

MINISTRY AND MISSION

343 Break Forth, O Living Light of God

Frank von Christierson, 1900-

ST. PETER C.M.
Alexander R. Reinagle, 1799-1877

1 Break forth, O liv-ing light of God, Up - on the world's dark hour!
2 Re - move the veil of an-cient words, Their mess-age long ob - scure;
3 Show us the proph-ets and the priests, The kings, the com-mon men,
4 O let thy word be light a - new To ev - ery na - tion's life;
5 O may one Lord, one faith, one word, One Spir - it lead us still;

Show us the way the Mas-ter trod; Re - veal his sav - ing power.
Re - store to us thy truth, O God, And make its mean-ing sure.
Who kept the faith and walked with thee; O make them live a - gain!
U - nite us in thy will, O Lord, And end all sin - ful strife.
And one great Church go forth in might To work God's per-fect will. A-men.

Words from *Ten New Hymns on the Bible* copyright 1952 by The Hymn Society of America. Used by permission.

344 Lord, Speak to Me, that I May Speak

Frances R. Havergal, 1836-1879

HOLLEY L.M.
George Hews, 1806-1873

1 Lord, speak to me, that I may speak In liv - ing ech - oes of thy tone;
2 O teach me, Lord, that I may teach The pre-cious things thou dost im - part;
3 O fill me with thy ful - ness, Lord, Un - til my ver - y heart o'er-flow
4 O use me, Lord, use e - ven me, Just as thou wilt, and when, and where;

As thou hast sought, so let me seek Thy err - ing chil-dren lost and lone.
And wing my words, that they may reach The hid-den depths of man-y a heart.
In kind-ling thought and glow-ing word, Thy love to tell, thy praise to show.
Un - til thy bless-ed face I see, Thy rest, thy joy, thy glo - ry share. A-men.

MINISTRY AND MISSION

O God of Might, O Son of Light

Ross Coggins, 1927-

345

Indonesian Folk Tune
Arr. James Bigelow, 1956

1 O God of might, O Son of light, O Ho - ly Spir - it sweet,
2 With ho - ly fire my heart in - spire Thy Spir - it's sword to wield;

Thy church ex - pand till all shall stand At Je - sus' pierc - ed feet.
With bor - rowed might I'll take thy light, Till dark - ness' doom be sealed.

Let all who once thy Son dis-owned Re - joice to see him now en-throned;
If oth - ers stop to count the cost, For fear of earth - ly treas - ures lost,

Yet while one stray - ing soul there be, Send me, O Lord, send me.
I'll count it gain to die for thee; Send me, O Lord, send me.

MINISTRY AND MISSION

346   O Church of God in Every Land

Wilbur C. Christians, 1912-

WINDHAM L.M.
Daniel Read, 1757-1836

1 O Church of God in ev - ery land, O
2 O Lord of time and space and power, We
3 O Lord, our God, whose pres - ence now, We

force for right from God's own hand, Through thee God's love is
seek thee in this ho - ly hour. O grant us cour - age
sense in song and sa - cred vow. Grant us for - give - ness,

shown to all, To na - tions great, and chil - dren small.
to be free, In mind, in soul, in all, in thee.
in - ner peace, And then from sin a sure re - lease.

Words used by permission of the author.

347   Lord Christ, the Father's Mighty Son

Brian A. Wren, 1936-

HAMPTON POYLE 8.8.5.8.6.
Peter Warwick Cutts, 1937-

1 Lord Christ, the Fa - ther's might - y Son, Whose
2 To make us one your prayers were said, To
3 Lord Christ, for - give us, make us new! What
4 We will not ques - tion or re - fuse The

UNITY

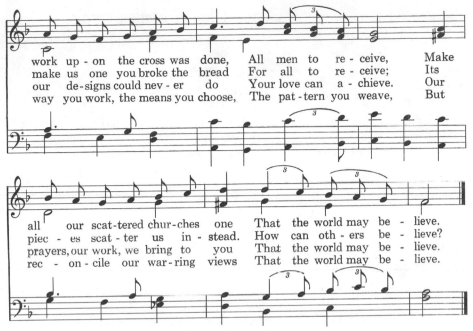

work up-on the cross was done, All men to re-ceive, Make
make us one you broke the bread For all to re-ceive; Its
our de-signs could nev-er do Your love can a-chieve. Our
way you work, the means you choose, The pat-tern you weave, But

all our scat-tered chur-ches one That the world may be-lieve.
piec-es scat-ter us in-stead. How can oth-ers be-lieve?
prayers, our work, we bring to you That the world may be-lieve.
rec-on-cile our war-ring views That the world may be-lieve.

From *Dunblane Praises I*; words by permission of Brian A. Wren, music by permission of Oxford University Press.

I Love Thy Kingdom, Lord 348

Timothy Dwight, 1752-1817

ST. THOMAS S.M.
Williams' *New Universal Psalmodist*, 1770

1 I love thy king-dom, Lord, The house of thine a-bode,
2 I love thy Church, O God! Her walls be-fore thee stand,
3 For her my tears shall fall, For her my prayers as-cend,
4 Be-yond my high-est joy I prize her heaven-ly ways,
5 Sure as thy truth shall last, To Zi-on shall be given

The Church our blest Re-deem-er saved With his own pre-cious blood.
Dear as the ap-ple of thine eye, And grav-en on thy hand.
To her my cares and toils be given, Till toils and cares shall end.
Her sweet com-mun-ion, sol-emn vows, Her hymns of love and praise.
The bright-est glo-ries earth can yield, And bright-er bliss of heaven. A-men.

UNITY

349 Built on the Rock the Church Doth Stand

Nicolai F. S. Grundtvig, 1783-1872
Tr. Carl Doving, 1867- 1937, alt.
Revised, Fred C. M. Hansen, 1888-

KIRKEN DEN ER ET 8.8.8.8.8.8.8.8.
Ludwig M. Lindeman, 1812-1887

1 Built on the Rock the church doth stand, E - ven when stee-ples are
2 Not in our tem - ples made with hands God, the al - might - y, is
3 We are God's house of liv - ing stones, Built for his own hab - i -

fall - ing; Crum-bled have spires in ev - ery land, Bells still are
dwell - ing; High in the heavens his tem - ple stands, All earth-ly
ta - tion; He fills our hearts, his hum - ble thrones, Grant-ing us

chim-ing and call - ing; Call-ing the young and old to rest, Call-ing the
tem-ples ex - cell - ing; Yet he who dwells in heaven a - bove Deigns to a -
life and sal - va - tion; Were two or three to seek his face, He in their

souls of men dis-tressed, Long-ing for life ev - er - last - ing.
bide with us in love, Mak-ing our bod-ies his tem - ple.
midst would show his grace, Bless-ings up - on them be - stow - ing. A-men.

UNITY

Forgive, O Lord, Our Severing Ways

350

John Greenleaf Whittier, 1807-1892, and others

EISENACH L.M.
Johann Hermann Schein, 1586-1630
Harm. J. S. Bach, 1685-1750

1 For-give, O Lord, our sev-ering ways, The ri-val al-tars that we raise, The wran-gling tongues that mar thy praise. Thy grace im-part; in time to be Shall one great tem-ple rise to thee— One church for all hu-man-i-ty.

2 A sweet-er song shall then be heard, Con-fess-ing, in a world's ac-cord, The in-ward Christ, the liv-ing Word. That song shall swell from shore to shore, One hope, one faith, one love re-store, The seam-less robe that Je-sus wore. A-men.

UNITY

351 Our Father, Thou Almighty God

Russell F. Harrison, 1918-

ALL SAINTS NEW C.M.D.
Henry S. Cutler, 1824-1902

1 Our Fa - ther, thou Al - might - y God, In song we voice our praise,
2 O God, whose great cre - a - tive power A - bounds on ev - ery hand,
3 Cre - a - tive God, whose love sus - tains, Whose spir - it can re - deem,
4 In Je - sus Christ, the world's great light, For this his - to - ric time,

For ev - ery gift so free - ly given, En - rich - ing all our days.
Fill men with love, that peace may dwell In each and ev - ery land.
E - rase the sin and pride of self; May truth in us be seen.
Bind close in Chris-tian fel - low-ship, In kin - ship all man - kind.

Ful - fill in us thy deep de - sire, Thy will for all man - kind.
May faith and hope find fer - tile soil For seeds of truth to grow,
Bring to our need - y u - ni-verse Thy wis - dom for this hour,
May all men see on earth this day, The light that bright - ly beams,

Re - move our sin and sel - fish-ness; Re - new each heart and mind.
Help men to turn from fu - tile ways; Thy pur-pose may they know.
Draw all thy chil-dren close to thee, That each may gain thy power.
To point the way; pro-claim to man: God's power the world re - deems. A - men.

UNITY

Lord, We Thank Thee for Our Brothers

352

Roger K. Powell, 1914-

AUSTRIAN HYMN 8.7.8.7.D.
Franz Joseph Haydn, 1732-1809

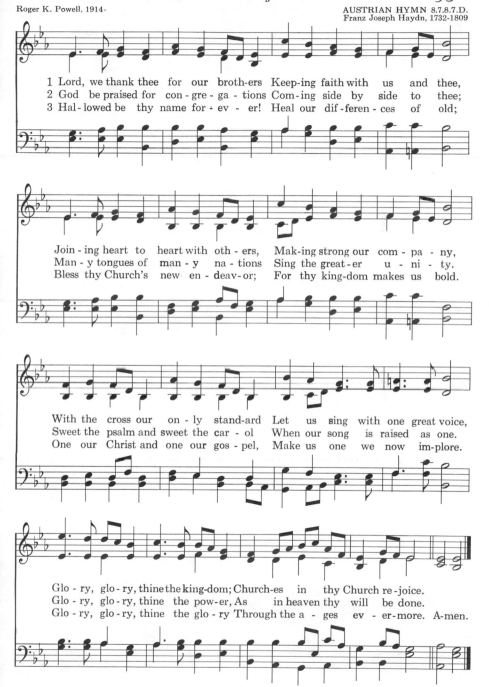

1 Lord, we thank thee for our broth-ers Keep-ing faith with us and thee,
2 God be praised for con-gre-ga-tions Com-ing side by side to thee;
3 Hal-lowed be thy name for ev-er! Heal our dif-feren-ces of old;

Join-ing heart to heart with oth-ers, Mak-ing strong our com-pa-ny,
Man-y tongues of man-y na-tions Sing the great-er u-ni-ty.
Bless thy Church's new en-deav-or; For thy king-dom makes us bold.

With the cross our on-ly stand-ard Let us sing with one great voice,
Sweet the psalm and sweet the car-ol When our song is raised as one.
One our Christ and one our gos-pel, Make us one we now im-plore.

Glo-ry, glo-ry, thine the king-dom; Church-es in thy Church re-joice.
Glo-ry, glo-ry, thine the pow-er, As in heaven thy will be done.
Glo-ry, glo-ry, thine the glo-ry Through the a-ges ev-er-more. A-men.

UNITY

O Church of God, Divided

Marion Franklin Ham, 1867-1956

BLOMSTERTID 7.6.7.6.D.
Swedish *Koralbok*, 1697

1 O Church of God, di - vid - ed And rent by end - less strife!
2 The sub - tle powers of dark - ness, Like foe - men in the night,
3 Dis - perse thy war - ring fac - tions, And bid their con - flicts cease;

Thy war - ring sects ob - scur - ing The way, the truth, the life;
Ad - vance up - on the strong - holds Of jus - tice, truth and right;
Lift high the fall - en stand - ard Of Christ, the Prince of Peace;

A strick - en world, de - spair - ing, Is call - ing un - to thee;
The might - y sway of e - vil Pre - vails in ev - ery land;
One Lord, one faith, one Spir - it, One God of all pro - claim;

O Church of Christ's e - van - gel, What shall thine an - swer be?
O Church of God's a - noint - ing, A - rise, and take thy stand!
Go forth, O Church, u - nit - ed, To con - quer in his name! A-men.

UNITY

Glorious Things of Thee Are Spoken

John Newton, 1725-1807

AUSTRIAN HYMN 8.7.8.7.D.
Franz Joseph Haydn, 1732-1809

354

1 Glo-rious things of thee are spo-ken, Zi-on, cit-y of our God;
2 See, the streams of liv-ing wa-ters, Springing from e-ter-nal love,
3 Round each hab-i-ta-tion hov-ering, See the cloud and fire ap-pear

He whose word can-not be bro-ken Formed thee for his own a-bode.
Well sup-ply thy sons and daughters, And all fear of want re-move.
For a glo-ry and a covering, Show-ing that the Lord is near!

On the Rock of A-ges founded, What can shake thy sure re-pose?
Who can faint, while such a riv-er Ev-er flows their thirst to as-suage?
Thus de-riv-ing from their ban-ner Light by night and shade by day,

With sal-va-tion's walls surrounded, Thou may'st smile at all thy foes.
Grace, which like the Lord, the Giver, Nev-er fails from age to age.
Safe they feed up-on the man-na Which he gives them when they pray. A-men.

UNITY

355
Christ Is the King!

George Kennedy Allen Bell, 1883-1958

SOUTH GORE 8.8.8.8 8.8.
Ronald Arnatt, 1930-

1 Christ is the King! O friends up - raise An - thems of
2 O Chris - tian wo - men, Chris - tian men, All the world
3 Let Love's un - con - quer - a - ble might Your scat - tered

joy and ho - ly praise For his brave
o - ver, seek a - gain The Way di -
com - pa - nies u - nite In ser - vice

saints of an - cient days, Who with a
sci - ples fol - lowed then. Christ through all
to the Lord of light; So shall God's

UNITY

faith / a - / will

for - ev - er / ges is / on earth

new / the / be

same: / done,

Fol - lowed the / Place the same / New lamps be

King, and round him drew / hope in his great Name, / lit, new tasks be - gun,

Thou-sands of faith - ful men and / With the same faith his word pro - / And the whole Church at last be

1, 2

true / claim.

3.

one.

A - men.

rall...en..tan....do....

UNITY

Thy Hand, O God, Has Guided

E. H. Plumptre, 1821-1891

REX SUMMAE MAJESTATIS 7.6.7.6.D.
A. Gregory Murray, 1905-

1 Thy hand, O God, has guid-ed Thy flock from age to age;
2 Thy her-alds brought glad tid-ings To great-est, as to least;
3 Through man-y a day of dark-ness, Through man-y a scene of strife,
4 Thy mer-cy will not fail us, Nor leave thy work un-done;

The won-drous tale is writ-ten, Full clear, on ev-ery page;
They bade men rise, and hast-en To share the great King's feast;
The faith-ful few fought brave-ly To guard the na-tion's life.
With thy right hand to help us, The vic-tory shall be won;

Our fa-thers owned thy good-ness, And we their deeds re-cord;
And this was all their teach-ing, In ev-ery deed and word,
Their gos-pel of re-demp-tion, Sin par-doned, man re-stored,
And then, by men and an-gels, Thy name shall be a-dored,

And both of this bear wit-ness, One Church, one Faith, one Lord.
To all a-like pro-claim-ing One Church, one Faith, one Lord.
Was all in this en-fold-ed, One Church, one Faith, one Lord.
And this shall be their an-them, One Church, one Faith, one Lord.

UNITY

Father, Let Me Dedicate

Lawrence Tuttiett, 1825-1897

DEDICATION 7.5.7.5.D.
G. A. Macfarren, 1813-1887

1 Fa - ther, let me de - di - cate All this year to thee,
2 Can a child pre - sume to choose Where or how to live?
3 If in mer - cy thou wilt spare Joys that yet are mine;
4 If thou call - est to the cross, And its shad - ow come,

In what - ev - er world - ly state Thou wilt have me be.
Can a fa - ther's love re - fuse All the best to give?
If on life, se - rene and fair, Bright - er rays may shine,
Turn-ing all my gain to loss, Shroud - ing heart and home,

Not for sor - row, pain, or care, Free - dom dare I claim;
More thou giv - est ev - ery day Than the best can claim,
Let my glad heart, while it sings, Thee in all pro - claim,
Let me think how thy dear Son To his glo - ry came,

This a - lone shall be my prayer: "Glo - ri - fy thy name."
Nor with-hold-est aught that may "Glo - ri - fy thy name."
And what-e'er the fu - ture brings, "Glo - ri - fy thy name."
And in deep-est woe pray on: "Glo - ri - fy thy name." A - men.

NEW YEAR AND CHANGING SEASONS

358
God Is Working His Purpose Out

Arthur C. Ainger, 1841-1919

PURPOSE Irregular
Martin Shaw, 1875-1958

1 God is work-ing his pur-pose out As year suc-
2 From ut - most east to ut-most west, Wher-e'er man's
3 March we forth in the strength of God With the ban-ner of
4 All we can do is noth-ing worth Un - less God

Octaves to the end

ceeds to year; God is work - ing his
foot hath trod, By the mouth of man - y
Christ un - furled, That the light of the glo - rious
bless-es the deed; Vain - ly we hope for the

pur - pose out, And the time is draw-ing near; Near - er and
mes - sen - gers Goes forth the voice of God; Give ear to
gos - pel of truth May shine through-out the world; Fight we the
har - vest-tide Till God gives life to the seed; Yet near - er and

NEW YEAR AND CHANGING SEASONS

near - er draws the time, The time that shall sure - ly be,
me, ye con - ti - nents, Ye isles, give ear to me,
fight with sorrow and sin To set their cap - tives free,
near - er draws the time, The time that shall sure - ly be,

When the earth shall be filled with the glo - ry of God
That the earth may be filled with the glo - ry of God
That the earth may be filled with the glo - ry of God
When the earth shall be filled with the glo - ry of God

St. 1, 2, 3   St. 4

As the wa - ters cov - er the sea.
As the wa - ters cov - er the sea.
As the wa - ters cov - er the sea.
As the wa - ters cov - er the sea.

Music from *Enlarged Songs of Praise* by permission
of Oxford University Press.

NEW YEAR AND CHANGING SEASONS

Another Year Is Dawning

Frances R. Havergal, 1836-1879

AURELIA 7.6.7.6.D.
Samuel Sebastian Wesley, 1810-1876

1 An - oth - er year is dawn - ing, Dear Fa - ther, let it be
2 An - oth - er year of mer - cies, Of faith - ful - ness and grace,
3 An - oth - er year of serv - ice, Of wit - ness for thy love,

In work-ing or in wait - ing An - oth - er year with thee;
An - oth - er year of glad - ness In the shin - ing of thy face,
An - oth - er year of train - ing For ho - lier work a - bove.

An - oth - er year of prog - ress, An - oth - er year of praise,
An - oth - er year of lean - ing Up - on thy lov - ing breast,
An - oth - er year is dawn - ing, Dear Fa - ther, let it be

An - oth - er year of prov - ing Thy pres - ence all the days;
An - oth - er year of trust - ing, Of qui - et, hap - py rest;
On earth, or else in heav - en, An - oth - er year for thee. A - men.

NEW YEAR AND CHANGING SEASONS

Lord, Thou Hast Set an Open Door

Roger K. Powell, 1914-

PARIS 8.10.10.10.
William Billings, 1746-1800

1 Lord, thou hast set an o - pen door
2 Thy hand hast led us in the past
3 An o - pen door that none can shut:
4 Grant us, O Lord, the strength of faith

In each un - fold - ing of an - oth - er year:
And beck - ons now to fol - low un - known ways.
A bright - er fu - ture is thy gift to men.
To serve thy peace with - in a world of strife,

A door of hope that lead - eth un - to thee,
We need not know the by - ways yet to come,
Re - deemed in Christ, we thank thee for thy grace
That pass - ing years may see thy king - dom come

If thou, O Fa - ther, let thy way ap - pear.
For in each lane of life we find thy praise.
Which makes us con - quer - ors of time a - gain.
When all men know thee as the Lord of life! A - men.

NEW YEAR AND CHANGING SEASONS

361 Sing to the Great Jehovah's Praise

Charles Wesley, 1707-1788

LOBT GOTT IHR CHRISTEN C.M.
Melody by Nikolaus Herman, c. 1485-1561

1 Sing to the great Jehovah's praise! All praise to him belongs; Who kindly lengthens out our days, Inspires our choicest songs, Inspires our choicest songs.

2 His providence hath brought us through Another various year; We all, with vows and anthems new, Before our God appear, Before our God appear.

3 O God, thy mercies past we own, And thy continued care; To thee presenting through thy Son What-e'er we have and are, What-e'er we have and are. A-men.

NEW YEAR AND CHANGING SEASONS

Praise to God, Your Praises Bring 362

William C. Gannett, 1840-1923, alt.

SAVANNAH 7.7.7.7.
The Foundery Collection, 1742

1 Praise to God, your prais-es bring; Hearts, bow down and voic - es, sing
2 Praise him for his bud-ding green, A - pril's res - ur - rec - tion scene;
3 Praise him for his sum-mer rain, Feed - ing, day and night, the grain;
4 Praise him for the win-ter's rest, Snow that falls on na - ture's breast;
5 For his year of won-der done, Praise to the all - glo-rious One!

Prais - es to the glo - rious One, All his year of won - der done.
Praise him for his shin - ing hours, Star - ring all the land with flowers.
Praise him for his tin - y seed, Hold - ing all his world shall need.
Praise for hap - py dreams of birth, Brood-ing in the qui - et earth.
Hearts, bow down and voic - es, sing Praise and love to na-ture's King! A-men.

Ring Out the Old, Ring In the New 363

Alfred Tennyson, 1809-1892

DEUS TUORUM MILITUM L.M.
Grenoble Antiphoner, 1868

1 Ring out the old, ring in the new; Ring, hap - py bells, a - cross the snow;
2 Ring out a slow-ly dy - ing cause, And an - cient forms of par - ty strife;
3 Ring out old shapes of foul dis-ease; Ring out the nar-rowing lust of gold;
4 Ring in the val-iant man and free; The larg - er heart, the kind-lier hand;

The year is go - ing, let him go; Ring out the false, ring in the true.
Ring in the no - bler modes of life, With sweet-er man - ners, pur - er laws.
Ring out the thou-sand wars of old, Ring in the thou-sand years of peace.
Ring out the dark-ness of the land, Ring in the Christ that is to be. A-men.

NEW YEAR AND CHANGING SEASONS

Great God, We Sing That Mighty Hand

Philip Doddridge, 1702-1751

WAREHAM L.M.
William Knapp, 1698-1768

1 Great God, we sing that might - y hand
2 By day, by night, at home, a - broad,
3 With grate - ful hearts the past we own;
4 In scenes ex - alt - ed or de - pressed,

By which sup - port - ed still we stand;
Still are we guard - ed by our God:
The fu - ture, all to us un - known,
Thou art our joy, and thou our rest;

The o - pening year thy mer - cy shows,
By his in - ces - sant boun - ty fed,
We to thy guard - ian care com - mit,
Thy good - ness all our hopes shall raise,

That mer - cy crowns it till it close.
By his un - err - ing coun - sel led.
And, peace - ful, leave be - fore thy feet.
A - dored through all our chang - ing days. A - men.

NEW YEAR AND CHANGING SEASONS

Lord of the Church, We Humbly Pray

365

Edward Osler, 1798-1863
Based on Charles Wesley, 1707-1788

CORNWALL 8.8.6.D.
Samuel Sebastian Wesley, 1810-1876

1 Lord of the church, we hum-bly pray For those who guide us in thy way, And speak thy ho-ly word. With love di-vine their hearts in-spire, And touch their lips with hal-lowed fire, And need-ful strength af-ford.

2 Help them to preach the truth of God, Re-demp-tion through the Sav-ior's blood: Nor let the Spir-it cease On all the church his gifts to shower: To them a mes-sen-ger of power, To us, of life and peace. A-men.

DEDICATION: MINISTER

366 In This House by Men Constructed

Herbert E. Hinton, 1890-

PLEADING SAVIOR 8.7.8.7.D.
Joshua Leavitt's *Christian Lyre*, 1830

1 In this house by men con-struct-ed, Wilt thou here thy
2 O - pen here the gates of heav - en, Let this house thy
3 Send us forth till all cre - a - tion Sing thy prais - es,

chil - dren meet, Hear our prayer, ac - cept our wor - ship,
thres - hold be; May all hearts in need of com - fort
own thy sway; Guide our church in lov - ing ser - vice,

Grant com - mu - nion pure and sweet? Come we here with
Here find life and peace in thee. Just as thou didst
By thy Light, thy Truth, thy Way. God of man, thou

prayer and prais - es, Come the lame, the lone, the sad;
lead our fa - thers Ev - er on - ward to the Light;
great Cre - a - tor, Thou the Arch - i - tect di - vine;

DEDICATION: CHURCH

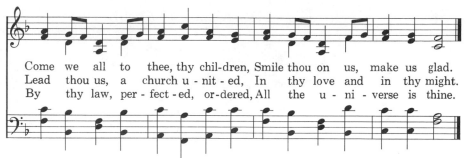

Come we all to thee, thy chil-dren, Smile thou on us, make us glad.
Lead thou us, a church u - nit - ed, In thy love and in thy might.
By thy law, per - fect - ed, or-dered, All the u - ni - verse is thine.

O Thou, Whose Own Vast Temple Stands 367

William Cullen Bryant, 1794-1878

DUNDEE C.M.
Scottish Psalter; 1615

1 O thou, whose own vast tem - ple stands Built
2 Lord, from thine in - most glo - ry send, With -
3 May err - ing minds that wor - ship here Be
4 May faith grow firm and love grow warm, And

o - ver earth and sea, Ac - cept the walls that
in these courts to a - bide, The peace that dwell - eth
taught the bet - ter way; And they who mourn and
pure de - vo - tion rise, While round these hal - lowed

hu - man hands Have raised to wor - ship thee.
with - out end Se - rene - ly by thy side.
they who fear Be strength - ened as they pray.
walls the storm Of earth - born pas - sion dies. A - men.

DEDICATION: CHURCH

368 Jesus, Friend, So Kind and Gentle

Philip E. Gregory, 1886-

DULCE CARMEN 8.7.8.7.8.7.
"An Essay on the Church Plain Chant," 1782

1 Je - sus, Friend, so kind and gen - tle, Lit - tle ones we
2 Thou who didst re - ceive the chil - dren To thy - self so
3 Grant to us a deep com - pas - sion For thy chil - dren

bring to thee; Grant to them thy dear - est bless - ing,
ten - der - ly, Give to all who teach and guide them,
ev - ery - where. May we see our hu - man fam - ily

Let thine arms a - round them be; Now en - fold them
Wis - dom and hu - mil - i - ty, Vi - sion true to
Free from sor - row and de - spair, And be - hold thy

in thy good - ness, From all dan - ger keep them free.
keep them no - ble, Love to serve them faith - ful - ly.
king - dom glo - rious, In our world so bright and fair. A - men.

DEDICATION: CHILDREN

God of the Nations, Who from Dawn of Days 369

W. Russell Bowie, 1882-1969

TOULON 10.10.10.10.
Abridged from *Genevan Psalter*, 1551

1 God of the na - tions, who from dawn of days
2 Thy hand has led a - cross the hun - gry sea
3 Then, for thy grace to grow in broth - er - hood,

Hast led thy peo - ple in their wid - ening ways,
The ea - ger peo - ples flock - ing to be free,
For hearts a - flame to serve thy des - tined good,

Through whose deep pur - pose stran - ger thou - sands stand
And from the breeds of earth, thy si - lent sway
For faith, and will to win what faith shall see,

Here in the bor - ders of our prom - ised land,
Fash - ions the na - tion of the broad - ening day.
God of thy peo - ple, hear us cry to thee! A - men.

THE NATION

Eternal Father, Strong to Save

William Whiting, 1825-1878, alt.

MELITA 8.8.8.8.8.8.
John B. Dykes, 1823-1876

1 E - ter - nal Fa - ther, strong to save, Whose arm doth bind the
2 O Sav - ior, whose al - might - y word, The winds and waves sub -
3 O Ho - ly Spir - it, who didst brood Up - on the cha - os
4 O Trin - i - ty of love and power! Our breth - ren shield in

rest - less wave, Who bidd'st the might - y o - cean deep Its
mis - sive heard, Who walk - edst on the foam - ing deep, And
dark and rude, Who bad'st its an - gry tu - mult cease, And
dan - ger's hour; From rock and tem - pest, fire and foe, Pro -

own ap - point - ed lim - its keep, O hear us when we
calm a - mid its rage didst sleep, O hear us when we
gav - est light, and life, and peace, O hear us when we
tect them where - so - e'er they go; Thus ev - er - more shall

cry to thee, For those in per - il on the sea.
cry to thee, For those in per - il on the sea.
cry to thee, For those in per - il on the sea.
rise to thee Glad hymns of praise from land and sea. A - men.

THE NATION

My Country, 'Tis of Thee

371

Samuel F. Smith, 1808-1895

AMERICA 6.6.4.6.6.6.4.
Anonymous in *Thesaurus Musicus*, 1744

1 My coun - try, 'tis of thee, Sweet land of lib - er - ty,
2 My na - tive coun - try, thee, Land of the no - ble free,
3 Let mu - sic swell the breeze, And ring from all the trees

Of thee I sing; Land where my fa - thers died, Land of the
Thy name I love; I love thy rocks and rills, Thy woods and
Sweet free-dom's song; Let mor - tal tongues a - wake; Let all that

pil - grims' pride, From ev - er - y moun-tain side Let free-dom ring.
tem - pled hills; My heart with rap - ture thrills Like that a - bove.
breathe par-take; Let rocks their si - lence break; The sound pro-long. A-men.

4 Our father's God, to thee,
Author of liberty,
   To thee we sing;
Long may our land be bright
With freedom's holy light;
Protect us by thy might,
   Great God, our King.

THE NATION

372   *Thou Judge by Whom Each Empire Fell*

Percy Dearmer, 1867-1936

NUN FREUT EUCH 8.7.8.7.8.8.7.
Klug's *Geistliche Lieder*, Wittenberg, 1535

1 Thou Judge by whom each em - pire fell, When pride of power o'er - came it,
2 Search, Lord, our spir - its in thy sight, In best and worst re - veal us;
3 Lo, fear-ing nought we come to thee, Though by our fault con - found - ed;

Con - vict us now, if we re - bel, Our na - tion judge, and shame it.
Shed on our souls a blaze of light, And judge, that thou may'st heal us.
Though self-ish, mean, and base we be, Thy jus - tice is un - bound - ed:

In each sharp cri - sis, Lord, ap - pear, For - give, and show our
The pres - ent be our judg - ment day, When all our lack thou
So large, it nought but love re - quires, And, judg - ing, pard - ons,

du - ty clear: To serve thee by re - pent - ance.
dost sur - vey: Show us our - selves and save us.
frees, in - spires. De - liv - er us from e - vil! A - men.

THE NATION

From *Enlarged Songs of Praise* by permission of Oxford University Press.

O God of Earth and Altar

Gilbert K. Chesterton, 1874-1936

LLANGLOFFAN 7.6.7.6.D.
Traditional Welsh Melody

1 O God of earth and al - tar, Bow down and hear our cry;
2 From all that ter - ror teach - es, From lies of tongue and pen,
3 Tie in a liv - ing teth - er The prince and priest and thrall;

Our earth - ly rul - ers fal - ter, Our peo - ple drift and die;
From all the eas - y speech - es That com - fort cru - el men,
Bind all our lives to - geth - er, Smite us and save us all;

The walls of gold en - tomb us, The swords of scorn di - vide;
From sale and prof - a - na - tion Of hon - or and the sword,
In fire and ex - ul - ta - tion A - flame with faith, and free,

Take not thy thun - der from us, But take a - way our pride.
From sleep and from dam - na - tion, De - liv - er us, O Lord!
Lift up a liv - ing na - tion, A sin - gle sword to thee. A - men.

Words by permission of Oxford University Press.

THE NATION

374 O Beautiful for Spacious Skies

Katharine Lee Bates, 1859-1929

MATERNA C.M.D.
Samuel A. Ward, 1847-1903

1 O beau-ti-ful for spa-cious skies, For am-ber waves of grain,
2 O beau-ti-ful for pil-grim feet, Whose stern, im-pas-sioned stress
3 O beau-ti-ful for he-roes proved In lib-er-at-ing strife,
4 O beau-ti-ful for pa-triot dream That sees be-yond the years

For pur-ple moun-tain maj-es-ties A-bove the fruit-ed plain!
A thor-ough-fare for free-dom beat A-cross the wil-der-ness!
Who more than self their coun-try loved, And mer-cy more than life!
Thine al-a-bas-ter cit-ies gleam, Un-dimmed by hu-man tears!

A-mer-i-ca! A-mer-i-ca! God shed his grace on thee,
A-mer-i-ca! A-mer-i-ca! God mend thine ev-ery flaw,
A-mer-i-ca! A-mer-i-ca! May God thy gold re-fine,
A-mer-i-ca! A-mer-i-ca! God shed his grace on thee,

And crown thy good with broth-er-hood From sea to shin-ing sea.
Con-firm thy soul in self-con-trol, Thy lib-er-ty in law.
Till all suc-cess be no-ble-ness, And ev-ery gain di-vine.
And crown thy good with broth-er-hood From sea to shin-ing sea. A-men.

THE NATION

Before Thee, Lord, We Join Our Hearts

375

Mildred Harner Foltz, 1910-

ROSEATE HUES C.M.D.
Joseph Barnby, 1838-1896

1 Be - fore thee, Lord, we join our hearts And hands in mar - riage now;
2 Then, help us find in com-mon tasks, With which each home is filled,
3 Though our own strength so of - ten fails We thank thee that we know

Be thou the guard-ian of this rite, And con - se - crate each vow.
The beau - ty and the lov - ing joy In which life's storms are stilled;
Thy prom-ise to a - bide with us Wher-ev - er we must go.

We would so build our home, O Lord, That it shall ev - er be
And give us gra - ti - tude to speak A word of thanks or praise
Be thou our glo-rious morn-ing song With ev - ery day be - gun:

A shel - ter from the stress of life, A ha - ven blest by thee.
To those who do the kind - ly things That glad-den all our days.
Be thou our clos-ing ves-per hymn When ev-ery day is done. A-men.

MARRIAGE

O Love Divine and Golden

John Samuel Bewley Monsell, 1811-1875

BLAIRGOWRIE (Dykes) 13.13.13.13.
John B. Dykes, 1823-1876

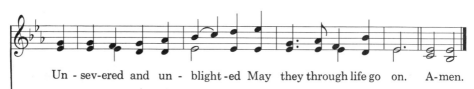

1 O Love di - vine and gold - en, Mys - ter - ious depth and height,

To thee the world be - hold - en, Looks up for life and light.

God bless these hands u - nit - ed; God bless these hearts made one!

Un - sev - ered and un - blight - ed May they through life go on. A - men.

MARRIAGE

O Thou Whose Favor Hallows All Occasions 377

Miriam Drury, 1900-

THOMAS CIRCLE 11.10.11.10.11.10.
Lawrence P. Schreiber, 1933-

1 O thou whose fa-vor hal-lows all oc-cas-ions, Be pre-sent at this
2 Long may they keep the sense of high ad-ven-ture, The gift of joy, the
3 Al-might-y God, Re-deem-er and De-fen-der, Be thou their stay what-

cov-e-nant-ing rite; May ev-ery pledge of true and last-ing pur-pose Be
mar-vel of a dream, Nor ev-er lose the vis-ion as they cher-ish Each
ev-er may be-tide; In-creas-ing-ly may each new year dis-cov-er Their

con-se-crat-ed in thy ho-ly sight; Con-fer on those be-fore thee
for the oth-er, hon-or and es-teem; En-rich them with the bless-ing
lives ma-tured, their mar-riage sanc-ti-fied, Their hearts firm fixed on this ex-

hea-ven-ly aid To keep the sol-emn vows that here are made.
of thy grace, And make their home thy con-stant dwell-ing place.
alt-ed goal: The praise of God whose name their vows ex-tol. A-men.

MARRIAGE

378

O Perfect Love
First Tune

Dorothy F. Gurney, 1858-1932

O PERFECT LOVE 11.10.11.10.
Joseph Barnby, 1838-1896

1 O per - fect Love, all hu - man thought tran - scend - ing,
2 O per - fect Life, be thou their full as - sur - ance
3 Grant them the joy which bright - ens earth - ly sor - row;

Low - ly we kneel in prayer be - fore thy throne,
Of ten - der char - i - ty and stead - fast faith,
Grant them the peace which calms all earth - ly strife,

That theirs may be the love which knows no end - ing,
Of pa - tient hope, and qui - et, brave en - dur - ance,
And to life's day the glo - rious un - known mor - row

Whom thou for - ev - er - more dost join in one.
With child - like trust that fears nor pain nor death.
That dawns up - on e - ter - nal love and life. A - men.

MARRIAGE

Words by permission of Oxford University Press.

O Perfect Love

Second Tune

Dorothy F. Gurney, 1858-1932

ZU MEINEM HERRN 11.10.11.10.
Johann G. Schicht, 1753-1823
Harm. David Evans, 1874-1948

379

1 O per-fect Love, all hu-man thought tran-scend-ing,
2 O per-fect Life, be thou their full as-sur-ance
3 Grant them the joy which bright-ens earth-ly sor-row;

Low-ly we kneel in prayer be-fore thy throne,
Of ten-der char-i-ty and stead-fast faith,
Grant them the peace which calms all earth-ly strife,

That theirs may be the love which knows no end-ing,
Of pa-tient hope, and qui-et, brave en-dur-ance,
And to life's day the glo-rious un-known mor-row

Whom thou for-ev-er-more dost join in one.
With child-like trust that fears nor pain nor death.
That dawns up-on e-ter-nal love and life. A-men.

MARRIAGE

380 As We Before Thine Altar Bow

Franklin P. Frye, 1903-

EMMANUEL L.M.
Carl C. N. Balle, 1806-1855

1 As we be - fore thine al - tar bow
2 As here each sol - emn vow we take,
3 As years go by may we ful - fill

We pray that thou wilt bless us now,
We seek thy strength, that we may make
The pur - pose of thy ho - ly will,

And may our mar - riage ev - er be
Our hearts and home thy dwell - ing place.
And faith - ful - ly with one ac - cord

A un - ion, hal - lowed, Lord, by thee.
Our lives a wit - ness to thy grace.
Serve thee, our ev - er - liv - ing Lord. A - men.

MARRIAGE

O Father, All Creating

381

John Ellerton, 1826-1893

NYLAND 7.6.7.6.D.
Finnish Melody
Adapt. David Evans, 1874-1948; arranged

1 O Fa-ther, all cre-a-ting, Whose wis-dom, love, and power
2 O Sav-ior, Guest most boun-teous Of old in Gal-i-lee,
3 Ex-cept thou build it, Fa-ther, The house is built in vain;

First bound two lives to-geth-er In E-den's pri-mal hour,
Vouch-safe to-day thy pres-ence With these who call on thee;
Ex-cept thou, Sav-ior, bless it, The joy will turn to pain;

To-day to these thy chil-dren Thine ear-liest gifts re-new,
Their store of earth-ly glad-ness Trans-form to heaven-ly wine,
But nought can break the u-nion Of hearts in thee made one;

A home by thee made hap-py, A love by thee kept true.
And teach them, in the tast-ing, To know the gift is thine.
And love thy Spir-it hal-lows Is end-less love be-gun. A-men.

MARRIAGE

Service Music

Come, Bless the Lord

382

Psalm 134:2

Austin C. Lovelace, 1919-

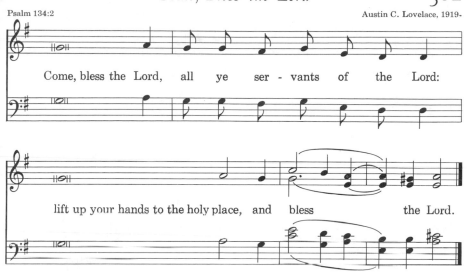

Come, bless the Lord, all ye ser - vants of the Lord:

lift up your hands to the holy place, and bless the Lord.

Enrich, Lord, Heart, Mouth, Hands in Me

383

George Herbert, 1593-1632, alt.

WULFRUN 8.8.8.
George W. Briggs, 1875-1959

En - rich, Lord, heart, mouth, hands in me, With faith, with hope, with

char - i - ty: That I may run, rise, rest with thee.

INTROITS

384

Psalm 122:1

I Was Glad

Austin C. Lovelace, 1919-

I was glad when they said un-to me, Let us go in-to the house of the Lord.

Music copyright by W. L. Jenkins; from *Service Music for the Adult Choir*; used by permission.

385

Glory to Thee, O God Most High

Philip Gell's *Psalms and Hymns*, 1815

MAINZER L.M.
Joseph Mainzer, 1801-1851
Alt. and harm. Austin C. Lovelace, 1919-

Glo - ry to thee, O God most high! Fa - ther, we praise thy

maj - es - ty, The Son, the Spir - it, we a -

dore: One God - head, blest for - ev - er - more.

Praise to the Holiest in the Height

386

John H. Newman, 1801-1890

ST. MARY C.M.
Melody, *Prys' Psalter*, 1621

Praise to the Ho-liest in the height And in the depth be praise; In

all his words most won-der - ful, Most sure in all his ways.

Lord, for the Mercies of the Night

387

John Mason, *c.* 1645-1694

FARRANT C.M
Attr. to Richard Farrant. *c.* 1530-1580

1 Lord, for the mer-cies of the night Our hum-ble thanks we pay,
2 Let this day praise thee, O Lord God, And so let all our days;

And un - to thee we ded - i - cate The first fruits of the day.
And O let heaven's e - ter - nal day Be thine e - ter - nal praise!

INTROITS

388   *Bless the Lord, O My Soul*

Minister: O all ye works of the Lord; bless ye the Lord; praise him and magnify him forever.

M. Ippolitof-Ivanoff, 1859-1935

Bless the Lord, O my soul, Bless-ed art thou, O Lord.

Minister: O ye servants of the Lord, bless ye the Lord; praise him, and magnify him forever.

Bless the Lord, O my soul, and all that is with-in me bless his ho - ly name.

Minister: O ye holy and humble men of heart, bless ye the Lord; praise him, and magnify him forever.

Bless the Lord, O my soul, and all that is with-in me bless his ho - ly name.

INTROITS

Glory Be to God the Father

Christopher Wordsworth, 1807-1885, alt.

REX GLORIAE 8.7.8.7.D.
Henry Smart, 1813-1879

Glo - ry be to God the Fa-ther; Glo - ry be to God the Son,

Dy - ing, risen, as - cend-ing for us; Who the heaven-ly realm has won;

Glo - ry to the Ho - ly Spir - it; To One God in Per-sons Three;

Glo - ry both in earth and heav-en, Glo - ry, end - less glo - ry be.

This Is the Day the Lord Hath Made

Isaac Watts, 1674-1748

TWENTY-FOURTH C.M.
Probably by Lucius Chapin, 1760-1842

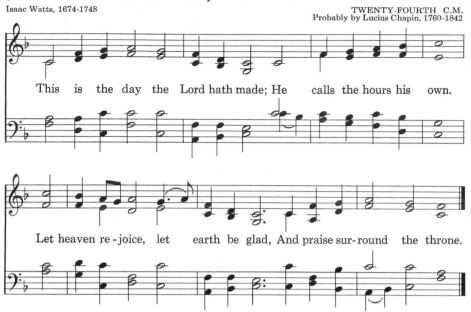

This is the day the Lord hath made; He calls the hours his own.

Let heaven re-joice, let earth be glad, And praise sur-round the throne.

Jesus, Stand Among Us

William Pennefather, 1816-1873

GLENFINLAS 6.5.6.5.
Kenneth G. Finlay, 1882-

Je-sus, stand a-mong us In thy ris-en power;

Let this time of wor-ship Be an ho-ly hour.

INTROITS

Music used by permission of Kenneth G. Finlay

Open Now Thy Gates of Beauty

Benjamin Schmolck, 1672-1737
Tr. Catherine Winkworth, 1827-1878

UNSER HERRSCHER 8.7.8.7.7.7.
Melody by Joachim Neander, 1650-1680

1 O - pen now thy gates of beau-ty, Zi - on, let me en - ter there,
2 Gra-cious God, I come be-fore thee, Come thou al - so un - to me;

Where my soul in joy - ful du - ty, Waits for him who an - swers prayer.
Where we find thee and a - dore thee, There a heaven on earth must be.

O how bless - ed is this place, Filled with sol - ace, light, and grace!
To my heart O en - ter thou, Let it be thy tem - ple now.

INTROITS

The Sacrifices of God

Psalm 51.17

Tonus Regius

The sacrifices of God are a bro-ken spir - it. A broken and a con-trite heart, O God, thou wilt not de-spise.

OFFERTORY

394

All Things Are Thine

John Greenleaf Whittier, 1807-1892

HERR JESU CHRIST L.M.
Pensum Sacrum, Gorlitz, 1648
Arr. Johann Sebastian Bach, 1685-1750

All things are thine: no gift have we, Lord of all gifts, to of-fer thee,

And hence with grate-ful hearts to-day, Thine own be-fore thy feet we lay.

395

Bless Thou the Gifts

First Tune

Samuel Longfellow, 1819-1892

CANONBURY L.M.
Robert Schumann, 1810-1856

Bless thou the gifts our hands have brought, Bless

thou the work our hearts have planned; Ours is the faith, the

will, the thought; The rest, O God, is in thy hand. A-men.

OFFERTORY

Bless Thou the Gifts

Second Tune

Samuel Longfellow, 1819-1892

EAST DALLAS L.M.
A. Eugene Ellsworth, 1910-

396

Bless thou the gifts our hands have brought, Bless thou the
work our hearts have planned; Ours is the faith, the will, the
thought, The rest, O God, is in Thy hand. A - men.

Bless Thou the Gifts

Third Tune

Samuel Longfellow, 1819-1892

BRESLAU L.M.
Melody, Leipzig, 1625

397

Bless thou the gifts our hands have brought, Bless thou the work our hearts have planned;

Ours is the faith, the will, the thought, The rest, O God, is in thy hand. A-men.

OFFERTORY

398 O King of Kings, Before Whose Throne

John Quarles, 1624-1665
Alt. Thomas Darling, 1816-1893

LEICESTER 8.8.8.8.8.8.
John Bishop, c. 1665-1737

O King of kings, be - fore whose throne The an - gels bow, no

gift can we Pre - sent that is in - deed our own, Since

heaven and earth be - long to thee; Yet this our souls through

grace im - part, The of - fering of a thank - ful heart. A-men.

OFFERTORY

All Things Come of Thee

1 Chronicles 29:14

Ludwig van Beethoven, 1770-1827

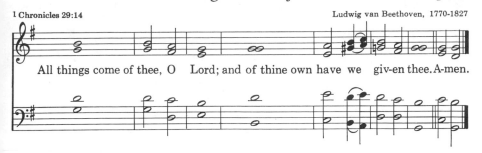

All things come of thee, O Lord; and of thine own have we giv-en thee. A-men.

We Give Thee But Thine Own

William Walsham How, 1823-1897

ST. ANDREW S.M.
Joseph Barnby, 1838-1896

We give thee but thine own, What - e'er the
gift may be; All that we have is
thine a - lone, A trust, O Lord, from thee. A - men.

Alternate tune No. 261.

OFFERTORY

401

Thy Word Have I Hid

Psalm 119: 11,12

CHESHIRE TUNE 8.8.8.5.
Este's Psalter, 1592

Thy word have I hid in my heart, that I might not sin a-gainst thee.

Bless-ed art thou, O Lord my God: teach me thy stat - utes.

402

Divine Instructor, Gracious Lord

Anne Steele, 1716-1778

TALLIS' ORDINAL C.M.
Thomas Tallis, *c.* 1505-1585

Di - vine in - struc - tor, gra-cious Lord, Be thou for - ev - er near;

Teach me to love thy sa - cred Word, And find my Sav - ior there. A-men.

SCRIPTURE

Teach Me, O Lord

403

Psalm 119: 33

William Henry Hewlett, 1873-

Teach me, O Lord, the way of thy stat - utes, and

I will keep it un - to the end.

Music arrangement by permission of the United Church Publishing House, Toronto.

O Lord, Open Thou Our Eyes

404

Psalm 119:18

John Camidge, 1735-1803

V. O Lord, open thou our eyes   R. That we may behold

won - drous things out of thy law.

Thanks Be to Thee 405

Thomas Tallis, c. 1505-1585

Thanks be to thee, O
Christ, for this thy } ho - ly gos - pel.

Praise Be to Thee 406

John Playford, 1674-1730

Praise be to thee, O Christ.

SCRIPTURE

407 Glory Be to Thee
Thomas Tallis, c. 1505-1585

Glo - ry be to thee, O Lord.

408 Glory Be to Thee
Thomas Tallis, c. 1505-1585

Glo - ry be to thee, O Lord.

409 Lord, Have Mercy Upon Us
John Merbecke, 1523-c. 1585

Lord, have mer-cy up-on us; Christ, have mer-cy up-on us; Lord, have mer-cy up-on us.

410 Lord, Have Mercy Upon Us
KYRIE
From a Lutheran Service of 1528

Lord, have mer-cy up-on us; Christ, have mer-cy up-on us; Lord, have mer-cy up-on us.

From *The Lutheran Service Book and Hymnal* by permission of the Commission on the Liturgy and Hymnal.

411 Write These Words
Ancient Chant

Write these words in our hearts, we be - seech thee, O Lord.

SCRIPTURE

Praise God, from Whom All Blessings Flow 412

Thomas Ken, 1637-1711

OLD HUNDREDTH L.M.
Attr. to Louis Bourgeois, c. 1510-1561
Genevan Psalter, 1551

Praise God from whom all bless-ings flow; Praise him, all crea-tures here be - low;

Praise him a-bove, ye heaven-ly host: Praise Fa-ther, Son, and Ho - ly Ghost. A-men.

Praise God, from Whom All Blessings Flow 413

Thomas Ken, 1637-1711

OLD HUNDREDTH L.M. (altered rhythm)
Attr. to Louis Bourgeois, c. 1510-1561
Genevan Psalter, 1551

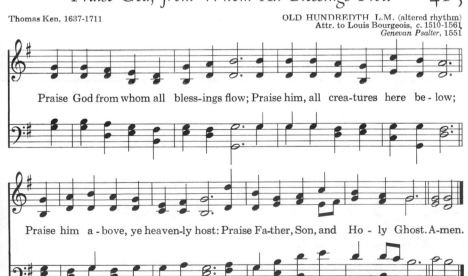

Praise God from whom all bless-ings flow; Praise him, all crea-tures here be - low;

Praise him a - bove, ye heaven-ly host: Praise Fa-ther, Son, and Ho - ly Ghost. A-men.

DOXOLOGIES

414

Gloria Patri

Henry W. Greatorex, 1813-1858

Glo - ry be to the Fa-ther, and to the Son, and to the Ho - ly Ghost; As it

was in the be-gin-ning, is now, and ev-er shall be, world with-out end. A-men. A - men.

415

Gloria Patri

Charles Meineke, 1782-1850

Glo - ry be to the Fa - ther, and to the Son, and to the

Ho - ly Ghost; As it was in the be - gin - ning, is

now, and ev - er shall be, world with-out end. A - men. A - men.

GLORIA PATRIS

Gloria Patri

Old Scottish Chant

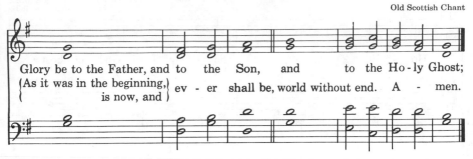

Glory be to the Father, and to the Son, and to the Ho-ly Ghost;
(As it was in the beginning,) ev - er shall be, world without end. A - men.
is now, and)

GLORIA PATRI

Holy, Holy, Holy

Peter C. Lutkin, 1858-1931

In unison

Ho - ly, ho - ly, ho - ly, Lord

God of hosts, Heaven and earth are full of thy

glo - ry: Glo - ry be to thee, O Lord most high. A-men.

SANCTUS

Holy, Holy, Holy

Communion Service in E Minor
Philip R. Dietterich, 1931-

Ho - ly, ho - ly, ho - ly, Lord God of hosts;

Heav - en and earth are full of thy glo - ry;

Glo - ry be to thee, O Lord most high. A - men.

SANCTUS

Music copyright © 1964 by Abingdon Press.

Holy, Holy, Holy

419

John Merbecke, 1523-c. 1585

In unison

Ho - ly, ho - ly, ho - ly, Lord God of hosts, Heaven and earth are

full of thy glo - ry: Glo-ry be to thee, O Lord most high. A - men.

SANCTUS

The Lord Be with You

420

Thomas Tallis, c. 1505-1585

To be said or sung: *Choir and Congregation:*

The {Lord be / with you,} And with thy spir - it. Let us pray.

(O Lord, show / thy mercy up-) on us, And grant us thy sal - va - tion.

(O God, make clean / our hearts with-) in us. And take not thy Ho - ly Spir - it from us.

CALL TO PRAYER

The Lord Be with You

To be said or sung: *Choir and Congregation:* Traditional

The {Lord be / with you,} And with thy spir - it. Let us pray.

{O Lord, show / thy mercy up-} on us, And grant us thy sal - va - tion.

{O God, make clean / our hearts with-} in us. And take not thy Holy Spirit from us.

CALL TO PRAYER

422

Hear Our Prayer

Psalm 143:1 George Whelpton, 1847-1930

Hear our prayer, O Lord, Hear our prayer, O Lord,

In - cline thine ear to us, And grant us thy peace. A - men.

PRAYER RESPONSES

Our Father, Who Art in Heaven

Anonymous

Harold W. Friedell, 1905-1958

Our Fa - ther, who art in heav - en, we

art   in heaven,

pray   thee to send in - to our hearts, and in - to the

hearts   of   all   men   ev - ery - where, the

Spir - it   of   our   Lord   Je - sus Christ.

PRAYER RESPONSES

Day by Day, Dear Lord

St. Richard of Chichester, 1197-1253   Harold W. Friedell, 1905-1958

Day by day, Dear Lord, of thee three things I
pray: To see thee more clear - ly, Love thee more dear - ly,
To see thee, Love thee,
Fol - low thee more near - ly, Day by day.

Music copyright © 1960 by H. W. Gray Company. Copyright assigned to
Belwin-Mills Publishing Corp. Used by permission.

Father of All Grace

Arden D. Keen, 1930-

Fa - ther of all grace, Fa - ther of all glo - ry,

Hear and an - swer us We pray thee. A - men.

PRAYER RESPONSES   Used by permission of Arden D. Keen.

Lead Me, Lord

426

Based on Psalms 5:8 and 4:8

Samuel S. Wesley, 1810-1876

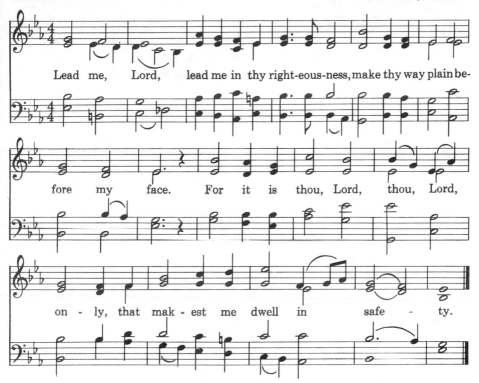

Lead me, Lord, lead me in thy right-eous-ness, make thy way plain be-

fore my face. For it is thou, Lord, thou, Lord,

on - ly, that mak - est me dwell in safe - ty.

May the Words of Our Mouths

427

Psalm 19:14, alt.

Alan Walker, 1927-

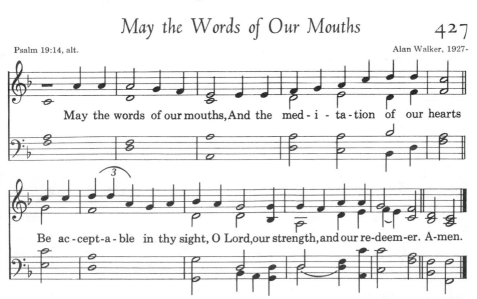

May the words of our mouths, And the med - i - ta - tion of our hearts

Be ac - cept - a - ble in thy sight, O Lord, our strength, and our re-deem-er. A-men.

PRAYER RESPONSES

428   O Thou Who Hearest Prayer

Unknown

6.6.6.6.8.8.
Welsh Melody

O thou who hear - est prayer, Give ear un - to our cry;

O let thy chil - dren share thy bless - ing from on high.

We plead the prom-ise of thy word, O grant us peace, al - might-y Lord! A-men.

429   Almighty Father, Hear Our Prayer

Arr. from Felix Mendelssohn, 1809-1847

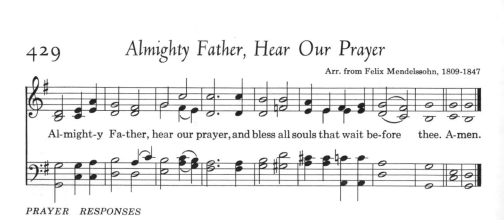

Al-might-y Fa-ther, hear our prayer, and bless all souls that wait be-fore thee. A-men

PRAYER RESPONSES

To My Humble Supplication

430

Joseph Bryan, c. 1610; alt., 1955

MON DIEU, PRÊTE-MOI L'OREILLE 8.8.7.7.
Genevan Psalter, 1543

1 To my hum-ble sup-pli - ca - tion, Lord, give ear and ac - cep - ta - tion
2 Heaven-ly Tu- tor, of thy kind-ness, Teach my dull-ness, guide my blind-ness

Save thy serv-ant, who doth own Help and hope in thee a - lone.
That my steps thy paths may tread, Which to end - less bliss do lead. A -men.

Spirit of Truth, of Life

431

Horace Westwood, 1884-

MENDON L.M.
German melody
Arr. Samuel Dyer, 1785- 1835

Spir - it of Truth, of Life, of Power, We bring our-selves as gifts to thee.

Oh, bind our hearts this sa - cred hour In faith and hope and char - i - ty. A -men.

PRAYER RESPONSES

432

Sarum Primer, 1558

God Be in My Head

LYTLINGTON Irregular
Sydney H. Nicholson, 1875-1947

God be in my head, And in my un-der-stand-ing;

God be in mine eyes, And in my look-ing;

God be in my mouth, And in my speak-ing;

God be in my heart, And in my think-ing;

God be at mine end, And at my de-part-ing.

BENEDICTION

The Lord Bless You and Keep You

433

Numbers 6: 24-26

Peter C. Lutkin, 1858-1931

The Lord bless you and keep you; The Lord lift his coun-te-nance up-

on you, and give you peace; and give you peace, The Lord

and give you peace, ... and give you peace, ... the Lord

Lord make his face and be gra - cious un-to

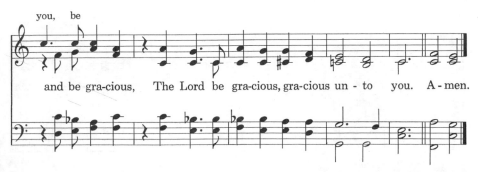

make his face to shine up-on you, and be gra-cious,

you, be

and be gra-cious, The Lord be gra-cious, gra-cious un-to you. A-men.

BENEDICTION

434

To Thee Before the Close of Day

Latin, c. 7th century
Tr. John M. Neale, 1818-1866

JAM LUCIS L.M.
Plainsong, Mode VI

Unison

To thee be-fore the close of day, Cre-a-tor of the

world, we pray That, with thy wont-ed fa-vor, thou

Wouldst be our guard and keep-er now. A - men.

435

Thou Wilt Keep Him in Perfect Peace

Isaiah 26:3

DUKE'S TUNE 8.6.
Scottish Psalter, 1615, abridged

Thou wilt keep him in per-fect peace Whose mind is stayed on thee. A-men.

BENEDICTION

May the Grace of Christ Our Savior 436

John Newton, 1725-1807

OMNI DEI 8.7.8.7.
Corner's *Gesangbuch*, 1631
Harm. Hubert Lamb, 1909-

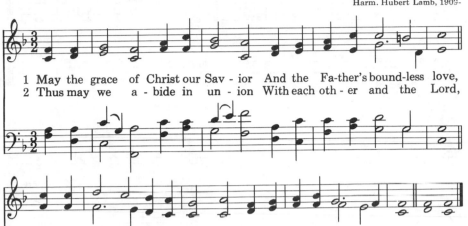

1 May the grace of Christ our Sav - ior And the Fa-ther's bound-less love,
2 Thus may we a - bide in un - ion With each oth - er and the Lord,

With the Ho - ly Spir-it's fav - or, Rest up - on us from a - bove.
And pos - sess in sweet com-mun-ion Joys which earth can-not af - ford. A - men.

Music by permission of Milton Academy from *The Milton Hymnal* and Middlesex
School from *The Middlesex Hymn Book*.

Father, Give Thy Benediction 437

Samuel Longfellow, 1819-1892

ALTA TRINITÀ BEATA 8.7.8.7.
Laudi Spirituali, 14th century

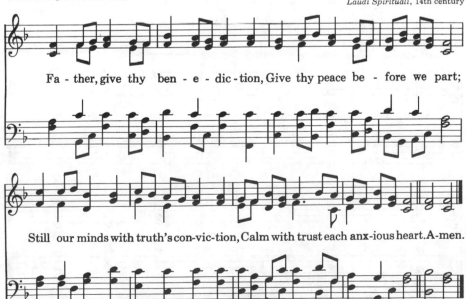

Fa - ther, give thy ben - e - dic - tion, Give thy peace be - fore we part;

Still our minds with truth's con-vic-tion, Calm with trust each anx-ious heart. A-men.

BENEDICTION

438 William Crotch, 1775-1847

A - - - men, A - - - men.

439 J. Alcock

A - - men, A - - - - men.

440 William Henry Walter, 1825-1893

A - - - - men, A - - - men.

441 Based on Tertius Noble, 1867-1953

A - men. A - men. A - - - - men.

Organ

AMENS These Amens are from *The Lutheran Service Book and Hymnal*; by permission of the Commission on Liturgy and Hymnal.

442

A — men, A — men.

443

A - men, A - - men.

444

A — men, A-men, A - men.

445

A-men, A-men, A - - men.

446

Eric DeLamarter, 1880-1953

A - - - men, A - men.

447

Louis Bourgeois, *c.* 1510-*c.* 1561

A - - - - - - - men.

AMENS

448

Franklin E. Perkins, 1929-

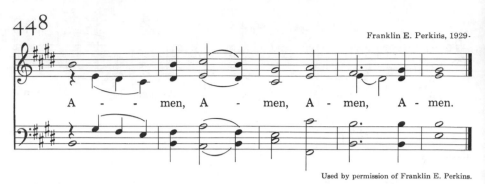

A - men, A - men, A - men, A - men.

449

Arden D. Keen, 1930-

450

Franklin E. Perkins, 1929-

A - men, A - men, A - men.

A - men, A - men.

451

John Stainer, 1840-1901

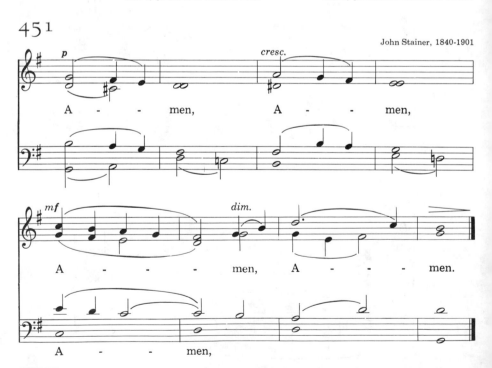

A - men, A - men,

A - men, A - men.

A - men,

AMENS

John Stainer, 1840-1901

A - men, A - - - men,

A - men, A - men, A - men, A - - men, A -

A - men, A - men,

A - - - men,

- - - men, A - - - men, A - men.

A - men,

453
Vincent Persichetti, 1915-

A - - - men, A - - - men.

From *Hymns and Responses for the Church Year* by Vincent Persichetti. Used by permission of Elkan-Vogel Co., Inc.

454
Vincent Persichetti, 1915-

A - - - men, A - - men, A - men.

From *Hymns and Responses for the Church Year* by Vincent Persichetti. Used by permission of Elkan-Vogel Co., Inc.

AMENS

The Written Word

Adoration and Praise

Litanies

Affirmation of Faith

Scripture Readings

Psalms

Prayers of Worship

Offering

The Lord's Supper

    SCRIPTURES

    INVITATION

    PRAYERS

Baptism

Benedictions

Adoration and Praise

455

O God, thou source of all pure desires and holy affections, give me now a quiet mind and a reverent heart, that I may worthily worship thee at this time.

456

O Lord, enable me this day to worship thee in spirit and in truth. Keep me from vain affections and wandering thoughts. Help me to join heartily in the praises and prayers of thy people. Cause me to take heed how I hear thy Word. O teach me this day by the mouth of thy minister so that I may better know and do thy will. Give me understanding in spiritual things, and may I receive the message thou dost send with all humility and eagerness to be instructed and made better. Forgive all wherein I come amiss, and accept and bless me for Jesus' sake. *Amen.*

457

O God, who makest thyself known in the stillness, let me feel thy presence in this sacred place; make me to be of the company of earnest souls who have worshiped here in spirit and in truth; through the voices of men and the instruments of praise help me to lift my heart to thee; and so, O Lord, purify my life, that, going forth into the world, I may go in thy strength and in thy love; through Jesus Christ our Lord. *Amen.*

458

"But the hour is coming, and now is, when the true worshipers will worship the Father in spirit and truth, for such the Father seeks to worship him. God is spirit, and those who worship him must worship in spirit and truth."
John 4:23-24

459

For thus said the Lord G OD , the Holy One of Israel,
   "In returning and rest you shall be saved;
   in quietness and in trust shall be your strength."
Isaiah 30:15

460

As a hart longs
   for flowing streams,
so longs my soul
   for thee, O God.
My soul thirsts for God,
   for the living God.
Psalm 42:1-2

461

For God alone my soul waits in silence;
   from him comes my salvation.
He only is my rock and my salvation,
   my fortress; I shall not be greatly moved.
Psalm 62:1-2

462

O God, thou art my God, I seek thee,
   my soul thirsts for thee;
my flesh faints for thee,
   as in a dry and weary land where no water is.
So I have looked upon thee in the sanctuary,
   beholding thy power and glory.
Because thy steadfast love is better than life,
   my lips will praise thee.
So I will bless thee as long as I live;
   I will lift up my hands and call on thy name.
Psalm 63:1-4

463

My heart is steadfast, O God, my heart is steadfast!
I will sing, and make melody!
   Awake, my soul!

I will give thanks to thee, O LORD, among the peoples,
    I will sing praises to thee among the nations.
For thy steadfast love is great above the heavens,
    thy faithfulness reaches to the clouds.

Psalm 108:1, 3, 4

464

"My soul magnifies the Lord,
and my spirit rejoices in God my Savior,
for he who is mighty has done great things for me,
and holy is his name."

Luke 1:46b, 47, 49

465

I will bless the LORD at all times;
    his praise shall continually be in my mouth.
My soul makes its boast in the LORD;
    let the afflicted hear and be glad.
O magnify the LORD with me,
    and let us exalt his name together!
The LORD redeems the life of his servants;
    none of those who take refuge in him will be condemned.

Psalm 34:1-3, 22

466

O come, let us sing to the LORD;
    let us make a joyful noise to the rock of our salvation!
Let us come into his presence with thanksgiving;
    let us make a joyful noise to him with songs of praise!
For the LORD is a great God,
    and a great King above all gods.
In his hand are the depths of the earth;
    the heights of the mountains are his also.
The sea is his, for he made it;
    for his hands formed the dry land.
O come, let us worship and bow down.

Psalm 95:1-6a

467

O come, let us worship and bow down,
    let us kneel before the LORD, our Maker!
For he is our God,
    and we are the people of his pasture,
    and the sheep of his hand.
Psalm 95:6-7

468

Have you not known? Have you not heard?
The LORD is the everlasting God,
    the Creator of the ends of the earth.
He does not faint or grow weary,
    his understanding is unsearchable.
He gives power to the faint,
    and to him who has no might he increases strength.
But they who wait for the LORD shall renew their strength,
    they shall mount up with wings like eagles,
they shall run and not be weary,
    they shall walk and not faint.
Isaiah 40:28-29, 31

469

Praise the LORD!
Praise, O servants of the LORD,
    praise the name of the LORD!
Blessed be the name of the LORD
    from this time forth and for evermore!
From the rising of the sun to its setting
    the name of the LORD is to be praised!
The LORD is high above all the nations,
    and his glory above the heavens!
Praise the LORD!
Psalm 113:1-4, 9b

470

Arise, shine; for your light has come,
and the glory of the LORD has risen upon you.
For behold, darkness shall cover the earth,

and thick darkness the peoples;
but the LORD will arise upon you,
   and his glory will be seen upon you.
And nations shall come to your light,
   and kings to the brightness of your rising
Lift up your eyes round about, and see.
Then you shall see and be radiant,
   your heart shall thrill and rejoice.

Isaiah 60:1-4a, 5a

471

O give thanks to the LORD, call on his name,
   make known his deeds among the peoples!
Sing to him, sing praises to him,
   tell of all his wonderful works!
Glory in his holy name;
   let the hearts of those who seek the LORD rejoice!
Seek the LORD and his strength,
   seek his presence continually!

Psalm 105:1-4

472

Praise the LORD!
For it is good to sing praises to our God;
   for he is gracious, and a song of praise is seemly.
He heals the brokenhearted,
   and binds up their wounds.

The Lord *is gracious and merciful,*
   slow to anger and abounding in steadfast love.
The Lord *is good to all,*
   and his compassion is over all that he has made.

Psalms 147:1, 3; 145:8-9

473

Blessed be the name of the LORD
   from this time forth and for evermore!
From the rising of the sun to its setting
   the name of the LORD is to be praised!

The L<small>ORD</small> is high above all nations,
    and his glory above the heavens!

Praise the Lord!
Praise the Lord, *O my soul!*
    I will praise the Lord *as long as I live;*
        I will sing praises to my God while I have being.

Psalms 113:2-4; 146:1-2

474

"Seek the L<small>ORD</small> while he may be found,
    call upon him while he is near;
let the wicked forsake his way,
    and the unrighteous man his thoughts;
let him return to the L<small>ORD</small>, that he may have mercy on him,
    and to our God, for he will abundantly pardon."

Isaiah 55:6-7

475

"Come to me, all who labor and are heavy laden, and I will give you rest. Take my yoke upon you, and learn from me; for I am gentle and lowly in heart, and you will find rest for your souls. For my yoke is easy, and my burden is light."

Matthew 11:28-30

476

Therefore, if any one is in Christ, he is a new creation; the old has passed away, behold, the new has come. All this is from God, who through Christ reconciled us to himself and gave us the ministry of reconciliation; that is, God was in Christ reconciling the world to himself, not counting their trespasses against them. For our sake he made him to be sin who knew no sin, so that in him we might become the righteousness of God.

2 Corinthians 5:17-19a, 21

477

But God, who is rich in mercy, out of the great love with which he loved us, even when we were dead through our trespasses, made us alive together with Christ (by grace you have been saved), and raised us up with him, and made us sit with him in the heavenly places in Christ Jesus, that in the coming ages he might show the immeasurable riches of his grace in kindness toward us in Christ Jesus. For by grace you have been saved through faith; and this is not your own doing, it is the gift of God.

Ephesians 2:4-8

478

While we were yet helpless, at the right time Christ died for the ungodly. God shows his love for us in that while we were yet sinners Christ died for us.

Romans 5:6, 8

479

The LORD is merciful and gracious,
    slow to anger and abounding in steadfast love.
He will not always chide,
    nor will he keep his anger for ever.
He does not deal with us according to our sins,
    nor requite us according to our iniquities.
For as the heavens are high above the earth,
    so great is his steadfast love toward those who fear him;
as far as the east is from the west,
    so far does he remove our transgressions from us.

Psalm 103:8-12

480

When the righteous cry for help, the LORD hears,
    and delivers them out of all their troubles.
The LORD is near to the brokenhearted,
    and saves the crushed in spirit.

Psalm 34:17-18

Litanies

481

O Thou the Source of every good and perfect gift; from thee comes grace sufficient for all our strivings, our suffering, our sin. For all that thou art and for the unnumbered blessings received from thine outstretched hand,

Accept our heartfelt thanksgiving.

From that coldness of heart which does not acknowledge thy goodness; from the self-centeredness which denies our need of thy grace; from our preoccupation with things immediate which makes us forget our dependence upon thee for health of body, mind and spirit,

Deliver us, dear Lord.

That our eyes may behold thy glory revealed in the world, with its every living thing; that our minds may perceive thy truth about life and death; that our hearts, filled with thy love, may respond in thy name to every human need,

Be pleased to hear us, good Lord.

That our thanksgiving may be expressed by worship that is sincere and true, by service to others that is unselfish and gladhearted, by humility when confronted by our inestimable debt to thee for thy manifold mercies,

Hear us, O Lord.

Praise God from whom all blessings flow;
  Praise him all creatures here below;
Praise him above, ye heavenly hosts;
  Praise Father, Son, and Holy Ghost. *Amen.*

482

Heavenly Father, we wait upon thee now with trust and love, and in full devotion to thy holy will. By all thy works; by the remembrance of all thy mercies; by the revelation of thyself to the prophets of old:

Teach us and draw us ever nearer to thee.

By the memory of Jesus Christ our Lord; by his life and teaching; by his life laid down for our salvation, and by the work of his Spirit in the world:

Teach us and draw us ever nearer to thee.

By the noble example of all the saints and martyrs of the church; by all that we owe to Christian faith and devotion down the years:

Teach us and draw us ever nearer to thee.

By the joys of life; by human love; by the affection and fidelity of friends; by the capacity for pleasure, and the sense of humor; by the persistency in our hearts of optimism and hope:

Teach us and draw us ever nearer to thee.

By the sorrows of life; by our falls and failures; by our disappointments and disasters; by the stern discipline of loneliness, of unrealized dreams, and the heartache of unsatisfied desire:

Teach us and draw us ever nearer to thee.

By our want of thee; by the hunger within us for the eternal life; by our search for truth and by our hands outstretched in prayer:

Teach us and draw us ever nearer to thee.

483

In peace let us pray to the Lord.

Lord, have mercy.

For the peace that is from above, and for the salvation of our souls, let us pray to the Lord.

Lord, have mercy.

For the peace of the whole world, for the well-being of the churches of God, and for the unity of all, let us pray to the Lord.

Lord, have mercy.

For this holy house, and for them that in faith, piety, and fear of God offer here their worship and praise, let us pray to the Lord.

Lord, have mercy.

Help, save, pity, defend us, O God, by thy grace. *Amen.*

484

O Savior of the world, who by thy cross and precious blood hast redeemed us;

Save us and help us, we humbly beseech thee, O Lord.

From the impatience which prevents us from finding thy purpose in pain and sorrow,

Save us, good Lord.

From refusing to share the suffering of the world, from seeking only comfort and pleasure, from forgetting those in distress, from the selfishness which brings needless grief to others,

Save us, good Lord.

Almighty Father, who in the afflictions of thy people art thyself afflicted, and art full of compassion and tender mercy; as we pray for those who suffer, for the aged and the dying;

We beseech thee to hear us, good Lord.

For all who are hindered in the race of life through no fault of their own; for the defective and the delicate; and for those who have been maimed and disabled;

We beseech thee to hear us, good Lord.

For those whose livelihood is insecure; for the hungry, the homeless and the destitute; for those who are overworked, down-trodden and in despair;

We beseech thee to hear us, good Lord.

For those who have to bear their burdens alone; for those who are in doubt and anguish of soul; for those who are oversensitive, and for those who suffer through their own wrongdoing;

We beseech thee to hear us, good Lord.

For all who do not pray for themselves, for all who have not the consolation of the prayers of others, and for all whose anguish is unrelieved by the knowledge of thy love;

We beseech thee to hear us, good Lord.

485

O God of grace and glory, we acknowledge before thee our unpayable indebtedness; we are the children of sacrifice; our choicest benedictions have been bought with the price of other blood and tears than our own; thou hast given us the inheritance of them that feared thy name.

O Lord, make us thankful.

For all saints and martyrs, prophets and apostles; for all soldiers of the common good who served thee in scorn of consequence and fell on sleep unashamed, of whom the world was not worthy,

O Lord, make us thankful.

For the cross of Christ and his exceeding bitter sacrifice; for the truths which there were brought to light, the love unbounded which there was freely given, and the costly salvation which there visited thy people,

O Lord, make us thankful.

By his loneliness in the Garden; by his betrayal and his trial; by the humiliation of his people's hate, the mockery of his thorny crown, and the bitterness of scourging; by the anguish of his cross; by his unfailing faith in thee and love for man,

O Lord, make us thankful.

Eternal God, may we, who owe our spiritual blessings to so great a cloud of witnessess, who have suffered before us, and to Christ, whose cross is our peace, walk as become those who are debtors to thy grace. From ingratitude, pride, hardness of heart, and all manner of evil requiting,

Good Lord, deliver us.

From neglect of blessing dearly purchased; from selfish use of opportunities for which good men died; from growing within our hearts the venomous roots of covetousness; from pampering ourselves with vain superfluities; and from all spendthrift wasting of our costly heritage,

Good Lord, deliver us.

Gird us, we beseech thee, with gratitude and fidelity; devote us to the service of mankind with more courageous zeal; free us from the detaining reluctance of our fear, selfishness, and unbelief; and at this altar of remembrance, may we, O Christ, join afresh the honorable company of thy true servants who in sacrificial living share the fellowship of thy cross.

Lord, have mercy upon us and grant us this blessing. Amen.

486

O God, before whose face the empires of the past have risen and fallen away, establish this nation in righteousness; and in personal character and public integrity make her foundations sure.

Lord, hear our prayer and mercifully bless this people.

From the ravages of crime, the disgrace of political corruption, and all malicious designs of lawless men,

Good Lord, deliver us.

From prejudice of race and color, making schism in the common wealth; from all inequity that, causing a few to be rich and many poor, begets ill will and spoils fraternity; from all loss of liberties bequeathed us by our sires and from careless acceptance of our heritage and neglect of its responsibilities,

Good Lord, deliver us.

From the decline of pure religion, from failure of moral fiber in our citizenship, from all accounting of things material above virtues spiritual; from vulgarity of life, loss of social conscience, and collapse of national character,

Good Lord, deliver us.

By the deep faiths on which the foundations of our land were laid and by the sacrifices of its pioneers,

We beseech thee to hear us, O Lord.

By the memory of leaders in the nation, whose wisdom has saved us, whose devotion has chastened us, whose characters have inspired us,

We beseech thee to hear us, O Lord.

By the undeserved wealth of a great continent committed to us and by our trusteeship of power to work weal or woe on the earth,

We beseech thee to hear us, O Lord.

Keep us from pride of mind, and from boasting tongues deliver us; save our national loyalty from narrowness and our flag from selfish shame; by our love for our land may we measure the love of others for their lands, honoring their devotion as we honor our own; and acknowledging thee one God, may we see all mankind one family and so govern our national affairs that the whole world may become one brotherhood of peoples.

Lord, hear our prayer and mercifully bless this people. Amen.

487

Jesus said, "And preach as you go, saying, 'The kingdom of heaven is at hand.' Heal the sick, raise the dead, cleanse lepers, cast out demons. You received without pay, give without pay."

Our Father who art in heaven,
Thy kingdom come,

Thy will be done,
On earth as it is in heaven.

At that time the disciples came to Jesus, saying, "Who is the greatest in the kingdom of heaven?" And calling to him a child, he put him in the midst of them, and said, "Truly, I say to you, unless you turn and become like children, you will never enter the kingdom of heaven."

Our Father who art in heaven,
Thy kingdom come,
Thy will be done,
On earth as it is in heaven.

"Every one then who hears these words of mine and does them will be like a wise man who built his house upon the rock; and the rain fell, and the floods came, and the winds blew and beat upon that house, but it did not fall, because it had been founded on the rock."

Our Father who art in heaven,
Thy kingdom come,
Thy will be done,
On earth as it is in heaven.

"When the Son of man comes in his glory, and all the angels with him, then he will sit on his glorious throne. Before him will be gathered all the nations, and he will separate them one from another as a shepherd separates the sheep from the goats."

Our Father who art in heaven,
Thy kingdom come,
Thy will be done,
On earth as it is in heaven.

Jesus said to them, "The light is with you for a little longer. Walk while you have the light, lest the darkness overtake you; he who walks in the darkness does not know where he goes. While you have the light, believe in the light, that you may become sons of light."

Our Father who art in heaven,
Thy kingdom come,
Thy will be done,
On earth as it is in heaven.

488

For the whole church of Christ, scattered abroad in five continents, and bearing many names, that it may be no longer torn asunder, divided in itself or weak, but may become a glorious church, without spot or blemish, fulfilling the perfect will:

Thy will be done in thy church, we beseech thee, O Lord.

For the churches that are passing through times of suffering and persecution, that their faith and courage may not fail nor their love grow cold:

Save them and us, we beseech thee, O Lord.

For the churches that are strong in faith, that they may abound in grace and in knowledge and love of thee:

Use them and us, we beseech thee, O Lord.

For all weak and struggling churches, that they may persevere and be strong, overcoming those forces which hinder their growth or threaten their existence:

Sustain them and us, we beseech thee, O Lord.

For the younger churches of Asia, Africa, and the islands of the sea, that they may grow into full stature of the completeness of Christ, bringing new treasures into the church of the ages:

Direct their steps and ours, we beseech thee, O Lord.

For the older churches of the east and the west, that they increase in wisdom and humility and find new ways to make the message of the gospel understood in the world of today:

Renew them and us, we beseech thee, O Lord.

For our brotherhood, that we may hold fast to the truth, be delivered from all error, and walk with one another in the way of love and unity:

Teach us and guide us, we beseech thee, O Lord.

For the several councils of the churches that through them Christians may the sooner overcome their reluctance to cooperate with one another, transcend their differences, and be knit more closely together in a fellowship of understanding love.

Draw all churches nearer to one another,
we beseech thee, O Lord.

O sovereign and almighty God, bless all thy people and all thy flock; give thy peace, thy help, thy love to us thy servants, the sheep of thy fold, that we may be united in the bond of peace, one body and one Spirit, in one hope of our calling, in thy divine boundless love, for the sake of Jesus Christ, the great Shepherd of the sheep. *Amen.*

489

All have sinned
and come short of the glory of God.
ST. PAUL'S LETTER TO THE ROMANS

The hatred which divides nation from nation, race from race, class from class,

Father, forgive.

The covetous desires of men and nations to possess what is not their own,

Father, forgive.

The greed which exploits the labors of men, and lays waste the earth,

Father, forgive.

Our envy of the welfare and happiness of others,

Father, forgive.

Our indifference to the plight of the homeless and the refugee,

Father, forgive.

The lust which uses for ignoble ends the bodies of men and women,

Father, forgive.

The pride which leads us to trust in ourselves, and not in God,

Father, forgive.

Be kind one to another, tenderhearted,
forgiving one another,
as God in Christ forgave you.

ST. PAUL'S LETTER TO THE EPHESIANS

Affirmation of Faith

490

We confess that Jesus is the Christ, the Son of the living God, and proclaim him Lord and Savior of the world. In his name and by his grace we accept our mission of witness and service to mankind. We rejoice in God our Father, maker of heaven and earth, and in the covenant of love by which he has bound us to himself. Through baptism into Christ we enter into newness of life and are made one with the whole people of God. In the fellowship and communion of the Holy Spirit we are joined to one another in brotherhood and in obedience to Christ. At the table of the Lord we celebrate with thanksgiving his saving acts and his presence. Within the universal church we receive the gift of ministry and the light of scripture. In the bonds of Christian faith we yield ourselves to God, that we may serve him whose kingdom has no end. Blessing, glory, and honor be to him forever. *Amen.*

491

I believe in God the Father Almighty, Maker of heaven and earth, and in Jesus Christ his only son our Lord, who was conceived by the Holy Ghost, born of the Virgin Mary, suffered under Pontius Pilate, was crucified, dead, and buried. He descended into hell; the third day he rose again from the dead; he ascended into heaven, and sitteth on the right hand of God the Father Almighty. From thence he shall come to judge the quick and the dead.

I believe in the Holy Ghost, the holy Catholic Church, the communion of saints, the forgiveness of sins, the resurrection of the body, and the life everlasting. *Amen.*

492

I believe in one God the Father Almighty, Maker of heaven and earth, and of all things visible and invisible:

And in one Lord Jesus Christ, the only-begotten Son of God; begotten of his Father before all worlds, God of God, Light of Light, Very God of very God; Begotten, not made, Being of one substance with the Father, By whom all things were made: Who for us men and for our salvation came down from heaven; And was incarnate by the Holy Ghost of the Virgin Mary, and was made man; And was crucified also for us under Pontius Pilate. He suffered and was buried: And the third day he rose again according to the Scriptures: And ascended into heaven, And sitteth on the right hand of the Father: And he shall come again, with glory, to judge both the quick and the dead; Whose kingdom shall have no end.

And I believe in the Holy Ghost, the Lord, and Giver of Life, Who proceedeth from the Father and the Son, Who with the Father and the Son together is worshiped and glorified; Who spake by the Prophets: And I believe one Catholic and Apostolic Church; I acknowledge one Baptism for the remission of sins; And I look for the Resurrection of the dead; And the Life of the world to come. *Amen.*

493

We believe that God is Spirit, and they who worship him must worship in spirit and truth.

We believe that God is Light, and if we walk in the light, as he is in the light, we have fellowship with one another.

We believe that God is Love, and he who loves is born of God and knows God.

We believe that Jesus is the Son of God; and as many as are led by the spirit of God, they are sons of God.

We believe that Jesus is the Way, the Truth, and the Life; and that God sent his Son into the world that the world should be saved through him.

We believe that we are children of God, and that God gave us eternal life, and this life is in his Son.

We believe that if we confess our sins, he is faithful and just to forgive us our sins.

We believe that the world passes away, and the lust of it; but he who does the will of God abides forever.

494

We believe in God, the Eternal Spirit, Father of our Lord Jesus Christ and our Father, and to his deeds we testify:

He calls the worlds into being,
  creates man in his own image
  and sets before him the ways of life and death.

He seeks in holy love to save all people from aimlessness and sin.

He judges men and nations by his righteous will declared through prophets and apostles.

In Jesus Christ, the man of Nazareth, our crucified and risen Lord,
  he has come to us
  and shared our common lot,
  conquering sin and death
  and reconciling the world to himself.

He bestows upon us his Holy Spirit,
  creating and renewing the Church of Jesus Christ,
  binding in covenant faithful people of all ages,
  tongues, and races.

He calls us into his church
  to accept the cost and joy of discipleship,
  to be his servants in the service of men,
  to proclaim the gospel to all the world,
  and resist the powers of evil,
  to share in Christ's baptism and eat at his table,
  to join him in his passion and victory.

He promises to all who trust him
  forgiveness of sins and fullness of grace,
  courage in the struggle for justice and peace,
  his presence in trial and rejoicing,
  and eternal life in his kingdom which has no end.

Blessing and honor, glory and power be unto him. *Amen.*

Scripture Readings

495

In the beginning God created the heavens and the earth. The earth was without form and void, and darkness was upon the face of the deep; and the Spirit of God was moving over the face of the waters.

And God said, "Let there be light"; and there was light. And God saw that the light was good; and God separated the light from the darkness. God called the light Day, and the darkness he called Night. And there was evening and there was morning, one day.

Genesis 1:1-5

496

And God spoke all these words, saying,

"I am the LORD your God, who brought you out of the land of Egypt, out of the house of bondage.

"You shall have no other gods before me.

"You shall not make for yourself a graven image, or any likeness of anything that is in heaven above, or that is in the earth beneath, or that is in the water under the earth; you shall not bow down to them or serve them; for I the LORD your God am a jealous God, visiting the iniquity of the fathers upon the children to the third and the fourth generation of those who hate me, but showing steadfast love to thousands of those who love me and keep my commandments.

"You shall not take the name of the LORD your God in vain; for the LORD will not hold him guiltless who takes his name in vain.

"Remember the sabbath day, to keep it holy. Six days you shall labor, and do all your work; but the seventh day is a sabbath to the LORD your God; in it you shall not do any work, you, or your son, or your daughter, your manservant, or your maidservant, or your cattle, or the sojourner who is within your gates; for in six days the LORD made heaven and earth, the sea, and all that is in them, and rested the seventh day; therefore the LORD blessed the sabbath day and hallowed it.

"Honor your father and your mother, that your days may be long in the land which the LORD your God gives you.

"You shall not kill.

"You shall not commit adultery.

"You shall not steal.

"You shall not bear false witness against your neighbor.

"You shall not covet your neighbor's house; you shall not covet your neighbor's wife, or his manservant, or his maidservant, or his ox, or his ass, or anything that is your neighbor's."

Exodus 20:1-17

497

"Hear, O Israel: The LORD our God is one LORD; and you shall love the LORD your God with all your heart, and with all your soul, and with all your might. And these words which I command you this day shall be upon your heart; and you shall teach them diligently to your children, and shall talk of them when you sit in your house, and when you walk by the way, and when you lie down, and when you rise. And you shall bind them as a sign upon your hand, and they shall be as frontlets between your eyes. And you shall write them on the doorposts of your house and on your gates."

Deuteronomy 6:4-9

498

"Blessed art thou, O LORD, the God of Israel our father, for ever and ever. Thine, O LORD, is the greatness, and the power, and the glory, and the victory, and the majesty; for all that is in the heavens and in the earth is thine; thine is the kingdom, O LORD, and thou art exalted as head above all. Both riches and honor come from thee, and thou rulest over all. In thy hand are power and might; and in thy hand it is to make great and to give strength to all. And now we thank thee, our God, and praise thy glorious name."

1 Chronicles 29:10b-13

499

Happy is the man who finds wisdom,
    and the man who gets understanding,
for the gain from it is better than gain from silver
    and its profit better than gold.

She is more precious than jewels,
    and nothing you desire can compare with her.
Long life is in her right hand;
    in her left hand are riches and honor.
Her ways are ways of pleasantness,
    and all her paths are peace.
She is a tree of life to those who lay hold of her;
    those who hold her fast are called happy.

The LORD by wisdom founded the earth;
    by understanding he established the heavens;
by his knowledge the deeps broke forth,
    and the clouds drop down the dew.

My son, keep sound wisdom and discretion;
    let them not escape from your sight,
and they will be life for your soul
    and adornment for your neck.
Then you will walk on your way securely
    and your foot will not stumble.
If you sit down, you will not be afraid;
    when you lie down, your sleep will be sweet.
Do not be afraid of sudden panic,
    or of the ruin of the wicked, when it comes;
for the LORD will be your confidence
    and will keep your foot from being caught.

Proverbs 3:13-26

500

In the year that King Uzziah died I saw the Lord sitting upon a throne, high and lifted up; and his train filled the temple. Above him stood the seraphim; each had six wings: with two he covered his face, and with two he covered his feet, and with two he flew. And one called to another and said:

"Holy, holy, holy is the LORD of hosts;
    the whole earth is full of his glory."

And the foundations of the thresholds shook at the voice of him who called, and the house was filled with smoke. And I said: "Woe is me! For I am lost;

for I am a man of unclean lips, and I dwell in the midst of a people of unclean lips; for my eyes have seen the King, the LORD of hosts!"

Then flew one of the seraphim to me, having in his hand a burning coal which he had taken with tongs from the altar. And he touched my mouth, and said: "Behold, this has touched your lips; your guilt is taken away, and your sin forgiven." And I heard the voice of the Lord saying, "Whom shall I send, and who will go for us?" Then I said, "Here am I! Send me."

Isaiah 6:1-8

501

The people who walked in darkness
    have seen a great light;
those who dwelt in a land of deep darkness,
    on them has light shined.
Thou hast multiplied the nation,
    thou hast increased its joy;
they rejoice before thee
    as with joy at the harvest,
    as men rejoice when they divide the spoil.
For the yoke of his burden,
    and the staff for his shoulder,
    the rod of his oppressor,
    thou hast broken as on the day of Midian.
For every boot of the tramping warrior in battle tumult
    and every garment rolled in blood
    will be burned as fuel for the fire.
For to us a child is born,
    to us a son is given;
and the government will be upon his shoulder,
    and his name will be called
"Wonderful Counselor, Mighty God,
    Everlasting Father, Prince of Peace."
Of the increase of his government and of peace
    there will be no end,
upon the throne of David, and over his kingdom,
    to establish it, and to uphold it
with justice and with righteousness
    from this time forth and for evermore.

Isaiah 9:2-7

502

There shall come forth a shoot from the stump of Jesse,
    and a branch shall grow out of his roots.
And the Spirit of the LORD shall rest upon him,
    the spirit of wisdom and understanding,
    the spirit of counsel and might,
    the spirit of knowledge and the fear of the LORD.
And his delight shall be in the fear of the LORD.

He shall not judge by what his eyes see,
    or decide by what his ears hear;
but with righteousness he shall judge the poor,
    and decide with equity for the meek of the earth;
and he shall smite the earth with the rod of his mouth,
    and with the breath of his lips he shall slay the wicked.
Righteousness shall be the girdle of his waist,
    and faithfulness the girdle of his loins.

The wolf shall dwell with the lamb,
    and the leopard shall lie down with the kid,
and the calf and the lion and the fatling together,
    and a little child shall lead them.
The cow and the bear shall feed;
    their young shall lie down together;
    and the lion shall eat straw like the ox.
The sucking child shall play over the hole of the asp,
    and the weaned child shall put his hand on the adder's den.
They shall not hurt or destroy
    in all my holy mountain;
for the earth shall be full of the knowledge of the LORD
    as the waters cover the sea.

In that day the root of Jesse shall stand as an ensign to the peoples; him
shall the nations seek, and his dwellings shall be glorious.

Isaiah 11:1-10

503

The wilderness and the dry land shall be glad,
    the desert shall rejoice and blossom;
like the crocus it shall blossom abundantly,
    and rejoice with joy and singing.

The glory of Lebanon shall be given to it,
 the majesty of Carmel and Sharon.
They shall see the glory of the LORD,
 the majesty of our God.

Strengthen the weak hands,
 and make firm the feeble knees.
Say to those who are of a fearful heart,
 "Be strong, fear not!
Behold, your God
 will come with vengeance,
with the recompense of God.
 He will come and save you."

Then the eyes of the blind shall be opened,
 and the ears of the deaf unstopped;
then shall the lame man leap like a hart,
 and the tongue of the dumb sing for joy.
For waters shall break forth in the wilderness,
 and streams in the desert;
the burning sand shall become a pool,
 and the thirsty ground springs of water;
the haunt of jackals shall become a swamp,
 the grass shall become reeds and rushes.

And a highway shall be there,
 and it shall be called the Holy Way;
the unclean shall not pass over it,
 and fools shall not err therein.
No lion shall be there,
 nor shall any ravenous beast come up on it;
they shall not be found there,
 but the redeemed shall walk there.
And the ransomed of the LORD shall return,
 and come to Zion with singing;
everlasting joy shall be upon their heads;
 they shall obtain joy and gladness,
 and sorrow and sighing shall flee away.

Isaiah 35

504

Comfort, comfort my people,
  says your God.
Speak tenderly to Jerusalem,
  and cry to her
that her warfare is ended,
  that her iniquity is pardoned,
that she has received from the LORD's hand
  double for all her sins.

A voice cries:
"In the wilderness prepare the way of the LORD,
  make straight in the desert a highway for our God.
Every valley shall be lifted up,
  and every mountain and hill be made low;
the uneven ground shall become level,
  and the rough places a plain.
And the glory of the LORD shall be revealed,
  and all flesh shall see it together,
  for the mouth of the LORD has spoken."

A voice says, "Cry!"
  And I said, "What shall I cry?"
All flesh is grass,
  and all its beauty is like the flower of the field.
The grass withers, the flower fades,
  when the breath of the LORD blows upon it;
  surely the people is grass.
The grass withers, the flower fades;
  but the word of our God will stand for ever.

Get you up to a high mountain,
  O Zion, herald of good tidings;
lift up your voice with strength,
  O Jerusalem, herald of good tidings,
  lift it up, fear not;
say to the cities of Judah,
  "Behold your God!"
Behold, the Lord GOD comes with might,
  and his arm rules for him;
  behold, his reward is with him,
  and his recompense before him.

He will feed his flock like a shepherd,
   he will gather the lambs in his arms,
he will carry them in his bosom,
   and gently lead those that are with young.
Isaiah 40:1-11

505

To whom then will you compare me,
   that I should be like him? says the Holy One.
Lift up your eyes on high and see:
   who created these?
He who brings out their host by number,
   calling them all by name;
by the greatness of his might,
   and because he is strong in power
   not one is missing.

Why do you say, O Jacob,
   and speak, O Israel.
"My way is hid from the LORD,
   and my right is disregarded by my God"?
Have you not known? Have you not heard?
The LORD is the everlasting God,
   the Creator of the ends of the earth.
He does not faint or grow weary,
   his understanding is unsearchable.
He gives power to the faint,
   and to him who has no might he increases strength.
Even youths shall faint and be weary,
   and young men shall fall exhausted;
but they who wait for the LORD shall renew their strength,
   they shall mount up with wings like eagles,
they shall run and not be weary,
   they shall walk and not faint.
Isaiah 40:25-31

506

Behold my servant, whom I uphold,
   my chosen, in whom my soul delights;
I have put my Spirit upon him,

he will bring forth justice to the nations.
He will not cry or lift up his voice,
    or make it heard in the street;
a bruised reed he will not break,
    and a dimly burning wick he will not quench;
    he will faithfully bring forth justice.
He will not fail or be discouraged
    till he has established justice in the earth;
    and the coastlands wait for his law.

Thus says God, the LORD,
    who created the heavens and stretched them out,
    who spread forth the earth and what comes from it,
who gives breath to the people upon it
    and spirit to those who walk in it:
"I am the LORD, I have called you in righteousness,
    I have taken you by the hand and kept you;
I have given you as a covenant to the people,
    a light to the nations,
    to open the eyes that are blind,
to bring out the prisoners from the dungeon,
    from the prison those who sit in darkness.
I am the LORD, that is my name;
    my glory I give to no other,
    nor my praise to graven images.
Behold, the former things have come to pass,
    and new things I now declare;
before they spring forth
    I tell you of them."

Sing to the LORD a new song,
    his praise from the end of the earth!
Isaiah 42:1-10a

507

Who has believed what we have heard?
    And to whom has the arm of the LORD been revealed?
For he grew up before him like a young plant,
    and like a root out of dry ground;
he had no form or comeliness that we should look at him,
    and no beauty that we should desire him.

He was despised and rejected by men;
    a man of sorrows, and acquainted with grief;
and as one from whom men hide their faces
    he was despised, and we esteemed him not.

Surely he has borne our griefs
    and carried our sorrows;
yet we esteemed him stricken,
    smitten by God, and afflicted.
But he was wounded for our transgressions,
    he was bruised for our iniquities;
upon him was the chastisement that made us whole,
    and with his stripes we are healed.
All we like sheep have gone astray;
    we have turned every one to his own way;
and the LORD has laid on him
    the iniquity of us all.

He was oppressed, and he was afflicted,
    yet he opened not his mouth;
like a lamb that is led to the slaughter,
    and like a sheep that before its shearers is dumb,
    so he opened not his mouth.
By oppression and judgment he was taken away;
    and as for his generation, who considered
that he was cut off out of the land of the living,
    stricken for the transgression of my people?
And they made his grave with the wicked
    and with a rich man in his death,
although he had done no violence,
    and there was no deceit in his mouth.

Yet it was the will of the LORD to bruise him;
    he has put him to grief;
when he makes himself an offering for sin,
    he shall see his offspring, he shall prolong his days;
the will of the LORD shall prosper in his hand;
    he shall see the fruit of the travail of his soul and be satisfied;
by his knowledge shall the righteous one, my servant,
    make many to be accounted righteous;
    and he shall bear their iniquities.
Therefore I will divide him a portion with the great,
    and he shall divide the spoil with the strong;

because he poured out his soul to death,
and was numbered with the transgressors;
yet he bore the sin of many,
and made intercession for the transgressors.

Isaiah 53

508

"Ho, every one who thirsts, come to the waters;
and he who has no money,
come, buy and eat!
Come, buy wine and milk
without money and without price.
Why do you spend your money for that which is not bread,
and your labor for that which does not satisfy?
Hearken diligently to me, and eat what is good,
and delight yourselves in fatness.
Incline your ear, and come to me;
hear, that your soul may live;
and I will make with you an everlasting covenant,
my steadfast, sure love for David.
Behold, I made him a witness to the peoples,
a leader and commander for the peoples.
Behold, you shall call nations that you know not,
and nations that knew you not shall run to you,
because of the LORD your God, and of the Holy One of Israel,
for he has glorified you.

"Seek the LORD while he may be found,
call upon him while he is near;
let the wicked forsake his way,
and the unrighteous man his thoughts;
let him return to the LORD, that he may have mercy on him,
and to our God, for he will abundantly pardon.
For my thoughts are not your thoughts,
neither are your ways my ways, says the LORD.
For as the heavens are higher than the earth,
so are my ways higher than your ways
and my thoughts than your thoughts.
"For as the rain and the snow come down from heaven,
and return not thither but water the earth,
making it bring forth and sprout,

giving seed to the sower and bread to the eater,
so shall my word be that goes forth from my mouth;
   it shall not return to me empty,
but it shall accomplish that which I purpose,
   and prosper in the thing for which I sent it.

"For you shall go out in joy,
   and be led forth in peace;
the mountains and the hills before you
      shall break forth into singing,
      and all the trees of the field shall clap their hands.
Instead of the thorn shall come up the cypress;
      instead of the brier shall come up the myrtle;
and it shall be to the LORD for a memorial,
      for an everlasting sign which shall not be cut off."

Isaiah 55

509

"Behold, the days are coming, says the LORD, when I will make a new covenant with the house of Israel and the house of Judah, not like the covenant which I made with their fathers when I took them by the hand to bring them out of the land of Egypt, my covenant which they broke, though I was their husband, says the LORD. But this is the covenant which I will make with the house of Israel after those days, says the LORD: I will put my law within them, and I will write it upon their hearts; and I will be their God, and they shall be my people. And no longer shall each man teach his neighbor and each his brother, saying, 'Know the LORD,' for they shall all know me, from the least of them to the greatest, says the LORD; for I will forgive their iniquity, and I will remember their sin no more."

Jeremiah 31:31-34

510

Seek good, and not evil,
   that you may live;
and so the LORD, the God of hosts, will be with you,
   as you have said.
Hate evil, and love good,
   and establish justice in the gate;
it may be that the LORD, the God of hosts,
      will be gracious to the remnant of Joseph.

"I hate, I despise your feasts,
    and I take no delight in your solemn assemblies.
Even though you offer me your burnt offerings and cereal offerings,
    I will not accept them,
and the peace offerings of your fatted beasts
    I will not look upon.
Take away from me the noise of your songs;
    to the melody of your harps I will not listen.
But let justice roll down like waters,
    and righteousness like an ever-flowing stream.

"With what shall I come before the LORD,
    and bow myself before God on high?
Shall I come before him with burnt offerings,
    with calves a year old?
Will the LORD be pleased with thousands of rams,
    with ten thousands of rivers of oil?
Shall I give my first-born for my transgression,
    the fruit of my body for the sin of my soul?"
He has showed you, O man, what is good;
    and what does the LORD require of you
but to do justice, and to love kindness,
    and to walk humbly with your God?
Amos 5:14-15, 21-24; Micah 6:6-8

511

Now when Jesus was born in Bethlehem of Judea in the days of Herod
the king, behold, wise men from the East came to Jerusalem, saying, "Where
is he who has been born king of the Jews? For we have seen his star in the
East, and have come to worship him." When Herod the king heard this, he
was troubled, and all Jerusalem with him; and assembling all the chief priests
and scribes of the people, he inquired of them where the Christ was to be
born. They told him, "In Bethlehem of Judea; for so it is written by the
prophet:
    'And you, O Bethlehem, in the land of Judah,
    are by no means least among the rulers of Judah;
    for from you shall come a ruler
    who will govern my people Israel.' "
    Then Herod summoned the wise men secretly and ascertained from them
what time the star appeared; and he sent them to Bethlehem, saying, "Go
and search diligently for the child, and when you have found him bring me

word, that I too may come and worship him." When they had heard the king they went their way; and lo, the star which they had seen in the East went before them, till it came to rest over the place where the child was. When they saw the star, they rejoiced exceedingly with great joy; and going into the house they saw the child with Mary his mother, and they fell down and worshiped him. Then, opening their treasures, they offered him gifts, gold and frankincense and myrrh. And being warned in a dream not to return to Herod, they departed to their own country by another way.

Now when they had departed, behold, an angel of the Lord appeared to Joseph in a dream and said, "Rise, take the child and his mother, and flee to Egypt, and remain there till I tell you; for Herod is about to search for the child, to destroy him," And he rose and took the child and his mother by night, and departed to Egypt, and remained there until the death of Herod. This was to fulfil what the Lord had spoken by the prophet, "Out of Egypt have I called my son."

Then Herod, when he saw that he had been tricked by the wise men, was in a furious rage, and he sent and killed all the male children in Bethlehem and in all that region who were two years old or under, according to the time which he had ascertained from the wise men.

Matthew 2:1-16

512

Seeing the crowds, he went up on the mountain, and when he sat down his disciples came to him. And he opened his mouth and taught them, saying:

"Blessed are the poor in spirit, for theirs is the kingdom of heaven.

"Blessed are those who mourn, for they shall be comforted.

"Blessed are the meek, for they shall inherit the earth.

"Blessed are those who hunger and thirst for righteousness, for they shall be satisfied.

"Blessed are the merciful, for they shall obtain mercy.

"Blessed are the pure in heart, for they shall see God.

"Blessed are the peacemakers, for they shall be called sons of God.

"Blessed are those who are persecuted for righteousness' sake, for theirs is the kingdom of heaven.

"Blessed are you when men revile you and persecute you and utter all kinds of evil against you falsely on my account. Rejoice and be glad, for your reward is great in heaven, for so men persecuted the prophets who were before you."

Matthew 5:1-12

513

"Beware of practicing your piety before men in order to be seen by them; for then you will have no reward from your Father who is in heaven.

"Thus, when you give alms, sound no trumpet before you, as the hypocrites do in the synagogues and in the streets, that they may be praised by men. Truly, I say to you, they have their reward. But when you give alms, do not let your left hand know what your right hand is doing, so that your alms may be in secret; and your Father who sees in secret will reward you.

"And when you pray, you must not be like the hypocrites; for they love to stand and pray in the synagogues and at the street corners, that they may be seen by men. Truly, I say to you, they have their reward. But when you pray, go into your room and shut the door and pray to your Father who is in secret; and your Father who sees in secret will reward you.

"And in praying do not heap up empty phrases as the Gentiles do; for they think that they will be heard for their many words. Do not be like them, for your Father knows what you need before you ask him. Pray then like this:

Our Father who art in heaven,
Hallowed be thy name.
Thy kingdom come,
Thy will be done,
    On earth as it is in heaven.
Give us this day our daily bread;
And forgive us our debts,
    As we also have forgiven our debtors;
And lead us not into temptation,
    But deliver us from evil.

For if you forgive men their trespasses, your heavenly Father also will forgive you; but if you do not forgive men their trespasses, neither will your Father forgive your trespasses."

Matthew 6:1-15

514

And Jesus went about all the cities and villages, teaching in their synagogues and preaching the gospel of the kingdom, and healing every disease and every infirmity. When he saw the crowds, he had compassion for them, because they were harassed and helpless, like sheep without a shepherd. Then he said to his disciples, "The harvest is plentiful, but the laborers are few; pray therefore the Lord of the harvest to send out laborers into his harvest."

And Jesus came and said to them, "All authority in heaven and on earth has been given to me. Go therefore and make disciples of all nations, baptizing them in the name of the Father and of the Son and of the Holy Spirit, teaching them to observe all that I have commanded you; and lo, I am with you always, to the close of the age."

Matthew 9:35-38; 28:18-20

5¹5

Now when Jesus came into the district of Caesarea Philippi, he asked his disciples, "Who do men say that the Son of man is?" And they said, "Some say John the Baptist, others say Elijah, and others Jeremiah or one of the prophets." He said to them, "But who do you say that I am?" Simon Peter replied, "You are the Christ, the Son of the living God." And Jesus answered him, "Blessed are you, Simon Bar-Jona! For flesh and blood has not revealed this to you, but my Father who is in heaven. And I tell you, you are Peter, and on this rock I will build my church, and the powers of death shall not prevail against it. I will give you the keys of the kingdom of heaven, and whatever you bind on earth shall be bound in heaven, and whatever you loose on earth shall be loosed in heaven." Then he strictly charged the disciples to tell no one that he was the Christ.

Then Jesus told his disciples, "If any man would come after me, let him deny himself and take up his cross and follow me. For whoever would save his life will lose it, and whoever loses his life for my sake will find it. For what will it profit a man, if he gains the whole world and forfeits his life? Or what shall a man give in return for his life? For the Son of man is to come with his angels in the glory of his Father, and then he will repay every man for what he has done. Truly, I say to you, there are some standing here who will not taste death before they see the Son of man coming in his kingdom."

Matthew 16:13-20; 24-28

5¹6

And when they drew near to Jerusalem and came to Bethphage, to the Mount of Olives, then Jesus sent two disciples, saying to them, "Go into the village opposite you, and immediately you will find an ass tied, and a colt with her; untie them and bring them to me. If any one says anything to you, you shall say, 'The Lord has need of them,' and he will send them immediately."

This took place to fulfill what was spoken by the prophet, saying,

"Tell the daughter of Zion,

Behold, your king is coming to you,
humble, and mounted on an ass,
and on a colt, the foal of an ass."

The disciples went and did as Jesus had directed them; they brought the ass and the colt, and put their garments on them, and he sat thereon.

Most of the crowd spread their garments on the road, and others cut branches from the trees and spread them on the road. And the crowds that went before him and that followed him shouted, "Hosanna to the Son of David! Blessed is he who comes in the name of the Lord! Hosanna in the highest!" And when he entered Jerusalem, all the city was stirred, saying, "Who is this?" And the crowds said, "This is the prophet Jesus from Nazareth of Galilee."

Matthew 21:1-11

517

"When the Son of man comes in his glory, and all the angels with him, then he will sit on his glorious throne. Before him will be gathered all the nations, and he will separate them one from another as a shepherd separates the sheep from the goats, and he will place the sheep at his right hand, but the goats at the left. Then the King will say to those at his right hand, 'Come, O blessed of my Father, inherit the kingdom prepared for you from the foundation of the world; for I was hungry and you gave me food, I was thirsty and you gave me drink, I was a stranger and you welcomed me, I was naked and you clothed me, I was sick and you visited me, I was in prison and you came to me.' Then the righteous will answer him. 'Lord, when did we see thee hungry and feed thee, or thirsty and give thee drink? And when did we see thee a stranger and welcome thee, or naked and clothe thee? And when did we see thee sick or in prison and visit thee?' And the King will answer them, 'Truly, I say to you, as you did it to one of the least of these my brethren, you did it to me.' Then he will say to those at his left hand, 'Depart from me, you cursed, into the eternal fire prepared for the devil and his angels; for I was hungry and you gave me no food, I was thirsty and you gave me no drink, I was a stranger and you did not welcome me, naked and you did not clothe me, sick and in prison and you did not visit me.' Then they also will answer, 'Lord, when did we see thee hungry or thirsty or a stranger or naked or sick or in prison, and did not minister to thee?' Then he will answer them, 'Truly, I say to you, as you did it not to one of the least of these, you did it not to me.' And they will go away into eternal punishment, but the righteous into eternal life."

Matthew 25:31-46

518

Now after the sabbath, toward the dawn of the first day of the week, Mary Magdalene and the other Mary went to see the sepulchre. And behold, there was a great earthquake; for an angel of the Lord descended from heaven and came and rolled back the stone, and sat upon it. His appearance was like lightning, and his raiment white as snow. And for fear of him the guards trembled and became like dead men. But the angel said to the women, "Do not be afraid; for I know that you seek Jesus who was crucified. He is not here; for he has risen, as he said. Come, see the place where he lay. Then go quickly and tell his disciples that he has risen from the dead, and behold, he is going before you to Galilee; there you will see him. Lo, I have told you." So they departed quickly from the tomb with fear and great joy, and ran to tell his disciples. And behold, Jesus met them and said, "Hail!" And they came up and took hold of his feet and worshiped him. Then Jesus said to them, "Do not be afraid; go and tell my brethren to go to Galilee, and there they will see me."

Matthew 28:1-10

519

And one of the scribes came up and heard them disputing with one another, and seeing that he answered them well, asked him, "Which commandment is the first of all?" Jesus answered, "The first is, 'Hear, O Israel: The Lord our God, the Lord is one; and you shall love the Lord your God with all your heart, and with all your soul, and with all your mind, and with all your strength.' The second is this, 'You shall love your neighbor as yourself.' There is no other commandment greater than these." And the scribe said to him, "You are right, Teacher; you have truly said that he is one, and there is no other but he; and to love him with all the heart, and with all the understanding, and with all the strength, and to love one's neighbor as oneself, is much more than all whole burnt offerings and sacrifices." And when Jesus saw that he answered wisely, he said to him, "You are not far from the kingdom of God." And after that no one dared to ask him any question.

Mark 12:28-34

520

And Mary said,
   "My soul magnifies the Lord,
and my spirit rejoices in God my Savior,
for he has regarded the low estate of his handmaiden.
For behold, henceforth all generations will call me blessed;

for he who is mighty has done great things for me,
and holy is his name.
And his mercy is on those who fear him
from generation to generation.
He has shown strength with his arm,
he has scattered the proud in the imagination of their hearts,
he has put down the mighty from their thrones,
and exalted those of low degree;
he has filled the hungry with good things,
and the rich he has sent empty away.
He has helped his servant Israel,
in remembrance of his mercy,
as he spoke to our fathers,
to Abraham and to his posterity for ever."
Luke 1:46-55

521

"Blessed be the Lord God of Israel,
for he has visited and redeemed his people,
and has raised up a horn of salvation for us
in the house of his servant David,
as he spoke by the mouth of his holy prophets from of old,
that we should be saved from our enemies,
and from the hand of all who hate us;
to perform the mercy promised to our fathers,
and to remember his holy covenant,
the oath which he swore to our father Abraham, to grant us
that we, being delivered from the hand of our enemies,
might serve him without fear,
in holiness and righteousness before him all the days of our life.
And you, child, will be called the prophet of the Most High;
for you will go before the Lord to prepare his ways,
to give knowledge of salvation to his people
in the forgiveness of their sins,
through the tender mercy of our God,
when the day shall dawn upon us from on high
to give light to those who sit in darkness and in the shadow of death,
to guide our feet into the way of peace."
Luke 1:68-79

522

In those days a decree went out from Caesar Augustus that all the world should be enrolled. This was the first enrollment, when Quirinius was governor of Syria. And all went to be enrolled, each to his own city. And Joseph also went up from Galilee, from the city of Nazareth, to Judea, to the city of David, which is called Bethlehem, because he was of the house and lineage of David, to be enrolled with Mary, his betrothed, who was with child. And while they were there, the time came for her to be delivered. And she gave birth to her first-born son and wrapped him in swaddling cloths, and laid him in a manger, because there was no place for them in the inn.

And in that region there were shepherds out in the field, keeping watch over their flock by night. And an angel of the Lord appeared to them, and the glory of the Lord shone around them, and they were filled with fear. And the angel said to them, "Be not afraid; for behold, I bring you good news of a great joy which will come to all the people; for to you is born this day in the city of David a Savior, who is Christ the Lord. And this will be a sign for you: you will find a babe wrapped in swaddling cloths and lying in a manger." And suddenly there was with the angel a multitude of the heavenly host praising God and saying,

"Glory to God in the highest,
and on earth peace among men with whom he is pleased!"

When the angels went away from them into heaven, the shepherds said to one another, "Let us go over to Bethlehem and see this thing that has happened, which the Lord has made known to us." And they went with haste, and found Mary and Joseph, and the babe lying in a manger. And when they saw it they made known the saying which had been told them concerning this child; and all who heard it wondered at what the shepherds told them. But Mary kept all these things, pondering them in her heart. And the shepherds returned, glorifying and praising God for all they had heard and seen, as it had been told them.

Luke 2:1-20

523

And he came to Nazareth, where he had been brought up; and he went to the synagogue, as his custom was, on the sabbath day. And he stood up to read; and there was given to him the book of the prophet Isaiah. He opened the book and found the place where it was written,

"The Spirit of the Lord is upon me,
because he has anointed me to preach good news to the poor.
He has sent me to proclaim release to the captives

and recovering of sight to the blind,
to set at liberty those who are oppressed,
to proclaim the acceptable year of the Lord."
And he closed the book, and gave it back to the attendant, and sat down; and the eyes of all in the synagogue were fixed on him. And he began to say to them, "Today this scripture has been fulfilled in your hearing."
Luke 4:16-21

524

"But I say to you that hear, Love your enemies, do good to those who hate you, bless those who curse you, pray for those who abuse you. To him who strikes you on the cheek, offer the other also; and from him who takes away your cloak do not withold your coat as well. Give to every one who begs from you; and of him who takes away your goods do not ask them again. And as you wish that men would do to you, do so to them.

"If you love those who love you, what credit is that to you? For even sinners love those who love them. And if you do good to those who do good to you, what credit is that to you? For even sinners do the same. And if you lend to those from whom you hope to receive, what credit is that to you? Even sinners lend to sinners, to receive as much again. But love your enemies, and do good, and lend, expecting nothing in return; and your reward will be great, and you will be sons of the Most High; for he is kind to the ungrateful and the selfish. Be merciful, even as your Father is merciful.

"Judge not, and you will not be judged; condemn not, and you will not be condemned; forgive, and you will be forgiven; give, and it will be given to you; good measure, pressed down, shaken together, running over, will be put into your lap. For the measure you give will be the measure you get back."
Luke 6:27-38

525

And behold, a lawyer stood up to put him to the test, saying, "Teacher, what shall I do to inherit eternal life?" He said to him, "What is written in the law? How do you read?" And he answered, "You shall love the Lord your God with all your heart, and with all your soul, and with all your strength, and with all your mind; and your neighbor as yourself." And he said to him, "You have answered right; do this, and you will live."

But he, desiring to justify himself, said to Jesus, "And who is my neighbor?" Jesus replied, "A man was going down from Jerusalem to Jericho, and he fell among robbers, who stripped him and beat him, and departed, leaving him half dead. Now by chance a priest was going down the road; and when

he saw him he passed by on the other side. So likewise a Levite, when he came to the place and saw him, passed by on the other side. But a Samaritan, as he journeyed, came to where he was; and when he saw him, he had compassion, and went to him and bound up his wounds, pouring on oil and wine; then he set him on his own beast and brought him to an inn, and took care of him. And the next day he took out two denarii and gave them to the innkeeper, saying, 'Take care of him; and whatever more you spend, I will repay you when I come back.' Which of these three, do you think, proved neighbor to the man who fell among the robbers?" He said, "The one who showed mercy on him." And Jesus said to him, "Go and do likewise."
Luke 10:25-37

526

And he said, "There was a man who had two sons; and the younger of them said to his father, 'Father, give me the share of property that falls to me.' And he divided his living between them. Not many days later, the younger son gathered all he had and took his journey into a far country, and there he squandered his property in loose living. And when he had spent everything, a great famine arose in that country, and he began to be in want. So he went and joined himself to one of the citizens of that country, who sent him into his fields to feed swine. And he would gladly have fed on the pods that the swine ate; and no one gave him anything. But when he came to himself he said, 'How many of my father's hired servants have bread enough and to spare, but I perish here with hunger! I will arise and go to my father, and I will say to him, "Father, I have sinned against heaven and before you; I am no longer worthy to be called your son; treat me as one of your hired servants." ' And he arose and came to his father. But while he was yet at a distance, his father saw him and had compassion, and ran and embraced him and kissed him. And the son said to him, 'Father, I have sinned against heaven and before you; I am no longer worthy to be called your son.' But the father said to his servants, 'Bring quickly the best robe, and put it on him; and put a ring on his hand, and shoes on his feet; and bring the fatted calf and kill it, and let us eat and make merry; for this my son was dead, and is alive again; he was lost, and is found.' And they began to make merry.

"Now his elder son was in the field; and as he came and drew near to the house, he heard music and dancing. And he called one of the servants and asked what this meant. And he said to him, 'Your brother has come, and your father has killed the fatted calf, because he has received him safe and sound.' But he was angry and refused to go in. His father came out and entreated him, but he answered his father, 'Lo, these many years I have served you, and I never disobeyed your command; yet you never gave me a kid, that

I might make merry with my friends. But when this son of yours came, who has devoured your living with harlots, you killed for him the fatted calf!' And he said to him, 'Son, you are always with me, and all that is mine is yours. It was fitting to make merry and be glad, for this your brother was dead, and is alive; he was lost, and is found.' "

Luke 15:11-24, 25-32

527

That very day two of them were going to a village named Emmaus, about seven miles from Jerusalem, and talking with each other about all these things that had happened. While they were talking and discussing together, Jesus himself drew near and went with them. But their eyes were kept from recognizing him. And he said to them, "What is this conversation which you are holding with each other as you walk?" And they stood still, looking sad. Then one of them named Cleopas, answered him, "Are you the only visitor to Jerusalem who does not know the things that have happened there in these days?" And he said to them, "What things?" And they said to him, "Concerning Jesus of Nazareth, who was a prophet mighty in deed and word before God and all the people, and how our chief priests and rulers delivered him up to be condemned to death, and crucified him. But we had hoped that he was the one to redeem Israel. Yes, and besides all this, it is now the third day since this happened. Moreover, some women of our company amazed us. They were at the tomb early in the morning and did not find his body; and they came back saying that they had even seen a vision of angels, who said that he was alive. Some of those who were with us went to the tomb, and found it just as the women had said; but him they did not see." And he said to them, "O foolish men, and slow of heart to believe all that the prophets have spoken! Was it not necessary that the Christ should suffer these things and enter into his glory?" And beginning with Moses and all the prophets, he interpreted to them in all the scriptures the things concerning himself.

So they drew near to the village to which they were going. He appeared to be going further, but they constrained him, saying, "Stay with us, for it is toward evening and the day is now far spent." So he went in to stay with them. When he was at table with them, he took the bread and blessed, and broke it, and gave it to them. And their eyes were opened and they recognized him; and he vanished out of their sight. They said to each other, "Did not our hearts burn within us while he talked to us on the road, while he opened to us the scriptures?" And they rose that same hour and returned to Jerusalem; and they found the eleven gathered together and those who were with them, who said, "The Lord has risen indeed, and has appeared to

Simon!" Then they told what had happened on the road, and how he was known to them in the breaking of the bread.
Luke 24:13-35

528

In the beginning was the Word, and the Word was with God, and the Word was God. He was in the beginning with God; all things were made through him, and without him was not anything made that was made. In him was life, and the life was the light of men. The light shines in the darkness, and the darkness has not overcome it.

There was a man sent from God, whose name was John. He came for testimony, to bear witness to the light, that all might believe through him. He was not the light, but came to bear witness to the light.

The true light that enlightens every man was coming into the world. He was in the world, and the world was made through him, yet the world knew him not. He came to his own home, and his own people received him not. But to all who received him, who believed in his name, he gave power to become children of God; who were born, not of blood nor of the will of the flesh nor of the will of man, but of God.

And the Word became flesh and dwelt among us, full of grace and truth; we have beheld his glory, glory as of the only Son from the Father.
John 1:1-14

529

For God so loved the world that he gave his only Son, that whoever believes in him should not perish but have eternal life. For God sent the Son into the world, not to condemn the world, but that the world might be saved through him. He who believes in him is not condemned; he who does not believe is condemned already, because he has not believed in the name of the only Son of God. And this is the judgment, that the light has come into the world, and men loved darkness rather than light, because their deeds were evil. For every one who does evil hates the light, and does not come to the light, lest his deeds should be exposed. But he who does what is true comes to the light, that it may be clearly seen that his deeds have been wrought in God.
John 3:16-21

530

So Jesus again said to them, "Truly, truly, I say to you, I am the door of the sheep. All who came before me are thieves and robbers; but the sheep did not heed them. I am the door; if any one enters by me, he will be saved, and will go in and out and find pasture. The thief comes only to steal and kill and destroy; I came that they may have life, and have it abundantly. I am the good shepherd. The good shepherd lays down his life for the sheep. He who is a hireling and not a shepherd, whose own the sheep are not, sees the wolf coming and leaves the sheep and flees; and the wolf snatches them and scatters them. He flees because he is a hireling and cares nothing for the sheep. I am the good shepherd; I know my own and my own know me, as the Father knows me and I know the Father; and I lay down my life for the sheep. And I have other sheep, that are not of this fold; I must bring them also, and they will heed my voice. So there shall be one flock, one shepherd. For this reason the Father loves me, because I lay down my life, that I may take it again. No one takes it from me, but I lay it down of my own accord. I have power to lay it down, and I have power to take it again; this charge I have received from my Father."

John 10:7-18

53¹

"Let not your hearts be troubled; believe in God, believe also in me. In my Father's house are many rooms; if it were not so, would I have told you that I go to prepare a place for you? And when I go and prepare a place for you, I will come again and will take you to myself, that where I am you may be also. And you know the way where I am going." Thomas said to him, "Lord, we do not know where you are going; how can we know the way?" Jesus said to him, "I am the way, and the truth, and the life; no one comes to the Father, but by me. If you had known me, you would have known my Father also; henceforth you know him and have seen him."

Philip said to him, "Lord, show us the Father, and we shall be satisfied." Jesus said to him, "Have I been with you so long, and yet you do not know me, Philip? He who has seen me has seen the Father; how can you say, 'Show us the Father'? Do you not believe that I am in the Father and the Father in me? The words that I say to you I do not speak on my own authority; but the Father who dwells in me does his works. Believe me that I am in the Father and the Father in me; or else believe me for the sake of the works themselves.

"Truly, truly, I say to you, he who believes in me will also do the works that I do; and greater works than these will he do, because I go to the Father. Whatever you ask in my name, I will do it, that the Father may be glorified in the Son; if you ask anything in my name, I will do it."

John 14:1-14

532

"I am the true vine, and my Father is the vinedresser. Every branch of mine that bears no fruit, he takes away, and every branch that does bear fruit he prunes, that it may bear more fruit. You are already made clean by the word which I have spoken to you. Abide in me, and I in you. As the branch cannot bear fruit by itself, unless it abides in the vine, neither can you, unless you abide in me. I am the vine, you are the branches. He who abides in me, and I in him, he it is that bears much fruit, for apart from me you can do nothing. If a man does not abide in me, he is cast forth as a branch and withers; and the branches are gathered, thrown into the fire and burned. If you abide in me, and my words abide in you, ask whatever you will, and it shall be done for you. By this my Father is glorified, that you bear much fruit, and so prove to be my disciples. As the Father has loved me, so have I loved you; abide in my love. If you keep my commandments, you will abide in my love, just as I have kept my Father's commandments and abide in his love. These things I have spoken to you, that my joy may be in you, and that your joy may be full.

"This is my commandment, that you love one another as I have loved you. Greater love has no man than this, that a man lay down his life for his friends. You are my friends if you do what I command you. No longer do I call you servants, for the servant does not know what his master is doing; but I have called you friends, for all that I have heard from my Father I have made known to you. You did not choose me, but I chose you and appointed you that you should go and bear fruit and that your fruit should abide; so that whatever you ask the Father in my name, he may give it to you. This I command you, to love one another."
John 15:1-17

533

When the day of Pentecost had come, they were all together in one place. And suddenly a sound came from heaven like the rush of a mighty wind, and it filled all the house where they were sitting. And there appeared to them tongues as of fire, distributed and resting on each one of them. And they were all filled with the Holy Spirit and began to speak in other tongues, as the Spirit gave them utterance.

But Peter, standing with the eleven, lifted up his voice and addressed them, "Men of Judea and all who dwell in Jerusalem, let this be known to you, and give ear to my words.

"Jesus of Nazareth, a man attested to you by God with mighty works and wonders and signs which God did through him in your midst, as you yourselves know—this Jesus, delivered up according to the definite plan and foreknowledge of God, you crucified and killed by the hands of lawless men. But God raised him up, having loosed the pangs of death, because it was not possible for him to be held by it.

"Let all the house of Israel therefore know assuredly that God has made him both Lord and Christ, this Jesus whom you crucified."

Now when they heard this they were cut to the heart, and said to Peter and the rest of the apostles, "Brethren, what shall we do?" And Peter said to them, "Repent, and be baptized every one of you in the name of Jesus Christ for the forgiveness of your sins; and you shall receive the gift of the Holy Spirit. For the promise is to you and to your children and to all that are far off, every one whom the Lord our God calls to him." And he testified with many other words and exhorted them, saying, "Save yourselves from this crooked generation." So those who received his word were baptized, and there were added that day about three thousand souls. And they devoted themselves to the apostles' teaching and fellowship, to the breaking of bread and the prayers.

Acts 2:1-4; 14; 22b-24; 36-42

534

So Paul, standing in the middle of the Areopagus, said: "Men of Athens, I perceive that in every way you are very religious. For as I passed along and observed the objects of your worship, I found also an altar with this inscription, 'To an unknown god.' What therefore you worship as unknown, this I proclaim to you. The God who made the world and everything in it, being Lord of heaven and earth, does not live in shrines made by man, nor is he served by human hands, as though he needed anything, since he himself gives to all men life and breath and everything. And he made from one every nation of men to live on all the face of the earth, having determined allotted periods and the boundaries of their habitation, that they should seek God, in the hope that they might feel after him and find him. Yet he is not far from each one of us, for

'In him we live and move and have our being';
as even some of your poets have said,

'For we are indeed his offspring.'
Being then God's offspring, we ought not to think that the Deity is like gold, or silver, or stone, a representation by the art and imagination of man. The times of ignorance God overlooked, but now he commands all men everywhere to repent, because he has fixed a day on which he will judge the world in righteousness by a man whom he has appointed, and of this he has given assurance to all men by raising him from the dead."

Acts 17:22-31

535

Therefore, since we are justified by faith, we have peace with God through our Lord Jesus Christ. Through him we have obtained access to this grace in which we stand, and we rejoice in our hope of sharing the glory of God. More than that, we rejoice in our sufferings, knowing that suffering produces endurance, and endurance produces character, and character produces hope, and hope does not disappoint us, because God's love has been poured into our hearts through the Holy Spirit which has been given to us.

While we were yet helpless, at the right time Christ died for the ungodly. Why, one will hardly die for a righteous man—though perhaps for a good man one will dare even to die. But God shows his love for us in that while we were yet sinners Christ died for us.

Romans 5:1-8

536

We know that in everything God works for good with those who love him, who are called according to his purpose.

What then shall we say to this? If God is for us, who is against us? He who did not spare his own Son but gave him up for us all, will he not also give us all things with him? Who shall bring any charge against God's elect? It is God who justifies; who is to condemn? Is it Christ Jesus, who died, yes, who was raised from the dead, who is at the right hand of God, who indeed intercedes for us? Who shall separate us from the love of Christ? Shall tribulation, or distress, or persecution, or famine, or nakedness, or peril, or sword? As it is written,

"For thy sake we are being killed all the day long;
    we are regarded as sheep to be slaughtered."

No, in all these things we are more than conquerors through him who loved us. For I am sure that neither death, nor life, nor angels, nor principalities, nor things present, nor things to come, nor powers, nor height, nor depth, nor anything else in all creation, will be able to separate us from the love of God in Christ Jesus our Lord.

Romans 8:28, 31-39

537

The word is near you, on your lips and in your heart (that is, the word of faith which we preach); because, if you confess with your lips that Jesus is Lord and believe in your heart that God raised him from the dead, you will be saved. For man believes with his heart and so is justified, and he confesses with his lips and so is saved. The scripture says, "No one who believes in him will be put to shame." For there is no distinction between Jew and Greek; the same Lord is Lord of all and bestows his riches upon all who call upon him. For, "every one who calls upon the name of the Lord will be saved." But how are men to call upon him in whom they have not believed? And how are they to believe in him of whom they have never heard? And how are they to hear without a preacher? And how can men preach unless they are sent? As it is written, "How beautiful are the feet of those who preach good news!" So faith comes from what is heard, and what is heard comes by the preaching of Christ.

Romans 10:8b-15, 17

538

I appeal to you therefore, brethren, by the mercies of God, to present your bodies as a living sacrifice, holy and acceptable to God, which is your spiritual worship. Do not be conformed to this world but be transformed by the renewal of your mind, that you may prove what is the will of God, what is good and acceptable and perfect.

Let love be genuine; hate what is evil, hold fast to what is good; love one another with brotherly affection; outdo one another in showing honor. Never flag in zeal, be aglow with the Spirit, serve the Lord. Rejoice in your hope, be patient in tribulation, be constant in prayer. Contribute to the needs of the saints, practice hospitality.

Bless those who persecute you; bless and do not curse them. Rejoice with those who rejoice, weep with those who weep. Live in harmony with one another; do not be haughty, but associate with the lowly; never be conceited. Repay no one evil for evil, but take thought for what is noble in the sight of all. If possible, so far as it depends upon you, live peaceably with all. Beloved, never avenge yourselves, but leave it to the wrath of God; for it is written, "Vengeance is mine, I will repay, says the Lord." No, "if your enemy is hungry, feed him; if he is thirsty, give him drink; for by so doing you will heap burning coals upon his head." Do not be overcome by evil, but overcome evil with good.

Romans 12:1-2, 9-21

539

Now there are varieties of gifts, but the same Spirit; and there are varieties of service, but the same Lord; and there are varieties of working, but it is the same God who inspires them all in every one. To each is given the manifestation of the Spirit for the common good. To one is given through the Spirit the utterance of wisdom, and to another the utterance of knowledge according to the same Spirit, to another faith by the same Spirit, to another gifts of healing by the one Spirit, to another the working of miracles, to another prophecy, to another the ability to distinguish between spirits, to another various kinds of tongues, to another the interpretation of tongues. All these are inspired by one and the same Spirit, who apportions to each one individually as he wills.

For just as the body is one and has many members, and all the members of the body, though many, are one body, so it is with Christ. For by one Spirit we were all baptized into one body—Jews or Greeks, slaves or free— and all were made to drink of one Spirit.

1 Corinthians 12:4-13

540

Now you are the body of Christ and individually members of it. And God has appointed in the church first apostles, second prophets, third teachers, then workers of miracles, then healers, helpers, administrators, speakers in various kinds of tongues. Are all apostles? Are all prophets? Are all teachers? Do all work miracles? Do all possess gifts of healing? Do all speak with tongues? Do all interpret? But earnestly desire the higher gifts.

And I will show you a still more excellent way.

If I speak in the tongues of men and of angels, but have not love, I am a noisy gong or a clanging cymbal. And if I have prophetic powers, and understand all mysteries and all knowledge, and if I have all faith, so as to remove mountains, but have not love, I am nothing. If I give away all I have, and if I deliver my body to be burned, but have not love, I gain nothing.

Love is patient and kind; love is not jealous or boastful; it is not arrogant or rude. Love does not insist on its own way; it is not irritable or resentful; it does not rejoice at wrong, but rejoices in the right. Love bears all things, believes all things, hopes all things, endures all things.

Love never ends; as for prophecies, they will pass away; as for tongues, they will cease; as for knowledge, it will pass away. For our knowledge is imperfect and our prophecy is imperfect; but when the perfect comes, the imperfect will pass away. When I was a child, I spoke like a child, I thought like a child, I reasoned like a child; when I became a man, I gave up childish ways. For now we see in a mirror dimly, but then face to face. Now I know in part; then I shall understand fully, even as I have been fully understood. So faith, hope, love abide, these three; but the greatest of these is love.

1 Corinthians 12:27-31; 13

541

Now I would remind you, brethren, in what terms I preached to you the gospel, which you received, in which you stand, by which you are saved, if you hold it fast—unless you believed in vain.

For I delivered to you as of first importance what I also received, that Christ died for our sins in accordance with the scriptures, that he was buried, that he was raised on the third day in accordance with the scriptures, and that he appeared to Cephas, then to the twelve.

Lo! I tell you a mystery. We shall not all sleep, but we shall all be changed, in a moment, in the twinkling of an eye, at the last trumpet. For the trumpet will sound, and the dead will be raised imperishable, and we shall be changed. For this perishable nature must put on the imperishable, and this mortal nature must put on immortality. When the perishable puts on the imperishable, and the mortal puts on immortality, then shall come to pass the saying that is written:

"Death is swallowed up in victory."
"O death, where is thy victory?
O death, where is thy sting?"

The sting of death is sin, and the power of sin is the law. But thanks be to God, who gives us the victory through our Lord Jesus Christ.

Therefore, my beloved brethren, be steadfast, immovable, always abound ing in the work of the Lord, knowing that in the Lord your labor is not in vain.

1 Corinthians 15:1-5, 51-58

542

For what we preach is not ourselves, but Jesus Christ as Lord, with ourselves as your servants for Jesus' sake. For it is the God who said, "Let light shine out of darkness," who has shone in our hearts to give the light of the knowledge of the glory of God in the face of Christ.

But we have this treasure in earthen vessels, to show that the transcendent power belongs to God and not to us. We are afflicted in every way, but not crushed; perplexed, but not driven to despair; persecuted, but not forsaken; struck down, but not destroyed; always carrying in the body the death of Jesus, so that the life of Jesus may also be manifested in our bodies. For while we live we are always being given up to death for Jesus' sake, so that the life of Jesus may be manifested in our mortal flesh. So death is at work in us, but life in you.

2 Corinthians 4:5-12

543

For the love of Christ controls us, because we are convinced that one has died for all; therefore all have died. And he died for all, that those who live might live no longer for themselves but for him who for their sake died and was raised.

From now on, therefore, we regard no one from a human point of view; even though we once regarded Christ from a human point of view, we regard him thus no longer. Therefore, if any one is in Christ, he is a new creation; the old has passed away, behold, the new has come. All this is from God, who through Christ reconciled us to himself and gave us the ministry of reconciliation; that is, God was in Christ reconciling the world to himself, not counting their trespasses against them, and entrusting to us the message of reconciliation. So we are ambassadors for Christ, God making his appeal through us. We beseech you on behalf of Christ, be reconciled to God. For our sake he made him to be sin who knew no sin, so that in him we might become the righteousness of God.

2 Corinthians 5:14-21

544

For freedom Christ has set us free; stand fast therefore, and do not submit again to a yoke of slavery.

For you were called to freedom, brethren; only do not use your freedom as an opportunity for the flesh, but through love be servants of one another. For the whole law is fulfilled in one word, "You shall love your neighbor as yourself." But if you bite and devour one another take heed that you are not consumed by one another.

But I say, walk by the Spirit, and do not gratify the desires of the flesh. For the desires of the flesh are against the Spirit, and the desires of the Spirit are against the flesh; for these are opposed to each other, to prevent you from doing what you would. But if you are led by the Spirit you are not under the law. Now the works of the flesh are plain: immorality, impurity, licentiousness, idolatry, sorcery, enmity, strife, jealousy, anger, selfishness, dissension, party spirit, envy, drunkenness, carousing, and the like. I warn you, as I warned you before, that those who do such things shall not inherit the kingdom of God. But the fruit of the Spirit is love, joy, peace, patience, kindness, goodness, faithfulness, gentleness, self-control; against such there is no law. And those who belong to Christ Jesus have crucified the flesh with its passions and desires.

If we live by the Spirit, let us also walk by the Spirit.

Galatians 5:1, 13-25

545

I therefore, a prisoner for the Lord, beg you to lead a life worthy of the calling to which you have been called, with all lowliness and meekness, with patience, forbearing one another in love, eager to maintain the unity of the Spirit in the bond of peace. There is one body and one Spirit, just as you were called to the one hope that belongs to your call, one Lord, one faith, one baptism, one God and Father of us all, who is above all and through all and in all. But grace was given to each of us according to the measure of Christ's gift.

And his gifts were that some should be apostles, some prophets, some evangelists, some pastors and teachers, for the equipment of the saints, for the work of ministry, for building up the body of Christ, until we all attain to the unity of the faith and of the knowledge of the Son of God, to mature manhood, to the measure of the stature of the fulness of Christ; so that we may no longer be children, tossed to and fro and carried about with every wind of doctrine, by the cunning of men, by their craftiness in deceitful wiles. Rather, speaking the truth in love, we are to grow up in every way into him who is the head, into Christ, from whom the whole body, joined and knit together by every joint with which it is supplied, when each part is working properly, makes bodily growth and upbuilds itself in love.

Ephesians 4:1-7, 11-16

546

Have this mind among yourselves, which you have in Christ Jesus, who, though he was in the form of God, did not count equality with God a thing to be grasped, but emptied himself, taking the form of a servant, being born in the likeness of men. And being found in human form he humbled himself and became obedient unto death, even death on a cross. Therefore God has highly exalted him and bestowed on him the name which is above every name, that at the name of Jesus every knee should bow, in heaven and on earth and under the earth, and every tongue confess that Jesus Christ is Lord, to the glory of God the Father.

Philippians 2:5-11

547

May you be strengthened with all power, according to his glorious might, for all endurance and patience with joy, giving thanks to the Father, who has qualified us to share in the inheritance of the saints in light. He has delivered us from the dominion of darkness and transferred us to the kingdom of his beloved Son, in whom we have redemption, the forgiveness of sins.

He is the image of the invisible God, the first-born of all creation; for in him all things were created, in heaven and on earth, visible and invisible, whether thrones or dominions or principalities or authorities—all things were created through him and for him. He is before all things, and in him all things hold together. He is the head of the body, the church; he is the beginning, the first-born from the dead, that in everything he might be pre-eminent. For in him all the fulness of God was pleased to dwell, and through him to reconcile to himself all things, whether on earth or in heaven, making peace by the blood of his cross.

Colossians 1:11-20

548

If then you have been raised with Christ, seek the things that are above, where Christ is, seated at the right hand of God. Set your minds on things that are above, not on things that are on earth. For you have died, and your life is hid with Christ in God. When Christ who is our life appears, then you also will appear with him in glory.

Put on then, as God's chosen ones, holy and beloved, compassion, kindness, lowliness, meekness, and patience, forbearing one another and, if one has a complaint against another, forgiving each other; as the Lord has forgiven you, so you also must forgive. And above all these put on love, which binds everything together in perfect harmony. And let the peace of Christ rule in your hearts, to which indeed you were called in the one body. And be thankful. Let the word of Christ dwell in you richly, as you teach and admonish one another in all wisdom, and as you sing psalms and hymns and spiritual songs with thankfulness in your hearts to God. And whatever you do, in word or deed, do everything in the name of the Lord Jesus, giving thanks to God the Father through him.

Colossians 3:1-4; 12-17

549

Blessed be the God and Father of our Lord Jesus Christ! By his great mercy we have been born anew to a living hope through the resurrection of Jesus Christ from the dead, and to an inheritance which is imperishable, undefiled, and unfading, kept in heaven for you, who by God's power are guarded through faith for a salvation ready to be revealed in the last time.

In this you rejoice, though now for a little while you may have to suffer various trials, so that the genuineness of your faith, more precious than gold which though perishable is tested by fire, may redound to praise and glory and honor at the revelation of Jesus Christ. Without having seen him you love him; though you do not now see him you believe in him and rejoice with unutterable and exalted joy. As the outcome of your faith you obtain the salvation of your souls.

1 Peter 1:3-9

550

That which was from the beginning, which we have heard, which we have seen with our eyes, which we have looked upon and touched with our hands, concerning the word of life—the life was made manifest, and we saw it, and testify to it, and proclaim to you the eternal life which was with the Father and was made manifest to us—that which we have seen and heard we proclaim also to you, so that you may have fellowship with us; and our fellowship is with the Father and with his Son Jesus Christ. And we are writing this that our joy may be complete.

This is the message we have heard from him and proclaim to you, that God is light and in him is no darkness at all. If we say we have fellowship with him while we walk in darkness, we lie and do not live according to the truth; but if we walk in the light, as he is in the light, we have fellowship with one another, and the blood of Jesus his Son cleanses us from all sin. If we say we have no sin, we deceive ourselves, and the truth is not in us. If we confess our sins, he is faithful and just, and will forgive our sins and cleanse us from all unrighteousness. If we say we have not sinned, we make him a liar, and his word is not in us.

1 John 1:1-10

551

See what love the Father has given us, that we should be called children of God; and so we are. The reason why the world does not know us is that it did not know him. Beloved, we are God's children now; it does not yet appear what we shall be, but we know that when he appears we shall be like him, for we shall see him as he is. And every one who thus hopes in him purifies himself as he is pure.

Every one who commits sin is guilty of lawlessness; sin is lawlessness. You know that he appeared to take away sins, and in him there is no sin. No one who abides in him sins; no one who sins has either seen him or known him. Little children, let no one deceive you. He who does right is righteous, as he is righteous. He who commits sin is of the devil; for the devil has sinned from the beginning. The reason the Son of God appeared was to destroy the works of the devil. No one born of God commits sin; for God's nature abides in him, and he cannot sin because he is born of God. By this it may be seen who are the children of God, and who are the children of the devil: whoever does not do right is not of God, nor he who does not love his brother.

1 John 3:1-10

552

Beloved, let us love one another; for love is of God, and he who loves is born of God and knows God. He who does not love does not know God; for God is love. In this the love of God was made manifest among us, that God sent his only Son into the world, so that we might live through him. In this is love, not that we loved God but that he loved us and sent his Son to be the expiation for our sins. Beloved, if God so loved us, we also ought to love one another. No man has ever seen God; if we love one another, God abides in us and his love is perfected in us.

By this we know that we abide in him and he in us, because he has given us of his own Spirit. And we have seen and testify that the Father has sent his Son as the Savior of the world. Whoever confesses that Jesus is the Son of God, God abides in him, and he in God. So we know and believe the love God has for us. God is love, and he who abides in love abides in God, and God abides in him. In this is love perfected with us, that we may have confidence for the day of judgment, because as he is so are we in this world. There is no fear in love, but perfect love casts out fear. For fear has to do with punishment, and he who fears is not perfected in love. We love, because he first loved us. If any one says, "I love God," and hates his brother, he is a liar; for he who does not love his brother whom he has seen, cannot love God whom he has not seen. And this commandment we have from him, that he who loves God should love his brother also.

1 John 4:7-21

553

Then I saw a new heaven and a new earth; for the first heaven and the first earth had passed away, and the sea was no more. And I saw the holy city, new Jerusalem, coming down out of heaven from God, prepared as a bride adorned for her husband; and I heard a great voice from the throne saying, "Behold, the dwelling of God is with men. He will dwell with them, and they shall be his people, and God himself will be with them; he will wipe away every tear from their eyes, and death shall be no more, neither shall there be mourning nor crying nor pain any more, for the former things have passed away."

And he who sat upon the throne said, "Behold, I make all things new." Also he said, "Write this, for these words are trustworthy and true." And he said to me, "It is done! I am the Alpha and the Omega, the beginning and the end. To the thirsty I will give water without price from the fountain of the water of life. He who conquers shall have this heritage, and I will be his God and he shall be my son."

Revelation 21:1-7

Psalms

554

Blessed is the man
  who walks not in the counsel of
  the wicked,
nor stands in the way of sinners,
  nor sits in the seat of scoffers;

but his delight is in the law of the
  Lord,
  and on his law he meditates day
  and night.

He is like a tree
  planted by streams of water,
that yields its fruit in its season,
  and its leaf does not wither.
In all that he does, he prospers.

The wicked are not so,
  but are like chaff which the wind
  drives away.

Therefore the wicked will not stand
  in the judgment,
  nor sinners in the congregation of
  the righteous;

for the Lord *knows the way of the*
  righteous,
  but the way of the wicked will
  perish.

Psalm 1

555

O Lord, rebuke me not in thy
  anger,
  nor chasten me in thy wrath.

Be gracious to me, O Lord, *for*
I am languishing;
  O Lord, *heal me, for my bones*
  are troubled.

My soul also is sorely troubled.
  But thou, O Lord—how long?
Turn, O Lord, save my life;
  deliver me for the sake of thy
  steadfast love.

For in death there is no remem-
  brance of thee;
  in Sheol who can give thee
  praise?

I am weary with my moaning;
  every night I flood my bed with
  tears;
  I drench my couch with my
  weeping.

My eye wastes away because of
  grief,
  it grows weak because of all my
  foes.

Depart from me, all you workers of
evil;
for the LORD has heard the sound
of my weeping.

The Lord *has heard my supplication;*
the Lord *accepts my prayer.*
All my enemies shall be ashamed
and sorely troubled;
they shall turn back, and be put .
to shame in a moment.

Psalm 6

556

O LORD, our Lord,
how majestic is thy name in all
the earth!

Thou whose glory above the
heavens is chanted
by the mouth of babes and
infants,
thou hast founded a bulwark be-
cause of thy foes,
to still the enemy and the
avenger.

When I look at thy heavens, the
work of thy fingers,
the moon and the stars which
thou hast established;
what is man that thou art mindful
of him,
and the son of man that thou dost
care for him?

Yet thou hast made him little less
than God,
and dost crown him with glory
and honor.

Thou hast given him dominion over
the works of thy hands;

thou hast put all things under his
feet,
all sheep and oxen,
and also the beasts of the field,
the birds of the air, and the fish of
the sea,
whatever passes along the paths
of the sea.

O Lord, *our Lord,*
how majestic is thy name in all
the earth!

Psalm 8

557

How long, O LORD? Wilt thou for-
get me for ever?
How long wilt thou hide thy face
from me?
How long must I bear pain in my
soul,
and have sorrow in my heart all
the day?
How long shall my enemy be
exalted over me?

Consider and answer me, O LORD
my God;
lighten my eyes, lest I sleep the
sleep of death;

lest my enemy say, "I have pre-
vailed over him";
lest my foes rejoice because I
am shaken.

But I have trusted in thy steadfast
love;
my heart shall rejoice in thy
salvation.

I will sing to the Lord,
because he has dealt bountifully
with me.

Psalm 13

558

Preserve me, O God, for in thee
I take refuge.

I say to the Lord, *"Thou art my
Lord,
I have no good apart from thee."*

The LORD is my chosen portion and
my cup;
thou holdest my lot.
The lines have fallen for me in
pleasant places;
yea, I have a goodly heritage.

I bless the Lord *who gives me
counsel;
in the night also my heart instructs me.*

I keep the LORD always before me;
because he is at my right hand,
I shall not be moved.

*Therefore my heart is glad, and my
soul rejoices;
my body also dwells secure.*

For thou dost not give me up to
Sheol,
or let thy godly one see the Pit.

*Thou dost show me the path of life;
in thy presence there is fulness
of joy,
in thy right hand are pleasures
for evermore.*

Psalm 16:1-2, 5-11

559

I love thee, O LORD, my strength.
The LORD is my rock, and my
fortress, and my deliverer,

my God, my rock, in whom I
take refuge,
my shield, and the horn of my
salvation, my stronghold.

I call upon the Lord, *who is worthy
to be praised,
and I am saved from my enemies.*

The cords of death encompassed
me,
the torrents of perdition assailed
me;
the cords of Sheol entangled me,
the snares of death confronted
me.

*In my distress I called upon the
Lord,
to my God I cried for help.
From his temple he heard my voice,
and my cry to him reached his
ears.*

He reached from on high, he took
me,
he drew me out of many waters.

*He delivered me from my strong
enemy,
and from those who hated me;
for they were too mighty for me.*

They came upon me in the day of
my calamity;
but the LORD was my stay.

*He brought me forth into a broad
place;
he delivered me, because he de-
lighted in me.*

Psalm 18:1-6, 16-19

560

The heavens are telling the glory
of God;
and the firmament proclaims his
handiwork.
Day to day pours forth speech,
and night to night declares
knowledge.

There is no speech, nor are there
words;
their voice is not heard;

yet their voice goes out through all
the earth,
and their words to the end of the
world.

In them he has set a tent for the
sun,
which comes forth like a bride-
groom leaving his chamber,
and like a strong man runs its
course with joy.

Its rising is from the end of the
heavens,
and its circuit to the end of them;
and there is nothing hid from its
heat.

The law of the LORD is perfect,
reviving the soul;
the testimony of the LORD is sure,
making wise the simple;

the precepts of the Lord *are right,*
rejoicing the heart;
the commandment of the Lord *is*
pure,
enlightening the eyes;

the fear of the LORD is clean,
enduring for ever;

the ordinances of the LORD are
true,
and righteous altogether.

More to be desired are they than
gold,
even much fine gold;
sweeter also than honey
and drippings of the honeycomb.

Moreover by them is thy servant
warned;
in keeping them there is great
reward.

But who can discern his errors?
Clear thou me from hidden
faults.

Keep back thy servant also from
presumptuous sins;
let them not have dominion over
me!
Then I shall be blameless,
and innocent of great transgression.

Let the words of my mouth and
the meditation of my heart
be acceptable in thy sight,
O Lord, *my rock and my re-*
deemer.
Psalm 19

561

The Lord *is my shepherd, I shall*
not want;
he makes me lie down in green
pastures.
He leads me beside still waters;
he restores my soul.
He leads me in paths of righteous-
ness
for his name's sake.

Even though I walk through the
    valley of the shadow of death,
    I fear no evil;
for thou art with me;
    thy rod and thy staff,
    they comfort me.
Thou preparest a table before me
    in the presence of my enemies;
thou anointest my head with oil,
    my cup overflows.
Surely goodness and mercy shall fol-
    low me
    all the days of my life;
and I shall dwell in the house of
    the Lord
    for ever.

Psalm 23

562

The earth is the LORD'S and the
    fulness thereof,
    the world and those who dwell
    therein;

for he has founded it upon the
    seas,
    and established it upon the rivers.

Who shall ascend the hill of the
    LORD?
    And who shall stand in his holy
    place?

He who has clean hands and a
    pure heart,
    who does not lift up his soul to
    what is false,
    and does not swear deceitfully.

He will receive blessing from the
    LORD,
    and vindication from the God of
    his salvation.

Such is the generation of those who
    seek him,
    who seek the face of the God of
    Jacob.

Lift up your heads, O gates!
    and be lifted up, O ancient doors!
    that the King of glory may come
    in.

Who is the King of glory?
    The Lord, strong and mighty,
    the Lord, mighty in battle!

Lift up your heads, O gates!
    and be lifted up, O ancient doors!
    that the King of glory may come
    in!

Who is this King of glory?
    The Lord of hosts,
    he is the King of glory!

Psalm 24

563

To thee, O LORD, I lift up my soul.

O my God, in thee I trust,
    let me not be put to shame;
    let not my enemies exult over
    me.

Yea, let none that wait for thee be
    put to shame;
    let them be ashamed who are
    wantonly treacherous.

Make me to know thy ways, O
    Lord;
    teach me thy paths.

Lead me in thy truth, and teach me,
    for thou art the God of my
    salvation;
    for thee I wait all day long.

Be mindful of thy mercy, O Lord,
and of thy steadfast love,
for they have been from of old.

Remember not the sins of my youth,
or my transgressions;
according to thy steadfast love
remember me,
for thy goodness' sake, O LORD!

Good and upright is the Lord;
therefore he instructs sinners in
the way.

He leads the humble in what is
right,
and teaches the humble his way.

All the paths of the Lord *are stead-*
fast love and faithfulness,
for those who keep his covenant
and his testimonies.

Psalm 25:1-10

564

The LORD is my light and my salvation;
whom shall I fear?
The LORD is the stronghold of my
life;
of whom shall I be afraid?

When evildoers assail me,
uttering slanders against me,
my adversaries and foes,
they shall stumble and fall.

Though a host encamp against me,
my heart shall not fear;
though war arise against me,
yet I will be confident.

One thing have I asked of the Lord,
that will I seek after;

that I may dwell in the house
of the Lord
all the days of my life,
to behold the beauty of the Lord,
and to inquire in his temple.

For he will hide me in his shelter
in the day of trouble;
he will conceal me under the
cover of his tent.
he will set me high upon a rock.

And now my head shall be lifted up
above my enemies round about
me;
and I will offer in his tent
sacrifices with shouts of joy;
I will sing and make melody to
the Lord,

Psalm 27:1-6

565

In thee, O LORD, do I seek refuge;
let me never be put to shame;
in thy righteousness deliver me!

Incline thy ear to me,
rescue me speedily!
Be thou a rock of refuge for me,
a strong fortress to save me!

Yea, thou art my rock and my fortress;
for thy name's sake lead me and
guide me,
take me out of the net which is
hidden for me,
for thou art my refuge.

Into thy hand I commit my spirit;
thou hast redeemed me, O LORD,
faithful God.

*Thou hatest those who pay regard
    to vain idols;
    but I trust in the* Lord.

I will rejoice and be glad for thy
    steadfast love,
    because thou hast seen my af-
    fliction,
    *thou hast taken heed of my ad-
    versities,*
and hast not delivered me into the
    hand of the enemy;
    *thou hast set my feet in a broad
    place.*

Be gracious to me, O LORD, for I
    am in distress;
    my eye is wasted from grief,
    my soul and my body also.

*For my life is spent with sorrow,
    and my years with sighing;
my strength fails because of my
    misery,
    and my bones waste away.*

But I trust in thee, O LORD,
    I say, "Thou art my God."

*My times are in thy hand;
    deliver me from the hand of my
    enemies and persecutors!
Let thy face shine on thy servant;
    save me in thy steadfast love!*

Psalm 31:1-10, 14-16

566

Blessed is he whose transgression is
    forgiven,
    whose sin is covered.

*Blessed is the man to whom the
    Lord imputes no iniquity,*

*and in whose spirit there is no
    deceit.*

When I declared not my sin, my
    body wasted away
    through my groaning all day
    long.
*For day and night thy hand was
    heavy upon me;
    my strength was dried up as by
    the heat of summer.*

I acknowledged my sin to thee,
    and I did not hide my iniquity;
I said, 'I will confess my trans-
    gressions to the LORD";
    then thou didst forgive the guilt
    of my sin.

*Therefore let every one who is
    godly
    offer prayer to thee;
at a time of distress, in the rush
    of great waters,
    they shall not reach him.*

Thou art a hiding place for me,
    thou preservest me from trou-
    ble;
    thou dost encompass me with
    deliverance.

*I will instruct you and teach you
    the way you should go;
    I will counsel you with my eye
    upon you.*

Be not like a horse or a mule, with-
    out understanding,
    which must be curbed with bit
    and bridle,
    else it will not keep with you.

*Many are the pangs of the wicked;
    but steadfast love surrounds him
    who trusts in the Lord.*

Be glad in the L<small>ORD</small>, and rejoice,
O righteous,
and shout for joy, all you upright in heart!

Psalm 32

567

I will bless the L<small>ORD</small> at all times;
his praise shall continually be in
my mouth.

My soul makes its boast in the
Lord;
let the afflicted hear and be glad.

O magnify the L<small>ORD</small> with me,
and let us exalt his name together!

I sought the Lord, *and he an-*
swered me,
and delivered me from all my
fears.

Look to him, and be radiant;
so your faces shall never be
ashamed.

This poor man cried, and the Lord
heard him,
and saved him out of all his
troubles.

The angel of the L<small>ORD</small> encamps
around those who fear him, and
delivers them.

O taste and see that the Lord *is*
good!
Happy is the man who takes re-
fuge in him!

O fear the L<small>ORD</small>, you his saints,
for those who fear him have no
want!

The young lions suffer want and
hunger;
but those who seek the Lord *lack*
no good thing.

Come, O sons, listen to me,
I will teach you the fear of the
L<small>ORD</small>.

What man is there who desires life,
and covets many days, that he
may enjoy good?

Keep your tongue from evil,
and your lips from speaking de-
ceit.

Depart from evil, and do good;
seek peace, and pursue it.

The eyes of the L<small>ORD</small> are toward
the righteous,
and his ears toward their cry.

The face of the Lord *is against evil-*
doers,
to cut off the remembrance of
them from the earth.

When the righteous cry for help,
the L<small>ORD</small> hears,
and delivers them out of all their
troubles.

The Lord *is near to the broken-*
hearted,
and saves the crushed in spirit.

Many are the afflictions of the righteous;
but the L<small>ORD</small> delivers him out
of them all.

He keeps all his bones;
not one of them is broken.

Evil shall slay the wicked;
 and those who hate the righteous
  will be condemned.

The Lord *redeems the life of his
 servants;*
 *none of those who take refuge
  in him will be condemned.*

Psalm 34

568

O LORD, rebuke me not in thy anger,
 nor chasten me in thy wrath!

*For thy arrows have sunk into me,
 and thy hand has come down on
 me.*

There is no soundness in my flesh
 because of thy indignation;
there is no health in my bones
 because of my sin.

*For my iniquities have gone over
 my head;
 they weigh like a burden too
 heavy for me.*

I am utterly spent and crushed;
 I groan because of the tumult of
  my heart.

Lord, *all my longing is known to
 thee,
 my sighing is not hidden from
 thee.*

My heart throbs, my strength fails
 me;
 and the light of my eyes—it also
  has gone from me.
My friends and companions stand
 aloof from my plague,
 and my kinsmen stand afar off.

*Those who seek my life lay their
 snares,
 those who seek my hurt speak of
 ruin,
 and meditate treachery all the
 day long.*

But I am like a deaf man, I do not
 hear,
 like a dumb man who does not
  open his mouth.

*Yea, I am like a man who does not
 hear,
 and in whose mouth are no re-
 bukes.*

But for thee, O LORD, do I wait;
 it is thou, O LORD my God, who
  wilt answer.

*Do not forsake me, O Lord!
 O my God, be not far from me!
Make haste to help me,
 O Lord, my salvation!*

Psalm 38:1-4, 8-15, 21-22

569

I waited patiently for the LORD;
 he inclined to me and heard my
  cry.

*He drew me up from the desolate
 pit,
 out of the miry bog,
and set my feet upon a rock,
 making my steps secure.*

He put a new song in my mouth,
 a song of praise to our God.
Many will see and fear,
 and put their trust in the LORD.

Blessed is the man who makes
the Lord his trust,
who does not turn to the proud,
to those who go astray after
false gods!

Thou hast multiplied, O LORD my
God,
thy wondrous deeds and thy
thoughts toward us;
none can compare with thee!

Were I to proclaim and tell of
them,
they would be more than can
be numbered.

Sacrifice and offering thou dost not
desire;
but thou hast given me an open
ear.
Burnt offering and sin offering
thou hast not required.

Then I said, "Lo, I come;
in the roll of the book it is
written of me;
I delight to do thy will, O my God;
thy law is within my heart."

I have told the glad news of deliverance
in the great congregation;
lo, I have not restrained my lips,
as thou knowest, O LORD.

I have not hid thy saving help
within my heart,
I have spoken of thy faithfulness and thy salvation;
I have not concealed thy steadfast love and thy faithfulness
from the great congregation

Do not thou, O Lord, withhold
thy mercy from me,

let thy steadfast love and thy
faithfulness
ever preserve me!

Psalm 40:1-11

57o

As a hart longs
for flowing streams,
so longs my soul
for thee, O God.

My soul thirsts for God,
for the living God.
When shall I come and behold
the face of God?

My tears have been my food
day and night,
while men say to me continually,
"Where is your God?"

These things I remember,
as I pour out my soul:
how I went with the throng,
and led them in procession to
the house of God,
with glad shouts and songs of
thanksgiving,
a multitude keeping festival.

Why are you cast down, O my soul,
and why are you disquieted
within me?
Hope in God; for I shall again
praise him,
my help and my God.

By day the Lord commands his
steadfast love;
and at night his song is with me,
a prayer to the God of my life.

I say to God, my rock:
"Why hast thou forgotten me?

Why go I mourning
  because of the oppression of the
    enemy?"

As with a deadly wound in my
    body,
  my adversaries taunt me,
while they say to me continually,
  "Where is your God?"

Why are you cast down, O my soul,
  and why are you disquieted with-
    in me?
Hope in God; for I shall again
  praise him,
  my help and my God.
Psalm 42:1-5, 8-11

57¹

Vindicate me, O God, and defend
    my cause
  against an ungodly people;
from deceitful and unjust men
    deliver me!

For thou art the God in whom I
    take refuge;
  why hast thou cast me off?
Why go I mourning
  because of the oppression of the
    enemy?

Oh send out thy light and thy truth;
  let them lead me,
let them bring me to thy holy
    hill
  and to thy dwelling!

Then I will go to the altar of God,
  to God my exceeding joy;
and I will praise thee with the lyre,
  O God, my God.

Why are you cast down, O my soul,
  and why are you disquieted with-
    in me?

Hope in God; for I shall again
  praise him,
  my help and my God.
Psalm 43

57²

God is our refuge and strength,
  a very present help in trouble.

Therefore we will not fear though
  the earth should change,
  though the mountains shake in
    the heart of the sea;

though its waters roar and foam,
  though the mountains tremble
    with its tumult.

There is a river whose streams
  make glad the city of God,
  the holy habitation of the Most
    High.

God is in the midst of her, she shall
    not be moved;
  God will help her right early.

The nations rage, the kingdoms
  totter;
  he utters his voice, the earth
    melts.

The LORD of hosts is with us;
  the God of Jacob is our refuge.

Come, behold the works of the
  Lord;
  how he has wrought desolations
    in the earth.

He makes wars cease to the end of
    the earth;

he breaks the bow, and shatters
the spear,
he burns the chariots with fire!

"*Be still, and know that I am God.
I am exalted among the nations,
I am exalted in the earth!*"

The LORD of hosts is with us;
the God of Jacob is our refuge.

Psalm 46

573

Have mercy on me, O God,
according to thy steadfast love;
according to thy abundant
mercy
blot out my transgressions.

*Wash me thoroughly from my in-
iquity,
and cleanse me from my sin!*

For I know my transgressions,
and my sin is ever before me.

*Against thee, thee only, have I
sinned,
and done that which is evil in
thy sight,
so that thou are justified in thy sen-
tence
and blameless in thy judgment.*

Behold, I was brought forth in iniquity,
and in sin did my mother con-
ceive me.

*Behold, thou desirest truth in the
inward being;
therefore teach me wisdom in my
secret heart.*

Purge me with hyssop, and I shall
be clean;

wash me, and I shall be whiter
than snow.

*Fill me with joy and gladness;
let the bones which thou hast
broken rejoice.*

Hide thy face from my sins,
and blot out all my iniquities.

*Create in me a clean heart, O God,
and put a new and right spirit
within me.*

Cast me not away from thy presence,
and take not thy holy Spirit from
me.

*Restore to me the joy of thy salva-
tion,
and uphold me with a willing
spirit.*

Then I will teach transgressors thy
ways,
and sinners will return to thee.

*Deliver me from bloodguiltiness,
O God,
thou God of my salvation,
and my tongue will sing aloud
of thy deliverance.*

O Lord, open thou my lips,
and my mouth shall show forth
thy praise.

*For thou hast no delight in sacri-
fice;
were I to give a burnt offering,
thou wouldst not be pleased.*

The sacrifice acceptable to God is
a broken spirit;
a broken and contrite heart, O
God, thou wilt not despise.

Psalm 51:1-17

574

Hear my cry, O God,
  listen to my prayer;
from the end of the earth I call
  to thee,
  when my heart is faint.

Lead thou me
  to the rock that is higher than I;
for thou art my refuge,
  a strong tower against the enemy.

Let me dwell in thy tent for ever!
  Oh to be safe under the shelter
  of thy wings!

For thou, O God, hast heard my
  vows,
  thou hast given me the heritage
  of those who fear thy name.
So will I ever sing praises to thy
  name,
  as I pay my vows day after day.
Psalm 61:1-5, 8

575

O God, thou art my God, I seek
  thee,
  my soul thirsts for thee;
my flesh faints for thee,
  as in a dry and weary land
  where no water is.

So I have looked upon thee in the
  sanctuary,
  beholding thy power and glory.

Because thy steadfast love is better
  than life,
  my lips will praise thee.

So I will bless thee as long as I
  live;

I will lift up my hands and call
  on thy name.

My soul is feasted as with marrow
  and fat,
  and my mouth praises thee with
  joyful lips,
when I think of thee upon my bed,
  and meditate on thee in the
  watches of the night;

for thou hast been my help,
  and in the shadow of thy wings I
  sing for joy.
My soul clings to thee;
  thy right hand upholds me.
Psalm 63:1-8

576

Praise is due to thee,
  O God in Zion;
and to thee shall vows be performed,

  O thou who hearest prayer!
To thee shall all flesh come
  on account of sins.

When our transgressions prevail
  over us,
  thou dost forgive them.

Blessed is he whom thou dost
  choose and bring near,
  to dwell in thy courts!
We shall be satisfied with the
  goodness of thy house,
  thy holy temple!

By dread deeds thou dost answer us
  with deliverance,
  O God of our salvation,
who art the hope of all the ends
  of the earth,
  and of the farthest seas:

who by thy strength hast established
   the mountains,
   being girded with might;

who dost still the roaring of the
   seas,
   the roaring of their waves,
   the tumult of the peoples;

so that those who dwell at earth's
   farthest bounds
   are afraid at thy signs;
thou makest the outgoings of the
   morning and the evening
   to shout for joy.

Thou visitest the earth and waterest
   it,
   thou greatly enrichest it;
the river of God is full of water;
   thou providest their grain,
   for so thou hast prepared it.

Thou waterest its furrows abundantly,
   settling its ridges,
softening it with showers,
   and blessing its growth.

Thou crownest the year with thy
   bounty;
   the tracks of thy chariot drip
   with fatness.

The pastures of the wilderness drip,
   the hills gird themselves with
   joy,
the meadows clothe themselves with
   flocks,
   the valleys deck themselves with
   grain,
   they shout and sing together for
   joy.

Psalm 65

577

May God be gracious to us and
   bless us
   and make his face to shine upon
   us,

that thy way may be known upon
   earth,
   thy saving power among all nations.

Let the peoples praise thee, O God;
   let all the peoples praise thee!

Let the nations be glad and sing
   for joy,
   for thou dost judge the peoples
   with equity
   and guide the nations upon
   earth.

Let the peoples praise thee, O God;
   let all the peoples praise thee!

The earth has yielded its increase;
   God, our God, has blessed us.
God has blessed us;
   let all the ends of the earth fear
   him!

Psalm 67

578

How lovely is thy dwelling place,
   O LORD of hosts!

My soul longs, yea, faints
   for the courts of the Lord;
my heart and flesh sing for joy
   to the living God.

Even the sparrow finds a home,
   and the swallow a nest for her-
   self,

where she may lay her young,
at thy altars, O LORD of hosts,
my King and my God.

*Blessed are those who dwell in thy
house,
ever singing thy praise!*

Blessed are the men whose strength
is in thee,
in whose heart are the highways
to Zion.

O Lord *God of hosts, hear my
prayer;
give ear, O God of Jacob!*

Behold our shield, O God;
look upon the face of thine
anointed!

*For a day in thy courts is better
than a thousand elsewhere.*

I would rather be a doorkeeper
in the house of my God
than dwell in the tents of wicked-
ness.

For the Lord *God is a sun and
shield;
he bestows favor and honor.*

No good thing does the LORD with-
hold
from those who walk uprightly.

O Lord *of hosts,
blessed is the man who trusts in
thee!*

Psalm 84:1-5, 8-12

579

Incline thy ear, O LORD, and answer me,
for I am poor and needy.

*Preserve my life, for I am godly;
save thy servant who trusts in
thee.*

Thou art my God; be gracious to
me, O Lord,
for to thee do I cry all the day.

*Gladden the soul of thy servant,
for to thee, O Lord, do I lift
up my soul.*

For thou, O Lord, art good and forgiving,
abounding in steadfast love to all
who call on thee.

Give ear, O Lord, *to my prayer;
hearken to my cry of supplication.*

In the day of my trouble I call on
thee,
for thou dost answer me.

*There is none like thee among
the gods, O Lord,
nor are there any works like
thine.*

All the nations thou hast made shall
come
and bow down before thee, O
Lord,
and shall glorify thy name.

*For thou art great and doest won-
drous things,
thou alone art God.*

Teach me thy way, O LORD,
that I may walk in thy truth;
unite my heart to fear thy name.

*I give thanks to thee, O Lord, my
God, with my whole heart,
and I will glorify thy name for
ever.*

Psalm 86:1-12

580

Lord, thou hast been our dwelling
place
in all generations.

*Before the mountains were brought
forth,*
*or ever thou hadst formed the
earth and the world,*
*from everlasting to everlasting
thou art God.*

Thou turnest man back to the dust,
and sayest, "Turn back, O chil-
dren of men!"

*For a thousand years in thy sight
are but as yesterday when it is
past,*
or as a watch in the night.

Thou dost sweep men away; they
are like a dream,
like grass which is renewed in
the morning:

*in the morning it flourishes and is
renewed;*
*in the evening it fades and
withers*

For we are consumed by thy anger;
by thy wrath we are over-
whelmed.

*Thou hast set our iniquities before
thee,*
*our secret sins in the light of
thy countenance.*

For all our days pass away under
thy wrath,
our years come to an end like a
sigh.

*The years of our life are three-
score and ten,*

*or even by reason of strength
fourscore;*
yet their span is but toil and
trouble;
they are soon gone, and we fly
away.

*Who considers the power of thy
anger,*
*and thy wrath according to the
fear of thee?*

So teach us to number our days
that we may get a heart of
wisdom.

Return, O Lord! How long?
Have pity on thy servants!

Satisfy us in the morning with thy
steadfast love,
that we may rejoice and be glad
all our days.

*Make us glad as many days as thou
hast afflicted us,*
*and as many years as we have
seen evil.*

Let thy work be manifest to thy
servants,
and thy glorious power to their
children.

*Let the favor of the Lord our God
be upon us,*
*and establish thou the work of
our hands upon us,*
*yea, the work of our hands estab-
lish thou it.*

Psalm 90

581

He who dwells in the shelter of the
Most High,
who abides in the shadow of the
Almighty,

will say to the LORD, "My refuge,
and my fortress;
my God in whom I trust."

*For he will deliver you from the
snare of the fowler
and from the deadly pestilence;*

he will cover you with his pinions,
and under his wings you will
find refuge;
his faithfulness is a shield and
buckler.

*You will not fear the terror of the
night,
nor the arrow that flies by day,
nor the pestilence that stalks in
darkness,
nor the destruction that wastes
at noonday.*

A thousand may fall at your side,
ten thousand at your right hand;
but it will not come near you.

*You will only look with your eyes
and see the recompense of the
wicked.*

Because you have made the LORD
your refuge,
the Most High your habitation.
no evil shall befall you,
no scourge come near your tent.

*For he will give his angels charge
of you
to guard you in all your ways.*

On their hands they will bear you
up,
lest you dash your foot against
a stone.

*You will tread on the lion and the
adder,*

*the young lion and the serpent
you will trample under foot.*

Because he cleaves to me in love,
I will deliver him;
I will protect him, because he
knows my name.

*When he calls to me, I will answer
him;
I will be with him in trouble,
I will rescue him and honor him.
With long life I will satisfy him,
and show him my salvation.*

Psalm 91

582

O come, let us sing to the LORD;
let us make a joyful noise to the
rock of our salvation!

*Let us come into his presence with
thanksgiving;
let us make a joyful noise to
him with songs of praise!*

For the LORD is a great God,
and a great King above all gods.

*In his hand are the depths of the
earth;
the heights of the mountains are
his also.*
The sea is his, for he made it;
for his hands formed the dry
land.

*O come, let us worship and bow
down,
let us kneel before the Lord, our
Maker!*

For he is our God,
and we are the people of his
pasture,
and the sheep of his hand.

Psalm 95:1-7

583

O sing to the LORD a new song;
sing to the LORD, all the earth

Sing to the Lord, *bless his name;*
tell of his salvation from day
to day.

Declare his glory among the nations,
his marvelous works among all
the peoples!

For great is the Lord, *and greatly*
to be praised,
he is to be feared above all gods.

For all the gods of the peoples are
idols;
but the LORD made the heavens.

Honor and majesty are before him;
strength and beauty are in his
sanctuary.

Ascribe to the LORD, O families of
the peoples,
ascribe to the LORD glory and
strength!

Ascribe to the Lord *the glory due*
his name;
bring an offering, and come into
his courts!

Worship the LORD in holy array;
tremble before him, all the earth!

Say among the nations, "The Lord
reigns!

Yea the world is established, it
shall never be moved;
he will judge the peoples with
equity."

Let the heavens be glad, and let the
earth rejoice;
let the sea roar, and all that fills
it;
let the field exult, and everything
in it!

Then shall all the trees of the wood
sing for joy
before the Lord, *for he comes,*
for he comes to judge the earth.

He will judge the world with righteousness,
and the peoples with his truth.

Psalm 96

584

O sing to the LORD a new song,
for he has done marvelous
things!
His right hand and his holy arm
have gotten him victory.
The Lord *has made known his vic-*
tory,
he has revealed his vindication
in the sight of the nations.
He has remembered his steadfast
love and faithfulness
to the house of Israel.
All the ends of the earth have
seen
the victory of our God.
Make a joyful noise to the Lord,
all the earth;
break forth into joyous song and
sing praises!

Sing praises to the LORD with the
lyre,
with the lyre and the sound of
melody!
*With trumpets and the sound of the
horn*
*make a joyful noise before the
King, the Lord!*
Let the sea roar, and all that fills it;
the world and those who dwell in
it!
Let the floods clap their hands;
let the hills sing for joy together
before the Lord, for he comes
to judge the earth.
He will judge the world with righteousness,
and the peoples with equity.

Psalm 98

585

Make a joyful noise to the Lord
all the lands!
Serve the Lord with gladness!
*Come into his presence with
singing!*
Know that the Lord is God!
*It is he that made us, and we are
his;*
*we are his people, and the sheep
of his pasture.*
*Enter his gates with thanksgiving,
and his courts with praise!*
*Give thanks to him, bless his
name!*
For the Lord is good;
*his steadfast love endures for
ever,*
*and his faithfulness to all genera-
tions.*

Psalm 100

586

Hear my prayer, O LORD;
let my cry come to thee!

Do not hide thy face from me
in the day of my distress!
Incline thy ear to me;
*answer me speedily in the day
when I call!*

For my days pass away like smoke,
and my bones burn like a fur-
nace.

*My heart is smitten like grass, and
withered;*
I forget to eat my bread.

Because of my loud groaning
my bones cleave to my flesh.

*I am like a vulture of the wilder-
ness,*
like an owl of the waste places;
I lie awake,
*I am like a lonely bird on the
housetop.*

All the day my enemies taunt me,
those who deride me use my
name for a curse.

For I eat ashes like bread,
and mingle tears with my drink,
*because of thy indignation and an-
ger;*
*for thou hast taken me up and
thrown me away.*

My days are like an evening shadow;
I wither away like grass.

*But thou, O Lord, are enthroned
for ever;*
*thy name endures to all genera-
tions.*

Thou wilt arise and have pity on
  Zion;
  it is the time to favor her;
  the appointed time has come.

For thy servants hold her stones
  dear,
  and have pity on her dust.

The nations will fear the name of
  the LORD,
  and all the kings of the earth thy
  glory.

For the Lord will build up Zion,
  he will appear in his glory;

he will regard the prayer of the
  destitute,
  and will not despise their supplication.

Psalm 102:1-17

587

Bless the LORD, O my soul;
  and all that is within me,
  bless his holy name!

Bless the Lord, O my soul;
  and forget not all his benefits
who forgives all your iniquity,
  who heals all your diseases,

who redeems your life from the Pit,
  who crowns you with steadfast
  love and mercy,

who satisfies you with good as long
  as you live
  so that your youth is renewed
  like the eagle's.

The LORD works vindication
  and justice for all who are
  oppressed.

He made known his ways to Moses,
  his acts to the people of Israel.

The LORD is merciful and gracious,
  slow to anger and abounding in
  steadfast love.

He will not always chide,
  nor will he keep his anger for
  ever.

He does not deal with us according
  to our sins,
  nor requite us according to our
  iniquities.

For as the heavens are high above
  the earth,
  so great is his steadfast love
  toward those who fear him;

as far as the east is from the west,
  so far does he remove our transgressions from us.

As a father pities his children,
  so the Lord pities those who
  fear him.

For he knows our frame;
  he remembers that we are dust.

As for man, his days are like grass;
  he flourishes like a flower of the
  field;
  for the wind passes over it, and it is
  gone,
  and its place knows it no more.

But the steadfast love of the LORD
  is from everlasting to everlasting
  upon those who fear him,
  and his righteousness to chil-
  dren's children,
to those who keep his covenant
  and remember to do his commandments.

The Lord *has established his throne
in the heavens,
and his kingdom rules over all.*

Bless the LORD, O you his angels,
you mighty ones who do his
word,
hearkening to the voice of his
word!

Bless the Lord, *all his hosts,
his ministers that do his will!
Bless the* Lord, *all his works,
in all places of his dominion.
Bless the* Lord, *O my soul!*

Psalm 103

588

I love the LORD, because he has
heard
my voice and my supplications.

*Because he inclined his ear to me,
therefore I will call on him as
long as I live.*

The snares of death encompassed
me;
the pangs of Sheol laid hold on
me;
I suffered distress and anguish.

Then I called on the name of the
Lord:
"O Lord, *I beseech thee, save
my life!"*

Gracious is the LORD, and righteous;
our God is merciful.

The Lord *preserves the simple;
when I was brought low, he
saved me.*

Return, O my soul, to your rest;

for the LORD has dealt bountifully with you.

*For thou hast delivered my soul
from death,
my eyes from tears,
my feet from stumbling;*
I walk before the LORD
in the land of the living.

*I kept my faith, even when I said,
"I am greatly afflicted";
I said in my consternation,
"Men are all a vain hope."*

What shall I render to the LORD
for all his bounty to me?

*I will lift up the cup of salvation
and call on the name of the*
Lord,
I will pay my vows to the Lord
*in the presence of all his
people.*

Precious in the sight of the LORD
is the death of his saints.

O Lord, *I am thy servant;
I am thy servant, the son of thy
handmaid.
Thou hast loosed my bonds.*

I will offer to thee the sacrifice of
thanksgiving
and call on the name of the
LORD.

I will pay my vows to the Lord
*in the presence of all his
people,
in the courts of the house of the*
Lord,
*in your midst, O Jerusalem.
Praise the* Lord!

Psalm 116

589

I lift up my eyes to the hills.
  From whence does my help
    come?

My help comes from the Lord, *who
  made heaven and earth.*

He will not let your foot be moved,
  he who keeps you will not slum-
    ber.

*Behold, he who keeps Israel
  will neither slumber nor sleep.*

The LORD is your keeper;
  the LORD is your shade
  on your right hand.

*The sun shall not smite you by day,
  nor the moon by night.*

The LORD will keep you from all
  evil;
  he will keep your life.

The Lord *will keep
  your going out and your coming
    in
  from this time forth and for ever-
    more.*

Psalm 121

590

*To thee I lift up my eyes,
  O thou who art enthroned
  in the heavens!
Behold, as the eyes of servants
  look to the hand of their
    master,
as the eyes of a maid
  to the hand of her mistress,
so our eyes look to the* Lord *our
  God,
  till he have mercy upon us.*

Have mercy upon us, O Lord, *have
  mercy upon us,
  for we have had more than
    enough of contempt.*
*Too long our soul has been sated
  with the scorn of those who are
    at ease,
  the contempt of the proud.*

Psalm 123

591

*Out of the depths I cry to thee, O
  Lord!
  Lord, hear my voice!
Let thy ears be attentive
  to the voice of my supplications!
If thou, O* Lord, *shouldst mark in-
    iquities,
  Lord, who could stand?
But there is forgiveness with
  thee,
  that thou mayest be feared.
I wait for the* Lord, *my soul waits,
  and in his word I hope;
my soul waits for the* Lord
  *more than watchmen for the
    morning,
  more than watchmen for the
    morning.
O Israel, hope in the* Lord!
  For with the Lord *there is stead-
    fast love,
  and with him is plenteous re-
    demption.
And he will redeem Israel
  from all his iniquities.*

Psalm 130

592

O Lord, *my heart is not lifted up,
  my eyes are not raised too
    high;*

*I do not occupy myself with things
    too great and too marvelous for
    me.*
*But I have calmed and quieted my
    soul,*
        *like a child quieted at its
        mother's breast;*
        *like a child that is quieted is my
        soul.*
O Israel, hope in the Lord
    *from this time forth and for ever-
    more.*

Psalm 131

593

I give thee thanks, O Lord, with
    my whole heart;
    before the gods I sing thy praise;

*I bow down toward the holy temple
    and give thanks to thy name for
        thy steadfast love and thy
        faithfulness;*
*for thou hast exalted above
    everything
    thy name and thy word.*

On the day I called, thou didst an-
    swer me,
    my strength of soul thou didst
    increase.

*All the kings of the earth shall
    praise thee, O Lord,
    for they have heard the words of
    thy mouth;*

and they shall sing of the ways of
    the Lord,
    for great is the glory of the Lord.

*For though the Lord is high, he
    regards the lowly;*

*but the haughty he knows from
    afar.*
Though I walk in the midst of trou-
    ble,
    thou dost preserve my life;
thou dost stretch out thy hand
        against the wrath of my ene-
        mies,
    and thy right hand delivers me.

The Lord *will fulfill his purpose
    for me;
    thy steadfast love, O Lord, en-
    dures for ever.
    Do not forsake the work of thy
    hands.*

Psalm 138

594

O Lord, thou hast searched me and
    known me!

*Thou knowest when I sit down and
    when I rise up;
    thou discernest my thoughts from
    afar.*

Thou searchest out my path and my
    lying down,
    and art acquainted with all my
    ways.

*Even before a word is on my
    tongue,
    lo, O Lord, thou knowest it alto-
    gether.*

Thou dost beset me behind and be-
    fore,
    and layest thy hand upon me.

*Such knowledge is too wonderful
    for me;
    it is high, I cannot attain it.*

Whither shall I go from thy Spirit?
 Or whither shall I flee from thy
  presence?

If I ascend to heaven, thou art
  there!
 If I make my bed in Sheol, thou
  art there!

If I take the wings of the morning
 and dwell in the uttermost parts
  of the sea.
even there thy hand shall lead me,
 and thy right hand shall hold me.

If I say, "Let only darkness cover
  me,
 and the light about me be night."
even the darkness is not dark to
  thee,
 the night is bright as the day;
 for darkness is as light with thee.

How precious to me are thy
  thoughts, O God!
 How vast is the sum of them!

If I would count them, they are
  more than the sand.
 When I awake, I am still with
  thee.

Search me, O God, and know my
  heart!
 Try me and know my thoughts!

And see if there be any wicked way
  in me,
 and lead me in the way ever-
  lasting!

Psalm 139:1-12, 17-18, 23-24

595

Hear my prayer, O LORD;
 give ear to my supplications.

In thy faithfulness answer me, in
  thy righteousness!

Enter not into judgment with thy
  servant;
 for no man living is righteous
  before thee.

For the enemy has pursued me;
 he has crushed my life to the
  ground;
 he has made me sit in darkness
  like those long dead.

Therefore my spirit faints within
  me;
 my heart within me is appalled.

I remember the days of old,
 I meditate on all that thou hast
  done;
 I muse on what thy hands have
  wrought.

I stretch out my hands to thee;
 my soul thirsts for thee like a
  parched land.

Make haste to answer me, O LORD!
 My spirit fails!
Hide not thy face from me,
 lest I be like those who go down
  to the Pit.

Let me hear in the morning of thy
  steadfast love,
 for in thee I put my trust.
Teach me the way I should go,
 for to thee I lift up my soul.

Deliver me, O LORD, from my enemies!
 I have fled to thee for refuge!

Teach me to do thy will,
 for thou art my God!

*Let thy good spirit lead me
on a level path!*

For thy name's sake, O LORD, preserve my life!
In thy righteousness bring me
out of trouble!

Psalm 143:1-11

596

I will extol thee, my God and King,
and bless thy name for ever and
ever.

*Every day I will bless thee,
and praise thy name for ever
and ever.*

Great is the LORD, and greatly to be
praised,
and his greatness is unsearchable.

*One generation shall laud thy
works to another,
and shall declare thy mighty acts.*

On the glorious splendor of thy
majesty,
and on thy wondrous works, I
will meditate.

*Men shall proclaim the might of
thy terrible acts,
and I will declare thy greatness.*

They shall pour forth the fame of
thy abundant goodness,
and shall sing aloud of thy
righteousness.

*The Lord is gracious and merciful,
slow to anger and abounding in
steadfast love.*

The LORD is good to all,
and his compassion is over all
that he has made.

*All thy works shall give thanks to
thee, O Lord,
and all thy saints shall bless thee!*

They shall speak of the glory of thy
kingdom,
and tell of thy power,
to make known to the sons of men
thy mighty deeds,
and the glorious splendor of thy
kingdom.

*Thy kingdom is an everlasting
kingdom,
and thy dominion endures
throughout all generations.*

The LORD is faithful in all his
words,
and gracious in all his deeds.

*The Lord upholds all who are fall-
ing,
and raises up all who are bowed
down.*

The eyes of all look to thee,
and thou givest them their food
in due season.

*Thou openest thy hand,
thou satisfiest the desire of every
living thing.*

The LORD is just in all his ways,
and kind in all his doings.

*The Lord is near to all who call
upon him,
to all who call upon him in truth.*

He fulfills the desire of all who fear
him,

he also hears their cry, and saves
them.

The Lord *preserves all who love
him;*
*but all the wicked he will de-
stroy.*

My mouth will speak the praise of
the LORD,
and let all flesh bless his holy
name for ever and ever.

Psalm 145

597

Praise the LORD!
Praise the LORD, O my soul!

I will praise the Lord *as long as I
live;*
*I will sing praises to my God
while I have being.*

Put not your trust in princes,
in a son of man, in whom there
is no help.

*When his breath departs he returns
to his earth;*
on that very day his plans perish.

Happy is he whose help is the God
of Jacob,
whose hope is in the LORD his
God,

who made heaven and earth,
the sea, and all that is in them;
who keeps faith for ever;

who executes justice for the oppressed;
who gives food to the hungry.

The Lord *sets the prisoners free;*
the Lord *opens the eyes of the
blind.*
The Lord *lifts up those who are
bowed down;*
the Lord *loves the righteous.*

The LORD watches over the so-
journers,
he upholds the widow and the
fatherless;
but the way of the wicked he
brings to ruin.

The Lord *will reign for ever,*
*thy God, O Zion, to all genera-
tions.*
Praise the Lord!

Psalm 146

598

Praise the LORD!
For it is good to sing praises to
our God;
for he is gracious, and a song of
praise is seemly.

The Lord *builds up Jerusalem;*
he gathers the outcasts of Israel.

He heals the brokenhearted,
and binds up their wounds.

*He determines the number of the
stars,*
*he gives to all of them their
names.*

Great is our LORD, and abundant
in power;
his understanding is beyond measure.

The Lord *lifts up the downtrodden,*
  he casts the wicked to the
  ground.

Sing to the LORD with thanksgiving;
  make melody to our God upon
  the lyre!

He covers the heavens with clouds,
  he prepares rain for the earth,
  he makes grass grow upon the
  hills.

He gives to the beasts their food,
  and to the young ravens which
  cry.

His delight is not in the strength
  of the horse,
  nor his pleasure in the legs of a
  man;

but the LORD takes pleasure in those
  who fear him,
  in those who hope in his steadfast love.

Praise the Lord, *O Jerusalem!*
  Praise your God, O Zion!

For he strengthens the bars of your
  gates;
  he blesses your sons within you.

He makes peace in your borders;
  he fills you with the finest of
  the wheat.

He sends forth his command to the
  earth;
  his word runs swiftly.

He gives snow like wool;
  he scatters hoarfrost like ashes.

He casts forth his ice like morsels;
  who can stand before his cold?

He sends forth his word, and melts
  them;
  he makes his wind blow, and
  the waters flow.

He declares his word to Jacob,
  his statutes and ordinances to
  Israel.

He has not dealt thus with any
  other nation;
  they do not know his ordinances.
  Praise the Lord!

Psalm 147

599

Praise the LORD!
Praise the LORD from the heavens,
  praise him in the heights!

Praise him, all his angels,
  praise him, all his host!

Praise him, sun and moon,
  praise him, all you shining
  stars!

Praise him, you highest heavens,
  and you waters above the
  heavens!

Let them praise the name of the
  LORD!
  For he commanded and they
  were created.

And he established them for ever
  and ever;
  he fixed their bounds which
  cannot be passed.

Praise the LORD from the earth,
you sea monsters and all deeps,
fire and hail, snow and frost,
stormy wind fulfilling his command!

Mountains and all hills,
fruit trees and all cedars!
Beasts and all cattle,
creeping things and flying
birds!

Kings of the earth and all peoples,
princes and all rulers of the
earth!

Young men and maidens together,
old men and children!

Let them praise the name of
the LORD,
for his name alone is exalted;
his glory is above earth and
heaven.

He has raised up a horn for his
people,
praise for all his saints,

for the people of Israel who are
near to him.
Praise the Lord!

Psalm 148

600

Praise the LORD!
Praise God in his sanctuary;
praise him in his mighty firmament!

Praise him for his mighty deeds;
praise him according to his ex-
ceeding greatness!

Praise him with trumpet sound;
praise him with lute and harp!

Praise him with timbrel and dance;
praise him with strings and pipe!

Praise him with sounding cymbals;
praise him with loud clashing
cymbals!

Let everything that breathes praise
the Lord!
Praise the Lord!

Psalm 150

Prayers of Worship

601

O God, thou source of all pure desires and holy affections, give me now a quiet mind and a reverent heart, that I may worthily worship thee at this time. *Amen.*

602

Our Father, who art in heaven,
Hallowed be thy name.
Thy kingdom come,
Thy will be done,
    On earth as it is in heaven.
Give us this day our daily bread;
And forgive us our debts,
    As we also have forgiven our debtors;
And lead us not into temptation,
    But deliver us from evil.
For thine is the kingdom and the power
and the glory, forever. *Amen.*

603

Almighty God, unto whom all hearts are open, all desires known, and from whom no secrets are hid; Cleanse the thoughts of our hearts by the inspiration of thy Holy Spirit, that we may perfectly love thee, and worthily magnify thy holy Name; through Christ our Lord. *Amen.*

604

Almighty God, who pourest out upon all who desire it the spirit of grace and supplication: Deliver us, when we draw nigh unto thee, from coldness of heart and wanderings of mind; that with steadfast thoughts and kindled affections we may worship thee in spirit and in truth; through Jesus Christ our Lord. *Amen.*

605

O thou Eternal God, speak to each of us the word that we need, and let thy word abide with us until it has wrought in us thy holy will. Cleanse, quicken, and refresh our hearts; direct and increase our faith; and grant that we, by our worship at this time, may be enabled to see thee more clearly, to love thee more fully, and to serve thee more perfectly. *Amen.*

606

Almighty and everlasting God, in whom we live and move and have our being, who hast made us for thyself, so that our hearts are restless till they rest in thee: Grant us purity of heart and strength of purpose, that no selfish passion may hinder us from knowing thy will, no weakness from doing it; that in thy light we may see light clearly, and in thy service find perfect freedom. *Amen.*

607

Almighty God, who art beyond the reach of our highest thought, and yet within the heart of the lowliest; we pray thee to come to us in all the beauty of light, in all the tenderness of love, in all the liberty of truth, and make thyself known unto us. Mercifully help us in the struggle to be pure and good; encourage us in every effort to be true, loyal and loving; to do justly, to love mercy and to walk humbly with thee. Sanctify all our desires and purposes, and unto each of us let thy blessing rest. *Amen.*

608

Almighty God, whose glory the heavens are telling, the earth thy power, and sea thy might, and whose greatness all feeling and thinking creatures everywhere proclaim; to thee belongeth glory, honor, might, greatness, and magnificence, now and forever, and unto ages of ages, through Jesus Christ our Lord. *Amen.*

609

O Lord our God, grant us grace to desire thee with our whole heart; that so desiring we may seek and find thee; and so finding thee may love thee; and loving thee, may hate those sins from which thou has redeemed us. *Amen.*

610

Most holy and merciful Father, we confess in thy presence the sinfulness of our nature, and our shortcomings and offenses against thee. Thou alone knowest how often we have sinned, in wandering from thy ways, in wasting thy gifts, in forgetting thy love. Have mercy, O Lord, upon us, who are ashamed and sorry for all we have done to displease thee; and forgive our sins, through Jesus Christ thy Son, our Savior. *Amen.*

611

Almighty and most merciful Father; We have erred and strayed from thy ways like lost sheep. We have followed too much the devices and desires of our own hearts. We have offended against thy holy laws. We have left undone those things which we ought to have done; And we have done those things which we ought not to have done. . . . But thou, O Lord, have mercy upon us. . . . Spare thou those, O God, who confess their faults. Restore thou those who are penitent; According to thy promises declared unto mankind in Christ Jesus our Lord. And grant, O most merciful Father, for his sake; That we may hereafter live a godly, righteous, and sober life, To the glory of thy holy Name. *Amen.*

612

Almighty and most merciful Father, we humbly confess our manifold sins and shortcomings. We acknowledge our transgressions as a nation and people: our pride and vainglory, our self-sufficiency and forgetfulness of thee. We have been unthankful for thy great goodness to us. We have been slow to obey thy command to make disciples of all nations. We have broken the unity of thy church, and by our divisions have weakened thy cause and hindered the gospel of Christ. Blot out our transgressions, O Lord, we beseech thee. Revive thy work in the midst of the years, and cause thy power and glory to be seen in the sanctuary, as in the days of old, through Jesus Christ our Lord. Amen.

613

Heavenly Father, we confess that we have sinned against thee and our neighbor. We have walked in darkness rather than in light; we have named the name of Christ, but have not departed from iniquity. Have mercy upon us, we beseech thee; for the sake of Jesus Christ forgive us all our sins; cleanse us by thy Holy Spirit; quicken our consciences; and enable us to forgive others; that we may henceforth serve thee.in newness of life, to the glory of thy holy name. Amen.

614

O Thou who art the Light of the minds that know thee, the Life of the souls that love thee, and the strength of the wills that serve thee; help us so to know thee that we may truly love thee, so to love thee that we may fully serve thee, whom to serve is perfect freedom; through Jesus Christ our Lord. *Amen.*

615

Almighty God, who hast given us grace at this time with one accord to make our common supplications unto thee; and dost promise that when two or three are gathered together in thy name thou will grant their requests; Fulfill now, O Lord, the desires and petitions of thy servants, as may be most expedient for them; granting us in this world knowledge of thy truth, and in the world to come life everlasting. *Amen.*

616

Almighty and everlasting God, who art always more ready to hear than we to pray, and art wont to give more than either we desire or deserve; Pour down upon us the abundance of thy mercy; forgiving us those things whereof our conscience is afraid, and giving us those good things which we are not worthy to ask, but through the merits and mediation of Jesus Christ, thy Son, our Lord. *Amen.*

617

O Lord, support us all the day long, until the shadows lengthen and the evening comes, and the busy world is hushed, and the fever of life is over, and our work is done. Then in thy mercy grant us a safe lodging, and a holy rest, and peace at the last. *Amen.*

618

Almighty God, who in Jesus Christ taught us to pray, and promised that what we ask in his name will be given us, so guide us by thy Holy Spirit that our prayers for others may serve thy will and show thy steadfast love; through the same Jesus Christ our Lord. *Amen.*

619

Almighty God, Father of all mercies, we thine unworthy servants, do give thee most humble and hearty thanks for all thy goodness and loving-kindness to us, and to all men. We bless thee for our creation, preservation, and all the blessings of this life; but above all, for thine inestimable love in the redemption of the world by our Lord Jesus Christ; for the means of grace, and for the hope of glory. And, we beseech thee, give us that due sense of all thy mercies, that our hearts may be unfeignedly thankful; and that we show forth thy praise, not only with our lips, but in our lives, by giving up ourselves to thy service, and by walking before thee in holiness and righteousness all our days; through Jesus Christ our Lord, to whom, with thee and the Holy Spirit, be all honour and glory, world without end. *Amen.*

620

O Lord, who hast set before us the great hope that thy kingdom shall come on earth, and hast taught us to pray for its coming, make us ever ready to thank thee for the signs of its dawning, and to pray and work for that perfect day when thy will shall be done on earth as it is in heaven. *Amen.*

621

Almighty God, who dwellest in light unapproachable, whom no man hath seen or can see; grant that we may know thee in him whom thou hast given to be the light of the world, our Savior Jesus Christ, and in the joy of his gospel may worship thee in spirit and in truth. *Amen.*

622

O God, our Father, help us remember the birth of Jesus, that we may share in the song of the angels, the gladness of the shepherds, and the worship of the wisemen.

Close the door of hate, and open the door of love over the world. Let kindness come with every gift, and good desires with every greeting. Deliver us from evil by the blessing that Christ brings and teach us to be merry with clear hearts.

May the Christmas morning make us happy to be thy children, and the Christmas evening bring us to our beds with grateful thoughts, forgiving and forgiven, for Jesus' sake. *Amen.*

623

O God our Father, who hast brought us again to the glad season when we commemorate the birth of thy Son Jesus Christ our Lord: Grant that his Spirit may be born anew in our hearts this day and that we may joyfully welcome him to reign over us. Open our ears that we may hear again the angelic chorus of old. Open our lips that we too may sing with uplifted hearts, Glory to God in the highest, and on earth peace, good will toward men. *Amen.*

624

O Lord God, whose chosen dwelling is the heart of the lowly: We give thanks that thou didst reveal thyself in the Holy Child Jesus, thereby sanctifying all childhood in him. We beseech thee to make us humble in faith and love, that we may know the joy of the gospel that is hidden from the wise and prudent and revealed unto babes. This we ask in his name, who, wearing our mortal flesh, grew in wisdom and in favor with God and man. *Amen.*

625

O God of grace, who at this time didst give Jesus Christ to be our Savior: We beseech thee to overcome our darkness with his light, our selfishness with his love, our indolence and cowardice with his steadfast devotion, that we may live ever as in thy presence, and perform faithfully our appointed tasks, and finally come to everlasting life; through the same Jesus Christ our Lord. *Amen.*

626

Almighty and everlasting God, who hatest nothing that thou hast made, and dost forgive the sins of all those who are penitent; Create and make in us new and contrite hearts, that we, worthily lamenting our sins . . . , may obtain of thee, the God of all mercy, perfect remission and forgiveness; through Jesus Christ our Lord. *Amen.*

627

O God, who knowest us to be set in the midst of so many and great dangers, that by reason of the frailty of our nature we cannot always stand upright; Grant to us such strength and protection, as may support us in all dangers, and carry us through all temptations; through Jesus Christ our Lord. *Amen.*

628

Almighty God, who hast shown us in the life and teaching of thy Son the true way of blessedness, thou hast also showed us in his suffering and death that the path of love may lead to the cross, and the reward of faithfulness may be a crown of thorns. Give us grace to learn these hard lessons. May we take up our cross and follow Christ, in the strength of patience and the constancy of faith; and may we have such fellowship with him in his sorrow, that we may know the secret of his strength and peace, and see, even in our darkest hour . . . the shining of the eternal light. *Amen.*

629

Almighty God, whose most dear Son went not up to joy but first he suffered pain, and entered not into glory before he was crucified; Mercifully grant that we, walking in the way of the cross, may find it none other than the way of life and peace; through the same thy Son Jesus Christ our Lord. *Amen.*

630

O Lord most holy, God most mighty, who hast found us wanting and yet hast not forsaken us, deliver us in these days of Lenten devotion from all the luxuries and comforts of a smug private righteousness, and impel us by thy love for our fellowmen to set our faces steadfastly toward that great city of the world where power and pride corrupt and waste the life of man, turning the hope of God to no account. Lift up our hearts as we recall the labor of our Lord and grant us his grace to take upon ourselves the burden of that sin which darkens our time and will not be lightened except by the cross of suffering. *Amen.*

631

O Thou Eternal God, whose dearly beloved Son was, for our sakes, content to bear sorrow and want and death, and who looked upon the great city and was touched with pity: Grant unto us such a measure of thy Spirit that we may follow him in courage and self-denial, and help us by thy great love to comfort the afflicted, to relieve the needy and destitute, to share the burdens of the heavy laden, and to see thee in all who are poor and desolate; through Jesus Christ our Lord. *Amen.*

632

Almighty God, whose mercies are everlasting, and whose grace is infinite: remember us with the favor thou bearest unto thy people. As on this day we call to mind our Lord's triumphal entry into the city that was to reject him, we beseech thee to give us such grace that we may welcome and crown him, our Lord and King forevermore; through the same Jesus Christ our Lord. *Amen.*

633

Father Everlasting, who hast set us in the fellowship of thy Son Jesus Christ, be near to us in this hour of solemn meditation. May our hearts be open to every holy affection, and ready to receive and cherish every sacred memory and serious impression. Give us to know the power of that death which this day commemorates.

Let a portion of the spirit which led our Savior to the cross descend upon us and fill our hearts with the love of thee and man. Here and now may every selfish passion and desire be quieted, and may that peace which passeth all understanding keep our hearts and minds in Christ Jesus. *Amen.*

634

O God, as we remember on this day the suffering and death of our Lord Jesus Christ, grant that we may confess our share in the sins which crucified him, that we may also be partakers in that reconciliation which is assured to those who belong to thee, through the merit and mediation of the same Jesus Christ our Lord. *Amen.*

635

Lord of heaven and of earth, we pray thee for all thy servants who have entered into the victory of eternal life, whose living was light to our darkness, and whose death, revealing their immortal stature, bound us with powerful and tender ties to heaven and to thee, our God. *Amen.*

636

Grant, we beseech thee, merciful God, that thy church, being gathered together in unity by thy Holy Spirit, may manifest thy power among all peoples, to the glory of thy name; through Jesus Christ our Lord, who liveth and reigneth with thee and the same Spirit, one God, world without end. *Amen.*

637

O God, who in the exaltation of thy Son Jesus Christ dost sanctify thy universal church; shed abroad in every race and nation the gift of his Spirit; that the work wrought by his power at the first preaching of the gospel may be extended throughout the whole world; through the same our Lord Jesus Christ. *Amen.*

638

O God, the Father Almighty, who has promised to give the Holy Spirit to them that ask thee; look graciously upon us assembled with one accord in one place to make our prayer unto thee, and to wait for thy promise; and of thy abundant mercy renew in our longing hearts thy Holy Gift; through Jesus Christ our Lord. *Amen.*

639

Send, we beseech thee, Almighty God, thy Holy Spirit into our hearts, that he may direct and rule us according to thy will, comfort us in all our afflictions, defend us from all error, and lead us into all truth; through Jesus Christ, our Lord. *Amen.*

640

Almighty God, who makest all things new, and abidest forever the same, encourage us to reach forward and to set our hope upon thy promises; so that, going on into the new year with trustful hearts, we may be able in all that we do to please thy loving eyes, through Jesus Christ our Lord. *Amen.*

641

O Thou whom we cannot love unless we love our brother, remove from us and all men both hate and prejudice, that thy children may be reconciled with those whom they fear, resent, or threaten; and thereafter live in peace; through Jesus Christ our Lord. *Amen.*

642

O God our Father, good beyond all that is good, fair beyond all that is fair, in whom is calmness, peace, and concord; reconcile we pray thee thy servants separated one from another by dissension, and lead us back into a unity of love which may bear some likeness to thy sublime nature. And as thou art above all things, grant that we may be united in generosity of spirit; that by the bonds of love and ties of affection we may become spiritually one, as well within ourselves as with each other, through that peace of thine which maketh all things peaceful in the grace, mercy, and pity of thy beloved Son. *Amen.*

643

O God, we thank thee for this universe, our great home; for its vastness and its riches, and for the manifoldness of the life which teems upon it and of which we are part. We praise thee for the arching sky and the blessed winds, for the driving clouds and the constellations on high. We praise thee for the salt sea and the running water, for the everlasting hills, for the trees, and for the grass under our feet. We thank thee for our senses by which we can see the splendor of the morning, and hear the jubilant songs of love, and smell the breath of the springtime. Grant us, we pray thee, a heart wide open to all this joy and beauty, and save our souls from being so steeped in care or so darkened by passion that we pass heedless and unseeing when even the thornbush by the wayside is aflame with the glory of God.

Enlarge within us the sense of fellowship with all the living things, our little brothers, to whom thou hast given this earth as their home in common with us. We remember with shame that in the past we have exercised the high dominion of man with ruthless cruelty, so that the voice of the earth, which should have gone up to thee in song, has been a groan of travail. May we realize that they live, not for us alone, but for themselves and for thee, and that they love the sweetness of life even as we, and serve thee in their place better than we in ours.

When our use of this world is over and we make room for others, may we not leave anything ravished by our greed or spoiled by our ignorance, but may we hand on our common heritage fairer and sweeter through our use of it, undiminished in fertility and joy, that so our bodies may return in peace to the great mother who nourished them and our spirits may round the circle of a perfect life in thee. *Amen.*

644

O God, who hast made of one blood all nations to dwell on the face of the earth, and who hast revealed thy will for men by thy Son, the Prince of Peace: Give us charity, we pray thee, to regard all men as our brethren, and to share with them the heritage we have received from thee. Deliver us from pride, prejudice, and arrogance. Put far from us all selfishness and malice, suspicion, envy, and anger, and the unrighteous passions which make men to be enemies one of another. Turn all peoples unto thee, that following thy holy example and united in thy service, they may become one brotherhood in thee, and that thy peace may possess every heart and rule in all the nations of the world; through Jesus Christ thy Son our Lord. *Amen.*

645

Endue thy church, O God, with the spirit of wisdom and power in Christ, that where others question, thy church may affirm; where others flee, thy church may advance; and where others fall, thy church may stand, through the same Jesus Christ our Lord. *Amen.*

646

Gracious Father, we humbly beseech thee for thy universal church. Fill it with all truth, and in all truth with all peace. Where it is corrupt, purge it; and where it is in error, direct it; where it is superstitious, rectify it; where anything is amiss, reform it; where it is right, strengthen and confirm it; where it is in want, furnish it; where it is divided and rent asunder, make up the breaches thereof, O thou holy One of Israel; for the sake of Jesus Christ our Lord and Savior. *Amen.*

647

O God, we pray for thy church, which is set today amid the perplexities of a changing order, and face to face with a great new task. We remember with love the nurture she gave to our spiritual life in its infancy, the tasks she set for our growing strength, the influence of the devoted hearts she gathers, the steadfast power for good she has exerted. When we compare her with all other human institutions, we rejoice, for there is none like her.

But when we judge her by the mind of her Master, we bow in pity and contrition. Oh, baptize her afresh in the life-giving spirit of Jesus! . . . Put upon her lips the ancient gospel of her Lord. . . . Fill her with the prophet's scorn

of tyranny, and with a Christlike tenderness for the heavy-laden and down-
trodden. . . . Bid her cease from seeking her own life, lest she lose it. Make
her valiant to give up her life to humanity, that like her crucified Lord she
may mount by the path of the cross to a higher glory. *Amen.*

648

Eternal God, send peace on earth, and by thy grace put down the pride,
greed, and anger that turn man against man, and nation against nation.
Speed the day when wars are ended and all men call thee Father; through
Jesus Christ our Lord. *Amen.*

649

O Lord Jesus Christ, who hath established thy church as the bulwark of
true freedom, and hath committed to all believers the ministry of reconciliation, continue thy work of reforming and cleansing within the church and
within our own heart, that being renewed by thy spirit thy church may bear
faithful witness to the gospel, and we live out our days in thy service. We
pray in thine own strong Name. *Amen.*

Offering

650

Every man shall give as he is able, according to the blessing of the LORD your God which he has given you.

Deuteronomy 16:17

651

Honor the LORD with your substance,
and with the first fruits of all your produce.

Proverbs 3:9

652

"Do not lay up for yourselves treasures on earth, where moth and rust consume and where thieves break in and steal, but lay up for yourselves treasures in heaven, where neither moth nor rust consumes and where thieves do not break in and steal. For where your treasure is, there will your heart be also."

Matthew 6:19-21

653

"Give, and it will be given to you; good measure, pressed down, shaken together, running over, will be put into your lap. For the measure you give will be the measure you get back."

Luke 6:38

654

"In all things I have shown you that by so toiling one must help the weak, remembering the words of the Lord Jesus, how he said, 'It is more blessed to give than to receive.' "

Acts 20:35

655

Having gifts that differ according to the grace given to us, let us use them: if prophecy, in proportion to our faith; if service, in our serving; he who teaches, in his teaching; he who exhorts, in his exhortation; he who contributes, in liberality; he who gives aid, with zeal; he who does acts of mercy, with cheerfulness.

Romans 12:6-8

656

For you know the grace of our Lord Jesus Christ, that though he was rich, yet for your sake he became poor, so that by his poverty you might become rich.

2 Corinthians 8:9

657

The point is this: he who sows sparingly will also reap sparingly, and he who sows bountifully will also reap bountifully. Each one must do as he has made up his mind, not reluctantly or under compulsion, for God loves a cheerful giver. And God is able to provide you with every blessing in abundance, so that you may always have enough of everything and may provide in abundance for every good work.

2 Corinthians 9:6-8

658

You will be enriched in every way for great generosity, which through us will produce thanksgiving to God; for the rendering of this service not only supplies the wants of the saints but also overflows in many thanksgivings to God.

2 Corinthians 9:11-12

659

But if any one has the world's goods and sees his brother in need, yet closes his heart against him, how does God's love abide in him? Little children, let us not love in word or speech but in deed and in truth.

1 John 3:17-18

660

Loving Father, we remember in our offering today the needs of our fellow men in every part of the world, and the command of Christ that we share with them the good news of thy love. Bless the work of those servants of Christ who are supported by our gifts and our prayers. Enable them by thy power to kindle lights in the midst of darkness to the end that all people may know him who is the Light of the world. *Amen.*

661

Almighty God, Giver of every good and perfect gift, teach us to render unto thee all that we have and all that we are, that we may praise thee not with our lips only but with our whole lives, turning the duties, the sorrows, and the joys of each successive day into a living sacrifice to thee. *Amen.*

662

O God, the God of all goodness and grace, who art worthy of a greater love than we can either give or understand; Fill our hearts, we beseech thee, with such love toward thee that nothing may seem too hard for us to do or to suffer in obedience to thee; and grant that by thus loving, we may become daily more like unto thee and finally obtain the crown of life which thou hast promised to those who unfeignedly love thee; through Jesus Christ our Lord. *Amen.*

The Lord's Supper

SCRIPTURES

663

Now as they were eating, Jesus took bread, and blessed, and broke it, and gave it to the disciples and said, "Take, eat; this is my body." And he took a cup, and when he had given thanks he gave it to them, saying, "Drink of it, all of you; for this is my blood of the covenant, which is poured out for many for the forgiveness of sins. I tell you I shall not drink again of this fruit of the vine until that day when I drink it new with you in my Father's kingdom."

Matthew 26:26-29

664

"Do not labor for the food which perishes, but for the food which endures to eternal life, which the Son of man will give to you; for on him has God the Father set his seal." "For the bread of God is that which comes down from heaven, and gives life to the world."

John 6:27, 33

665

Jesus said to them, "I am the bread of life; he who comes to me shall not hunger, and he who believes in me shall never thirst. For this is the will of my Father, that every one who sees the Son and believes in him should have eternal life; and I will raise him up at the last day."

John 6:35, 40

666

"Truly, truly, I say to you, he who believes has eternal life. I am the bread of life. I am the living bread which came down from heaven; if any one eats of this bread, he will live for ever; and the bread which I shall give for the life of the world is my flesh."

John 6:47-48, 51

667

"A new commandment I give to you, that you love one another; even as I have loved you, that you also love one another. By this all men will know that you are my disciples, if you have love for one another."

John 13:34-35

668

The cup of blessing which we bless, is it not a participation in the blood of Christ? The bread which we break, is it not a participation in the body of Christ? Because there is one bread, we who are many are one body, for we all partake of the one bread.

1 Corinthians 10:16-17

669

For I received from the Lord what I also delivered to you, that the Lord Jesus on the night when he was betrayed took bread, and when he had given thanks, he broke it, and said, "This is my body which is for you. Do this in remembrance of me." In the same way also the cup, after supper, saying, "This cup is the new covenant in my blood. Do this, as often as you drink it, in remembrance of me." For as often as you eat this bread and drink the cup, you proclaim the Lord's death until he comes.

1 Corinthians 11:23-26

670

Whoever, therefore, eats the bread or drinks the cup of the Lord in an unworthy manner will be guilty of profaning the body and blood of the Lord. Let a man examine himself, and so eat of the bread and drink of the cup. For any one who eats and drinks without discerning the body eats and drinks judgment upon himself.

1 Corinthians 11:27-29

INVITATION

671

Ye who do truly and earnestly repent you of your sins, and are in love and charity with your neighbors, and intend to lead a new life, following the commandments of God, and walking from henceforth in his holy ways; Draw near with faith, and take this holy Sacrament to your comfort; and make your humble confession to Almighty God.

672

Come to this sacred table, not because you must but because you may; come to testify, not that you are righteous, but that you sincerely love our Lord Jesus Christ, and desire to be his true disciples: come, not because you are strong, but because you are weak; not because you have any claim on heaven's rewards, but because in your frailty and sin you stand in constant need of heaven's mercy and help: come, not to express an opinion, but to seek a Presence and to pray for a Spirit.

And now that the Supper of the Lord is spread before you, lift up your minds and hearts above all selfish fears and cares; let this bread and this wine be to you the witnesses and signs of the grace of our Lord Jesus Christ, the love of God, and the communion of the Holy Spirit. Before the throne of the heavenly Father and the cross of the Redeemer consecrate your lives to the Christian obedience and service, and pray for strength to do and to bear the holy and blessed will of God.

PRAYERS

673

O heavenly Father, who dost govern the thoughts of men: bring to our minds the upper room where the Lord Jesus broke the bread with his disciples in the night before he was crucified; grant to us that, being of that company, we may look into the face of him who gave himself for the world. While we eat of his bread and drink of his cup, fill our lives with his life and send us forth to think his thoughts, to say his words, to do his deeds; and so, O Father, grant that, though we may know it not, the light of his face may shine in our faces, and all men may take note that we have been with Jesus, who liveth and reigneth with thee and the Holy Spirit, the God of everlasting love, world without end. *Amen.*

674

O Master of life, who didst gather thy disciples round thee in the upper room to give them there the sacrament of thy body and thy blood; take us also, unworthy as we are, into the fellowship of those who would follow thee. We acknowledge our shortcomings and our sins, our inconstant minds and hearts, and our slackness in devotion. But thou dost not forsake us even when we fail thee. Accept us not for what we are, but for what thou canst create in us, O Savior who by thy sacrifice hast sealed us for thine own. *Amen.*

675

O Thou who art the God and Father of all who dwell upon the face of the earth, make us one family this day at the table of our Lord, that remembering the gift of his life laid down, we may take up our pilgrimage again renewed by the bread of life, and made glad by our common salvation, through Jesus Christ our Lord. *Amen.*

676

Holy Father, thy glory makes the earth a temple and all life a sacrament; in the house of thy presence we lift up our hearts in adoration. O thou whose love is our life, reveal thyself to us as we gather at the table of the Lord, to break the loaf broken for us by a broken hand. Lead us beyond the symbol into the mystery of his grace and truth: may it be a festival of his living presence, as when he broke the bread in the gloaming of the day.

God of the living, we praise thee for the company of those gone before, who by their love and loyalty have left us a legacy of faith and hope. We give thee thanks for the fellowship of those who gather here, our comrades and fellow workers, with whom we share thy mercy and adore thy name. Make us members one of another, unite us in one heart with all who seek thee, in one communion with all who love thee, in one steadfast purpose with all who serve thy holy will in faithfulness and joy.

Bless the lonely of soul with thy nearness, and the wounded of heart with thy healing. Give to the hungry of spirit thyself, his bread, even the hidden manna whereof if he eat he shall hunger no more. O thou who hearest what our words cannot tell, lift our spirits to a loftier melody, that our song on earth may blend with the song of the redeemed. *Amen.*

677

We do not presume to come to this thy table, O merciful Lord, trusting in our own righteousness, but in thy manifold and great mercies. We are not worthy so much as to gather up the crumbs under thy table. But thou art the same Lord, whose property is always to have mercy: Grant us therefore, gracious Lord, so to eat the flesh of thy dear Son Jesus Christ, and to drink his blood, that our sinful bodies may be made clean by his body, and our souls washed through his most precious blood, and that we may evermore dwell in him, and he in us. *Amen.*

678

Most merciful heavenly Father, in whose likeness we have been created, and by whose grace we have been redeemed, with grateful hearts we approach this thy table to commemorate the sufferings of our dear Lord. . . . We thank thee for the great love which caused thee to give us thy only-begotten Son to redeem us from sin through his own death for us. And we thank thee for the great privilege of being numbered among his disciples and counted worthy of a place at thy table. Assist us, we pray thee, our heavenly Father, to partake of this bread and wine worthily, discerning the Lord's body and blood; and as we partake of these material emblems, grant that we also may be partakers of Christ's spirit and life, so that, as he gave himself for us, we also may give ourselves freely to thy service and to one another in acts of brotherly love. Give us, we beseech thee, a realizing sense of thy spiritual presence that we may each be strengthened thereby; and thus go forward in life's duties, stronger and purer for thy service. And grant us at last the unspeakable joy of sitting down together, with the innumerable company of the redeemed, at the Marriage Supper of the Lamb in thy everlasting kingdom; through Jesus Christ our Lord. *Amen.*

679

Lift up your hearts.

We lift them up to the Lord.

Let us glorify God.

For all his goodness to us.

All glory is yours, Eternal God, who made the universe. We praise you for this earth, for life and breath, for beauty we have seen and wonders still to come. From the beginning, your living Word has guided and corrected us. Your prophets have called us from disobedience, and prepared us for the coming of your Son.

We praise you for the Christ, who chose to come as one of us, and lived among us full of grace and truth. For us he became poor, and knew the sadness in our days; and for us he died on the cross and was buried. In him we know forgiveness and the lifting of burdens. He brings light to our darkness and opens our eyes to your great glory.

For you raised him from the dead and set him over all creation. Through your Holy Spirit we are members of his body, the church, and heirs of the promise of eternal life. Therefore with grateful hearts we join the faithful who, in all times and places, praise your name, saying

> *Holy, holy, holy,*
> *God of power and majesty,*
> *Heaven and earth are full of your glory,*
> *O God Most High!*

Holy Father, we thank you that the Lord Jesus, on the night when he was arrested, took bread, and when he had given thanks, he broke it, and said, "This is my body which is for you. Do this in remembering me." In the same way, he took the cup, after supper, saying, "This cup is the new covenant in my blood. Do this, as often as you drink it, in remembering me."

We remember you, Lord Jesus, as you commanded, confident we shall know you in the breaking of bread. We remember you, O Christ, confident you will seal the new covenant in our hearts as we drink this cup.

O Holy Spirit, who brought us here to proclaim the risen Lord, unite us in one body with him who loved us and gave himself for us.

O God, who called us from death to life: we give ourselves to you; and with the church through all ages, we thank you for your saving love in Jesus Christ our Lord. Amen.

Our Father in heaven, may your name be honored. May your kingdom come and your will be done on earth as it is in heaven. Give us today the food we need; and forgive us our sins as we forgive those who have wronged us. Keep us clear of temptation, and save us from evil. For the kingdom and power and glory are yours forever. Amen.

680

Lift up your hearts.

We lift them to the Lord.

Let us give thanks to the Lord God.

It is good that we do.

We give you thanks, Lord God, Creator and Father, for bringing the worlds into being, for forming man in your likeness, for recalling us when we rebel against you, and for keeping the world in your steadfast love. We praise you especially for Jesus Christ; who was born of Mary and lived as one of us; who knew exactly the life we know, and yet was obedient to your purposes, even to his death on a cross. We thank you that you stamped his death with victory by raising him in power and by making him head over all things. We rejoice in the continuing presence of the Holy Spirit; in the church you have gathered; in its task of obedience; and in the promise of eternal life. With the faithful in every place and time, we praise with joy your holy name.

> *Holy, holy, holy,*
> *God of love and majesty;*
> *The whole universe speaks of your glory,*
> *O God, Most High.*

Therefore bless now, by your Word and Spirit, both us and these gifts of bread and wine, that in receiving them at this table, and in offering here our faith and praise, we may be united with Christ and one another, and remain faithful to the tasks he sets before us.

In the strength Christ gives we offer ourselves to you, giving thanks that you have called us to serve you. Amen.

681

Almighty God, we praise thee as the giver of all things that are good and true—life and health, material comforts, and the beauties of nature, and this fellowship together with those we love. More than all we thank thee for the gift of thy Son who offered up his life for the remission of our sins. Father, we know that we are not worthy to sit at the table where his first disciples sat, just as they were not worthy. Yet we approach this table with confidence, knowing that if we come with sincere repentance, thy pardoning grace will be given freely. So we ask thee to cleanse our hearts of all that is impure, or petty, or selfish. As we receive these emblems of the love of our Lord, make us receptive to the incoming of his spirit. Inspire us by thy presence to go from here to live lives of greater service so that others will see in us the image of the Master and be led to give their lives to him. In his name we pray. *Amen.*

682

The Lord be with you.

And with you also.

Lift up your hearts.

We lift them to the Lord.

Let us give thanks to the Lord our God.

It is right indeed that we should do so.

It is most right and proper, holy Lord, almighty Father, everlasting God, that we should at all times, and in all places, give thanks to you through Jesus Christ, your only Son, our Lord; through whom you have created all things from the beginning and made man in your own image; through whom in the fullness of time you redeemed us, when we had fallen into sin, giving him to be born as man; to die on the cross and to rise again for us; setting him in glory at your right hand; through whom you have made us a holy people by sending forth your holy and lifegiving Spirit; through him therefore with the faithful who rest in him and all the glorious company of heaven, joyfully we praise you and say:

Holy, Holy, Holy, Lord God of Hosts, heaven and earth are full of your glory. Glory to you, Lord most high. Blessed is he who comes in the name of the Lord, Hosanna in the highest.

All glory to you, heavenly Father, who in your tender mercy gave your only Son Jesus Christ that all who believe in him might have eternal life. Hear us, merciful Father, and grant that receiving this bread and this wine in remembrance of the death and passion of your Son and Savior Jesus Christ, we may be partakers of his most blessed body and blood; who the night before he gave himself to death, took bread, and when he had given thanks he broke it and gave it to his disciples and said, Take, eat, this is my body which is given for you: do this in remembrance of me. In the same way after supper he took the cup, and when he had given thanks he gave it to them, and said, Drink this, all of you, for this is my blood of the new covenant which is shed for you and for many, for the forgiveness of sins; do this, as often as you drink it, in remembrance of me.

His death, Father, we show forth, his resurrection we proclaim, his coming we await. Glory to you, Lord most high.

Therefore, Father, we do this as your Son commanded, offering to you our praise and thanksgiving for his one perfect sacrifice made on the cross for the sin of the world, for his mighty resurrection and glorious ascension, which we recall before you in this sacrament of the bread of life and the cup of salvation. Accept us, in him, we pray, with this our sacrifice of praise and thanksgiving, and grant that all we who are partakers of this holy communion may be filled with the Holy Spirit and made one in your holy church, the body of your Son, Jesus Christ our Lord, through whom and in whom, in the unity of the Holy Spirit, all honor and glory be to you, almighty Father, for ever and ever. *Amen.*

683

(FOR THE BREAD) All glory and praise be unto thee, O God, our Father, who of thy tender mercy, gave thine only Son, Jesus Christ our Lord, to suffer death upon the cross for us all. Mercifully grant that thy Holy Spirit and Word may sanctify us and this bread, which thou hast given to be the symbol of the body of our Lord, that it may be for us spiritual food, that by faith we may feed in our hearts on him who is our only Savior and Lord. For his name's sake. *Amen.*

(FOR THE CUP) We give thanks, O God, for this cup, symbol of the most precious blood of our Lord. We commemorate his Last Supper with his disciples, his death upon the cross, His glorious resurrection and exaltation, and his coming again to receive us to share in his heavenly banquet. We pray thee to grant that thy Holy Spirit and Word may so sanctify us and this cup that we may feed in our hearts by faith upon the blood of our Lord, and that this cup may be for us the cup of fellowship and salvation. Let thy grace be upon us now and bless us beyond our asking. Through Jesus Christ our Lord. *Amen.*

Baptism

684

And when Jesus was baptized, he went up immediately from the water, and behold, the heavens were opened and he saw the Spirit of God descending like a dove, and alighting on him; and lo, a voice from heaven, saying, "This is my beloved Son, with whom I am well pleased."

Matthew 3:16-17

685

And Jesus came and said to them, "All authority in heaven and on earth has been given to me. Go therefore and make disciples of all nations, baptizing them in the name of the Father and of the Son and of the Holy Spirit, teaching them to observe all that I have commanded you; and lo, I am with you always, to the close of the age."

Matthew 28:18-20

686

And Peter said to them, "Repent, and be baptized every one of you in the name of Jesus Christ for the forgiveness of your sins; and you shall receive the gift of the Holy Spirit."

Acts 2:38

687

Do you not know that all of us who have been baptized into Christ Jesus were baptized into his death? We were buried therefore with him by baptism into death, so that as Christ was raised from the dead by the glory of the Father, we too might walk in newness of life.

Romans 6:3-4

688

For just as the body is one and has many members, and all the members of the body, though many, are one body, so it is with Christ. For by one Spirit we were all baptized into one body—Jews or Greeks, slaves or free—and all were made to drink of one Spirit.

1 Corinthians 12:12-13

689

In Christ Jesus you are all sons of God, through faith. For as many of you as were baptized into Christ have put on Christ. There is neither Jew nor Greek, there is neither slave nor free, there is neither male nor female; for you are all one in Christ Jesus.

Galatians 3:26-28

690

There is one body and one Spirit, just as you were called to the one hope that belongs to your call, one Lord, one faith, one baptism, one God and Father of us all, who is above all and through all and in all.

Ephesians 4:4-6

691

For Christ also died for sins once for all, the righteous for the unrighteous, that he might bring us to God, being put to death in the flesh but made alive in the spirit. Baptism, which corresponds to this, now saves you, not as a removal of dirt from the body but as an appeal to God for a clear conscience, through the resurrection of Jesus Christ.

1 Peter 3:18, 21

Benedictions

692

The LORD bless you and keep you:
The LORD make his face to shine upon you, and be gracious to you:
The LORD lift up his countenance upon you, and give you peace.

Numbers 6:24-26

693

May God be gracious to us and bless us
  and make his face to shine upon us,
that thy way may be known upon earth,
  thy saving power among all nations.

Psalm 67:1-2

694

"Lord, now lettest thou thy servant depart in peace,
according to thy word;
for mine eyes have seen thy salvation
which thou hast prepared in the presence of all peoples,
a light for revelation to the Gentiles,
and for glory to thy people Israel."

Luke 2:29-32

695

Grace to you and peace from God our Father and the Lord Jesus Christ.
Romans 1:7b

696

May the God of steadfastness and encouragement grant you to live in such harmony with one another, in accord with Christ Jesus, that together you may with one voice glorify the God and Father of our Lord Jesus Christ.
Romans 15:5-6

697

May the God of hope fill you with all joy and peace in believing, so that by the power of the Holy Spirit you may abound in hope.
Romans 15:13

698

The grace of the Lord Jesus Christ, and the love of God and the fellowship of the Holy Spirit be with you all.
2 Corinthians 13:14

699

Now may the Lord of peace himself give you peace at all times in all ways. The Lord be with you all.
2 Thessalonians 3:16

700

May grace and peace be multiplied to you in the knowledge of God and of Jesus our Lord.
2 Peter 1:2

Acknowledgments

Acknowledgments

Grateful appreciation is extended to those publishers and individuals who have so kindly permitted us to use their copyrighted materials. Every effort has been made to trace ownership of the materials used and to make proper acknowledgment. If omissions are discovered, they will be included in future editions.

Scripture quotations are from The Revised Standard Version of the Bible, copyrighted 1946 and 1952 by the Division of Christian Education, National Council of Churches, and are used by permission.

456   From *The New Church Hymnal* edited by H. Augustine Smith, © 1937 by Fleming H. Revell Company.

457   From *The New Church Hymnal* edited by H. Augustine Smith, © 1937 by Fleming H. Revell Company.

481   By Thomas B. McDormand.

482   By James G. Clague.

483   From *The Lutheran Service Book and Hymnal,* by permission of the Commission on the Liturgy and Hymnal. Used by permission.

484   From *A Book of Worship for Free Churches.* Used by permission.

485   "A Litany of the Cross" from *A Book of Public Prayers* by Harry Emerson Fosdick. Copyright © 1959 by Harry Emerson Fosdick.

486   "A Litany of the Nation" from *A Book of Public Prayers* by Harry Emerson Fosdick. Copyright © 1959 by Harry Emerson Fosdick.

487   Arranged by Kenneth L. Potee and used by permission.

488   Source unknown.

489   This litany is recited on the ruins of Coventry Cathedral every Friday at noon. It is reprinted with the permission of the Provost of Coventry Cathedral.

490   From the Preamble to "A Provisional Design for the Christian Church (Disciples of Christ)."

491   The Apostles' Creed.

492   The Nicene Creed.

493   Adapted by Dr. Major and reprinted by permission of his son, H. M. A. Major, and the executors of the Estate of Dr. Major.

494 This statement of faith is used in the United Church of Christ.

603 From *The Book of Common Prayer.*

604 Adapted from *Christian Worship and Praise,* edited by Henry Hallam Tweedy (Harper & Row, 1939). Reprinted by permission of Harper & Row, Publishers.

605 From the book *Devotional Services* by John Hunter, D.D. Published by E. P. Dutton & Co., Inc. and reprinted with the permission of E. P. Dutton & Co., Inc. and of J. M. Dent & Sons Ltd.

606 From *The Book of Common Worship,* Revised, 1932, the Board of Christian Education, Presbyterian Church, U.S.A. Copyright renewed, 1960. Used by permission.

607 From the *Service Book and Ordinal of the Presbyterian Church of South Africa.*

608 Adapted from *A Book of Public Worship* by permission of Oxford University Press.

609 By Saint Anselm, 1033-1109.

611 Adapted from *The Book of Common Prayer.*

612 From *Prayers for the Christian Year* by permission of the Committee on Public Worship and Aids to Devotion of the Church of Scotland.

613 From *The Book of Common Worship of the Church of South India* by permission of the Synod of the Church of South India.

614 From the Gelasian Sacramentary, 5th century.

615 From *The Book of Common Prayer.*

616 From *The Book of Common Prayer.*

618 From *The Book of Common Worship,* Provisional Services. The Westminster Press. Copyright © 1966, W. L. Jenkins. Used by permission.

619 From *The Book of Common Prayer.*

620 From *The Kingdom, the Power, and the Glory,* American Edition. Copyright 1933. Used by permission of Oxford University Press.

621 By Hugh Cameron from *Service Book for Ministers* by Joseph E. McCabe. Copyright © 1961 by Joseph E. McCabe. Used by permission of McGraw-Hill Book Company.

623 From *The Book of Worship,* Abingdon Press.

625 From *A Book of Pastoral Prayer* by Ernest Fremont Tittle. Copyright 1951 by Pierce and Smith (Abingdon Press).

626 Adapted from *The Book of Common Prayer.*

627 From *The Book of Common Prayer.*

628 From *The Kingdom, the Power, and the Glory,* American Edition. Copyright 1933. Used by permission of Oxford University Press.

629 From *The Book of Common Prayer.*

630 From *Prayers for Daily Use* by Samuel H. Miller. Copyright © 1957 by Samuel H. Miller.

631 From *The Kingdom, the Power, and the Glory,* American Edition. Copyright 1933. Used by permission of Oxford University Press.

632 From *Prayers for the Christian Year* by permission of the

Committee on Public Worship and Aids to Devotion of the Church of Scotland.

633 From the book *Devotional Services* by John Hunter, D.D. Published by E. P. Dutton & Co., Inc. and reprinted by permission of E. P. Dutton & Co., Inc. and of J. M. Dent & Sons Ltd.

634 From *Service Book for Ministers* by Joseph E. McCabe. Copyright © 1961 by Joseph E. McCabe. Used by permission of McGraw-Hill Book Company.

635 From *Prayers for Daily Use* by Samuel H. Miller. Copyright © 1951 by Samuel H. Miller.

636 From *The Book of Common Prayer.*

637 From *The Kingdom, the Power, and the Glory,* American Edition. Copyright 1933. Used by permission of Oxford University Press.

638 From *Service Book for Ministers* by Joseph E. McCabe. Copyright © 1961 by Joseph E. McCabe. Used by permission of McGraw-Hill Book Company.

639 From *The Book of Common Prayer.*

640 From the Mozarabic Sacramentary.

641 From *The Book of Common Worship,* Provisional Services. The Westminster Press. Copyright © 1966, W. L. Jenkins. Used by permission.

642 Jacobite Liturgy of Saint Dionysius.

643 From *Prayers of the Social Awakening* by Walter Rauschenbusch. The Pilgrim Press.

644 From *The Book of Common Worship,* Revised, 1932, the Board of Christian Education, Presbyterian Church, USA.

Copyright renewed, 1960. Used by permission.

645 From *Prayers of the Christian Life* by John Underwood Stephens. Copyright © 1952 and reprinted by permission of Oxford University Press.

646 From *A Chain of Prayers Across the Ages* by Selina Fox. Copyright 1913. John Murray (Publishers) Ltd. Used by permission.

647 From *Prayers of the Social Awakening* by Walter Rauschenbusch. The Pilgrim Press.

648 From *The Book of Common Worship,* Provisional Services. The Westminster Press. Copyright © 1966, W. L. Jenkins. Used by permission.

649 From *Service Book for Ministers* by Joseph E. McCabe. Copyright © 1961 by Joseph E. McCabe. Used by permission of McGraw-Hill Book Company.

660 By Lloyd V. Channels.

661 From *Services of Religion.* Used by permission of Beacon Press.

672 From the book *Devotional Services* by John Hunter, D.D. Published by E. P. Dutton & Co., Inc. and reprinted with the permission of E. P. Dutton & Co., Inc. and of J. M. Dent & Sons Ltd.

673 By Charles Lewis Slattery from *The Table of the Lord* edited by Charles L. Wallis. Reprinted by permission of Harper & Row, Publishers.

674 From *Lift Up Your Hearts* by Walter Russell Bowie. Copyright 1956 by Pierce and Washabaugh (Abingdon Press).

675 From *Service Book for Ministers* by Joseph E. McCabe. Copyright © 1961 by Joseph E. McCabe. Used by permission of McGraw-Hill Book Company.

676 From *Altar Stairs* by Joseph Fort Newton. Copyright 1928. Used by permission of The Macmillan Company.

677 From *The Book of Common Prayer.*

678 Adapted from *Alone with God* by J. H. Garrison. Copyright 1918 by The Christian Board of Publication. Used by permission.

679 From *The Book of Common Worship,* Provisional Services. The Westminster Press. Copyright © 1966, W. L. Jenkins. Used by permission.

680 From *Services of Word and Sacrament.* United Church Press. Used by permission.

681 By Winworth Williams from *Elder at the Lord's Table,* edited by Thomas W. Toler. Copyright 1954 by The Bethany Press. Used by permission.

682 From "The Liturgy on Eucharist" by permission of The New Zealand Provincial Commission for Prayer Book Review.

683 Adapted from *The Administration of the Lord's Supper* by William Robinson. Used by permission of the Publishing Committee of Churches of Christ and Mrs. William Robinson.

Indexes

Index of Authors, Composers, and Sources

Index of Topics

ADORATION AND PRAISE

52-83

See also MORNING; EVENING

As the sun doth daily rise 24
Blessing and honor and glory and power 185
Before Jehovah's aweful throne 48
For the beauty of the earth 7
Joyful, joyful, we adore thee 1
Let us with a gladsome mind 3
Look, ye saints, the sight is glorious 186
Now thank we all our God 99, 100
Rejoice, ye pure in heart 97
Sing praise to God 26
The spacious firmament on high 6
We gather together 102
When morning gilds the skies 296

ADVENT

103-116

AMERICA

See THE NATION

ANNIVERSARIES

See DEDICATION: CHURCH

ANXIETY

See CONFLICT AND CHALLENGE

ASCENSION

See also JESUS CHRIST: ASCENSION AND REIGN

All hail the power of Jesus' name 284
Alleluia! sing to Jesus 294
At the name of Jesus 291
For all the saints 279
Hail to the Lord's anointed 113
What joy to think of that vast host 280

ASH WEDNESDAY

See JESUS CHRIST: PASSION

ASSURANCE

See GOD: HIS PROVIDENCE; CONSTANCY; FAITH, HOPE, LOVE

BAPTISM

298-301

BEGINNING OF WORSHIP

See ADORATION AND PRAISE; MORNING; SERVICE MUSIC

BIBLE

See SCRIPTURES

BROTHERHOOD AND SERVICE

264-273

See also CHURCH: MINISTRY AND MISSION

God is working his purpose out 358
I bind my heart this tide 219
Joyful, joyful, we adore thee 1

Lift up your heads, ye mighty gates 105

Lord, whose love through humble service 145

O God of earth and altar 373

O God, we praise thee, and confess 55

The voice of God is calling 271

When I survey the wondrous cross 171

CONFLICT AND CHALLENGE
245-258

See also CHURCH: MINISTRY AND MISSION

Before the cross of Jesus 160

Father, hear the prayer we offer 226

God of grace and God of glory 245

Jesus calls us o'er the tumult 204

O God whose love compels us 18

Take up thy cross 151

The son of God, our Christ 149

We are living, we are dwelling 342

CONSECRATION

See CONFESSION AND COMMITMENT; STEWARDSHIP

CONSTANCY

All my hope on God is founded 20

Before Jehovah's aweful throne 48

Faith of our fathers! living still 253

Father, long before creation 211

God almighty, God eternal 203

God hath spoken 34

How firm a foundation 35

O God, our help in ages past 23

Of the father's love begotten 139

The God of Abraham praise 81

We sing the mighty power of God 4

COURAGE

See CONFLICT AND CHALLENGE

CREATION

See GOD: HIS WORKS IN CREATION

CROSS

See JESUS CHRIST: PASSION

DEDICATION

CHILDREN

Jesus, friend, so kind and gentle 368

CHURCH

All things are thine; no gift have we 262

In this house by men constructed 366

O thou, whose own vast temple stands 367

MINISTRY

Lord of the church, we humbly pray 365

Lord, speak to me, that I may speak 344

The voice of God is calling 271

DISCIPLESHIP

See CONFLICT AND CHALLENGE; CHURCH: MINISTRY AND MISSION; GOSPEL CALL AND RESPONSE; STEWARDSHIP

DOXOLOGIES

See also SERVICE MUSIC

As the sun doth daily rise (Stanza 5) 24

Father, we praise thee, now the night is over (Stanza 3) 62

Jesus Christ is risen today (Stanza 4) 174

Now thank we all our God (Stanza 3) 99

FUNERAL SERVICES

See GOD: HIS ABIDING PRESENCE

GOD

HIS WORKS IN CREATION
1-9

HIS LOVE   11-19

HIS PROVIDENCE   20-28

HIS ABIDING PRESENCE
29-49

HIS FORGIVENESS

50-51

See also FORGIVENESS

GOOD FRIDAY

See JESUS CHRIST: PASSION

GOSPEL CALL AND RESPONSE

203-223

See also CONFESSION AND COM-
MITMENT; CHURCH: MINISTRY AND
MISSION

Before the cross of Jesus 160
Draw thou my soul, O Christ 332
Lord Jesus, think on me 255
My God, I love thee 84
Savior, thy dying love 260
Take my life, and let it be 94
Thou didst leave thy throne 150
The voice of God is calling 271

GRATITUDE

See also THANKSGIVING

For the beauty of the earth 7
My God, I love thee 84
Now thank we all our God 99, 100
O be joyful in the Lord 77
O God, thy great creation 9
When I survey the wondrous cross
171

GRIEF

See COMFORT; GOD: HIS ABIDING
PRESENCE

GUIDANCE

Father, lead me day by day 36
God of our fathers, whose almighty
hand 22
Guide me, O thou great Jehovah
251
He leadeth me, O blessed thought
45
How firm a foundation 35
If thou but suffer God to guide
thee 51
Jesus, still lead on 242
O God, in whom we live and move
42
Savior, like a shepherd lead us 220
We gather together 102

HEALING

Children of the heavenly Father 30
Father, we praise thee, now the
night is over 62
I'll praise my maker while I've
breath 74
Immortal love, forever full 12
Jesus, friend of thronging pilgrims
144
My shepherd will supply my need
10
Sing praise to God 26
Unto the hills around do I lift up 21

HOLY WEEK

See JESUS CHRIST: PASSION

HOME AND FAMILY

274-278

See also DEDICATION: CHILDREN;
MARRIAGE

Praise to God, immortal praise 95
Through all the changing scenes 25

OBEDIENCE

See CONFESSION AND COMMITMENT; GOSPEL CALL AND RESPONSE

PALM SUNDAY

See JESUS CHRIST: TRIUMPHAL ENTRY

PATRIOTISM

See THE NATION

PEACE

All glory be to God on high 58
God, the omnipotent 33
Hope of the world 236
I bind my heart this tide 219
Let there be light, Lord God of hosts 331
O brother man, fold to thy heart 264
O church of God in every land 346
O day of God, draw nigh 266
O Zion, haste, thy mission high fulfilling 330
The Savior's wondrous love 267

PENITENCE

See GOD: HIS FORGIVENESS; FORGIVENESS

PENTECOST

Lord God, the Holy Ghost 198
On this day, the first of days 91

PRAISE

See ADORATION AND PRAISE

PRAYER

224-233

PROCESSIONAL HYMNS

A mighty fortress 31
All creatures of our God and King 54
All glory, laud, and honor 155
All hail the power of Jesus' name 284
All people that on earth do dwell 71
All praise to thee, for thou, O King divine 59
Alleluia! sing to Jesus 294
As with gladness men of old 141
Christ, whose glory fills the skies 285
Come, ye thankful people, come 101
Crown him with many crowns 184
Declare, O heavens, the Lord of space 87
For the beauty of the earth 7
Glorious things of thee are spoken 354
God himself is with us 61
God of grace and God of glory 245
God of our fathers, whose almighty hand 22
Holy, holy, holy, Lord God Almighty 70
I love thy kingdom, Lord 348
Immortal, invisible God only wise 75
Jesus shall reign where'er the sun 288
Joyful, joyful, we adore thee 1
Lead on, O King eternal 246
Look, ye saints the sight is glorious 186
Love divine, all loves excelling 297
Men and children everywhere 8
Now thank we all our God 99
Praise, my soul, the King of heaven 73

Index of Meters

Index of Tunes

Index of Children's Hymns

CHRISTIAN LIVING

All things are thine; no gift have we 262

Be thou my vision, O Lord of my heart 90

Father, hear the prayer we offer 226

Gracious Spirit, dwell with me 194

He would valiant be 252

In Christ there is no east or west 269

Just as I am, thine own to be 217

O brother man, fold to thy heart thy brother 264

Teach me, my God and King 341

The voice of God is calling 271

The wise may bring their learning 263

We are living, we are dwelling 342

We walk by faith, and not by sight 243

When thy heart with joy o'erflowing 96

Where restless crowds are thronging 272

THE CHURCH

Be known to us in breaking bread 311

Built on the Rock the church doth stand 349

Lord, we thank thee for our brothers 352

Master, we thy footsteps follow 299

Rise up, O men of God 93

THE CHRISTIAN YEAR

Advent

Let all mortal flesh keep silence 114

Lo, he comes, with clouds descending 187

O come, O come Emmanuel 108, 109

Veiled in darkness Judah lay 111

Birth

See JESUS CHRIST

Epiphany

As with gladness men of old 141

What star is this, with beams so bright 142

New Year and Changing Seasons

God is working his purpose out 358

Ascension

Rejoice, the Lord is King 188

Thanksgiving

As men of old their first fruits brought 98

Come, ye thankful people, come come 101

Now thank we all our God 99, 100

Rejoice, ye pure in heart 97

SCRIPTURES

The heavens declare thy glory, Lord 325

Book of books, our people's strength 329

SPIRITUALS

Let us break bread together 315

Were you there when they crucified my Lord 161

Index of First Lines